MESOZOIC ERA

CENOZOIC ERA

Cretaceous Period:
144–65 millions of years ago

Tertiary Period:
65–2 millions
of years ago

Quaternary Period:
65–2 millions
of years ago

Roy,
Merry Christmas
with love
till the end of time. Enjoy!
Marcia

THE ENCYCLOPEDIA OF THE
AGE OF THE
DINOSAURS

· STEVE PARKER ·

THE ENCYCLOPEDIA OF THE
AGE OF THE
DINOSAURS

PEGASUS

Published 2000 by
Pegasus Publishing Limited, High Street, Limpsfield, Surrey RH8 0DY

Library of Congress Catalogue-in-publication Data
The Encyclopedia of the Age of the Dinosaurs
ISBN 1-902620-07-0

Project Editor and Manager Ingrid Cranfield

Design Manager John Strange

Designer Megra Mitchell
(Mitchell Strange Design)

Printed and bound in Italy

A word of caution
This book, like others about dinosaurs, shows realistic-looking animals and describes them with great confidence. But no human has even seen a real living dinosaur. Our knowledge about them comes mainly from fossils . Using fossils to work out what a dinosaur looked like and how it lived involves guesswork – very intelligent, well-informed, and scientifically based, but still guesswork. The fossil evidence can be interpreted in various ways, and new fossils regularly change our ideas. This is why the study of dinosaurs is filled with lively debate and heated discussion and is so fascinating!

CONTENTS

Introduction

Not for 65 million years has a dinosaur been seen on earth. Something killed them ñ and many other species – at the end of the Cretaceous Period. Old they certainly are; yet they remain new. Almost every week a find reveals a "new" dinosaur that has previously unknown features or that ranks as the largest of its kind. So *Brachiosaurus* (75 feet, 23 meters) was overtaken by *Diplodocus* (90 feet, 27 meters), then by *Argentinosaurus* (120 feet, 37 meters), *Seismosaurus*, *Ultrasaurus*, and *Supersaurus*. Details of a still bigger one were revealed in January 2000: it was a herbivore up to 167 feet (40 meters) long.

Why do we find dinosaurs so fascinating? For one thing, some of them were unimaginably big. The recent find – yet unnamed – was identified from a femur (thighbone) 6 feet 6$^1/_2$ inches (2 meters) long, the height of a very tall man, and two cervical vertebrae (neckbones) 3 feet 10 inches (1.2 meters) high. But not all dinosaurs were giants. Some were the size of a chicken. Their tremendous range and variety contribute to the interest they hold for us.

People love to be frightened by monsters, real or imaginary. Some of the great dinosaurs were real "monsters", but they lived so long ago that we can pretend to quake in terror before them – from a safe distance. It is as though we can see them, but they cannot see or touch us.

For another thing, the earth – all of it – holds secrets from the Age of the Dinosaurs. In the ground, right under where you are sitting, there may be fossilized dinosaur remains waiting to be discovered. Dinosaurs were everywhere. They truly ruled the world – for 140 million years.

In the Mesozoic era, the continents were not where they are now. Because of "continental drift", landmasses floated around on the earthís surface. Australia was joined to Antarctica, for instance, and that supercontinent was a long way north of the present South Pole. The worldís climate and even the proportion of oxygen in the air were different then too. So these strange creatures, the dinosaurs, lived in a world that would be equally strange to us now.

Dinosaur names are also fun. The word *dinosaur* – from the Greek *deinos* ("terrible") and *sauros* ("lizard") – was not coined until 1841 when the anatomist Richard Owen recognized that dinosaurs were reptiles unlike any that were known in modern times. Generally, dinosaur names are chosen by the scientists who first describe them, and they may tell us something about the creature – who found it (*Lambeosaurus*, *Herrerasaurus*), where it was found (*Edmontosaurus*, *Shantungosaurus*), or what was special about it (*Heterodontosaurus*, "varied-toothed lizard", *Baryonyx*, "terrible claw"). But disputes arise about who found what first, adding to the confusion and the entertainment.

Another interesting aspect of the study of dinosaurs is the detective work, the painstaking research, the careful piecing together, and the rich imagination needed to reconstruct a prehistoric creature and – almost – bring it back to life. Sometimes, all the paleontologists have to work with is a single fossilized bone. From its size, type, and similarity to bones of other animals, they can make assumptions about the kind of dinosaur it might have been.

It is one thing to create models of dinosaurs. They show us only how the animals looked. It is another to understand how the dinosaurs lived. What did they eat? Where did they live? What form of locomotion did they use – on land, in the air, or in the water; two-footed or four-footed? How did they breed – by laying eggs or by giving birth to live young? Did they care for their offspring? Did pairs mate only to reproduce or did they bond for a long time? How did dinosaurs mark and defend their territory? What did they prey on and what preyed on them? Were they warm-blooded or cold-blooded?

Meat-eaters must have been fairly few in number, otherwise they would have run out of food. Any bad event such as a natural disaster would pose the risk of wiping out the entire species. Plant-eaters, if warm-blooded, faced a different problem. The bigger a creature's body is, the more difficult it is to get rid of excess body heat. If it overheats, it may cook! Beside, any animal that is nearly as large as a Jumbo jet has to eat vast amounts of food to stay alive.

And finally, dinosaurs and their fellow creatures of the Jurassic and Cretaceous Periods died out, totally, quite suddenly, and still – to us – completely mysteriously. There are dozens of theories to explain the mass extinction that wiped dinosaurs off the face of the earth, but we do not know which one is correct. We may never know. What could be more exciting than that?

The Encyclopedia of the Age of the Dinosaurs sets out the important facts about dinosaurs and the speculation too. One of the most comprehensive books on the subject ever produced, it puts dinosaurs into context, covering the world in which they lived, all that is known about the animals and their lives, and the processes of finding, studying, and 'recreating' dinosaurs.

And it proves that dinosaurs are still big news.

What were the dinosaurs?

The word *dinosaur* means "terrible lizard" or "terrible reptile." The dinosaurs were indeed reptiles. But they were not lizards, and not all dinosaurs were that terrible!

Few other animals are as famous as dinosaurs. Which is odd, because no one has ever seen a living dinosaur. There are none in zoos or wildlife parks. There are no movies or photographs of real dinosaurs. (Although there are plenty of dinosaurs made by animation and computer special effects.) All dinosaurs died out millions of years ago.

The evidence of fossils

The main reason that we know about dinosaurs is from their fossils. Fossils are the remains of their bones, teeth, horns, claws, and other hard body parts preserved in the rocks and turned to stone (see page 24). The fossils are used as the basis for rebuilding or reconstructing dinosaurs and other long-gone creatures as they might have appeared when they were alive (see page 26).

Monsters from the past

Despite the lack of living members, the dinosaurs are still world-famous. They are truly "monsters from the past." They inspire wonder and amazement. We are astonished at their great size. We like to imagine how they hunted and what they ate. We love to be frightened by their sharp claws and fierce teeth.

Perhaps it is because dinosaurs are no longer here that they inspire such awe and fascination. An unexplained mystery is much more fun than a puzzle that has been solved.

Basic facts about dinosaurs

- The dinosaurs were animals that lived long ago.
- They belonged to the group of animals called reptiles.
- Dinosaurs first appeared on earth by the natural process of evolution around 230 million years ago.
- They evolved into many different kinds, perhaps more than one thousand species.
- Some were very numerous, others were scarce.
- Some were gigantic - among the biggest animals that ever lived. Others were much smaller, the size of our pet dogs and cats today.
- The last dinosaurs died out, or became extinct, about 65 million years ago.

Not all "terrible lizards"

Dinosaurs were reptiles. But they were not lizards. They were not crocodiles either. They were a group of reptiles separate from any of today's reptile groups. This was recognized by the British scientist Richard Owen in 1841.

▼ Fossil formation

All kinds of prehistoric animals and plants formed fossils, not just the dinosaurs. This sequence shows how even the light, flimsy body of an ancient bird such as *Archaeopteryx* dies, gets covered with mud and sand, and is turned to stone.

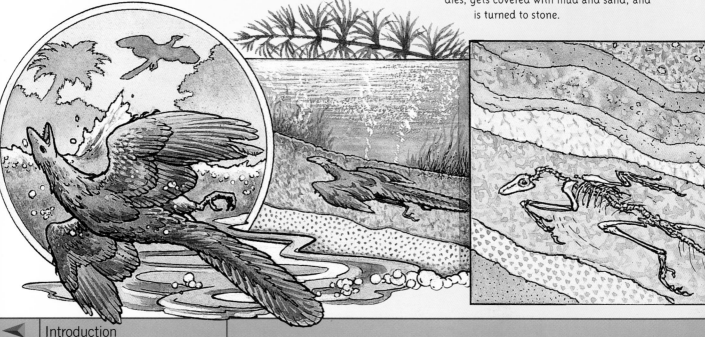

Owen was an anatomist - an expert in the parts and structures inside animal bodies. He had spent a few years studying some huge fossil bones and teeth. The animals they came from had been named *Megalosaurus*, *Hylaeosaurus*, and *Iguanodon*.

At first Owen saw that the bones had reptile features. He thought they might have belonged to long-dead types of lizards. But he soon saw that the bones, in particular the legbones, were quite different from those of any living reptile or any other animal. Also, they were huge, at least as big as elephants'. And so he invented a new name for them.

The Dinosauria are born

In 1841 the British Association for the Advancement of Science had a meeting in Plymouth, England. Richard Owen described his findings about the fossils. He proposed a new name for this group of huge, extinct reptiles. He called them *Dinosauria*. In one way, this is when the dinosaurs began.

So dinosaurs were dinosaurs, not lizards. Also, not all dinosaurs were terrible. Some were small plant-eaters that probably led quiet, peaceful lives. They had no sharp claws or long horns. Calling them "terrible" would be like calling a sheep "terrible."

The first dinosaurs

▲ **Fossil recovery**
Recovering or digging up fossils can be an arduous and lengthy process. Here workers chip carefully at solid rock in which the fossils of an armored dinosaur, *Saichania*, are embedded.

◄ **Fossil reconstruction**
The fossil bones, teeth, and other parts can be used to rebuild a lifelike version, as with this huge sauropod dinosaur *Diplodocus*.

The first dinosaurs

Dinosaurs were the largest and most important group of big land animals ever to walk the earth. They ruled for the longest time. They were incredibly varied, as shown in the other chapters of this book.

Yet, like all living things, the dinosaurs evolved from small beginnings. This chapter looks at the creatures that may have been the ancestors of the dinosaurs and how the dinosaurs themselves started out on their road to world domination.

Myths about dinosaurs ▶

Myths about dinosaurs

There are many popular ideas about dinosaurs, such as that they flew in the air or that they were hunted by people. As far as we know from fossils, the ones described here are not true. What's your favorite dinosaur myth?

All dinosaurs were huge
No. Some were, of course. One of the biggest was *Brachiosaurus*. It probably weighed 50 tons (51 tonnes), ten times more than an elephant. It was over 70 feet (21 meters) long. But some dinosaurs were as small as pet cats. One of the most-studied small dinosaurs, *Compsognathus*, was only the size of a chicken.

All dinosaurs were slow and stupid
No. Some dinosaurs were similar in size and shape to one of the fastest running animals alive today – the bird called the ostrich. These dinosaurs are known as ornithomimosaurs, or, more simply, "ostrich dinosaurs." They had long, muscular but slim back legs and they could probably run at speeds similar to the ostrich.

Dinosaurs evolved into mammals
No. The first mammals were probably small and slim, and from the outside they looked like the shrews or rats of today. They appeared on earth at about the same time as the first dinosaurs, around 230-220 million years ago. So

▲ **Dinosaurs and size**
Brachiosaurus was among the largest of dinosaurs and the biggest of all land animals. But some dinosaurs were 20,000 times smaller.

▲ **Dinosaurs and mammals**
Small, shrewlike mammals lived all through the Age of Dinosaurs. But none became larger than a pet cat.

dinosaurs could not have been the ancestors of mammals. The likely ancestors of mammals were the cynodonts, one of the groups of mammallike reptiles.

Dinosaurs ruled the earth for millions of years
No. It's true that dinosaurs were the largest and most common land animals for millions of years. So they did rule the land. But they never managed to rule two-thirds of the earth because it is covered by oceans and ...

Dinosaurs lived in the seas
No. Dinosaurs lived on land. There is no good evidence for any kind of dinosaur that stayed in water, either salty seawater or the freshwater of lakes and rivers. The animals that lived in seas and oceans during the Age of Dinosaurs belonged to different groups of

▲ Dinosaurs and the sea
No dinosaurs lived in the sea. Other reptiles such as
plesiosaurs did. Sharks (also shown above) were around long
before dinosaurs and long afterward too.

▲ Dinosaurs in the air
The first birds such as *Archaeopteryx* probably evolved from
small meat-eating dinosaurs. But mainstream science says the
possession of feathers makes them birds, not dinosaurs.

reptiles such as ichthyosaurs, plesiosaurs, and
mosasaurs (see Chapter 6). However, like most
reptiles and other wild animals, dinosaurs could
probably swim if they had to.

Dinosaurs soared through the air
No. Through the history of life there have been
  four main groups of true flying animals (as
  distinct from gliders).
- PTEROSAURS The animals that flew through
  the air during the Age of Dinosaurs
  belonged to a different group of reptiles
  known as pterosaurs (see chapter 6 in this
  book).
- BIRDS While the dinosaurs flourished, the
  first birds such as *Archaeopteryx* appeared
  on earth.
- INSECTS Flying insects such as dragonflies
  had already been around for many millions
  of years.
- BATS The flying mammals called bats did not
  evolve until after the dinosaurs died out.

The first people hunted dinosaurs
No. The last dinosaurs died out 65 million
years ago. The first humans or people
appeared less than five million years ago.
That's a gap of at least 60 million years. Early
humans probably evolved in Africa from an
apelike ancestor resembling a chimpanzee.
Gradually they became more upright and taller,

with bigger brains, and learnt how to use
tools. But they never saw a dinosaur.

All dinosaurs were green
No. Well, er ... Probably not. The truth is that
we do not know what color dinosaurs were.
However, it's unlikely that they were all green.
Only a few bits of fossilized dinosaur skin have
ever been found. Being fossils, they have lost
their original color. They have turned to stone
and so are the color of the stone. This is why
the pictures of dinosaurs in books like these
have made-up colors. The colors and patterns
are based on good guesses involving the
colors of similar animals today such as
crocodiles and lizards.

▼ Dinosaurs as they were
Science-based reconstructions produce lifelike scenes such as
this tyrannosaur *Albertosaurus* hunting a young duckbill
(hadrosaur) *Maiasaura*.

⇒ The prehistoric world

How long ago did dinosaurs live? Was it a long part of the history of the earth - or, like our own time here, the blink of an eye?

History goes back a long way. Grandparents sometimes seem very old. Yet the Pyramids of Ancient Egypt were built more than 4,000 years ago. Much further back, about half a million years ago, people lived in caves, used fire for warmth and cooking, and chipped stone tools.

However, these timespans are tiny compared with the immense length of prehistory – the time before history was written down or recorded in some way. Prehistoric time stretches back tens, hundreds, even thousands of millions of years. From the beginning of the earth some 4,600 million years ago, time can be divided into major units called eras. The eras are, in turn, divided into smaller spans of time known as periods. They are shown in the chart below.

4,600	550	500	450	400	350	300

Precambrian Era
4,600 million to
570 million
years ago

Paleozoic Era ("Ancient Life")
570 million to 248 million years ago

Cambrian Period
570-510 million years ago,
The first shelled animals such as trilobites, ammonites,
and brachiopods (lampshells)
Large seaweeds

Ordovician Period
510-438 million years ago
More types of shelled animals such as corals
The first animals with backbones — early fish,
without jaws or fins

Silurian Period
438-408 million years ago
Swarms of different kinds of shelled animals
in the seas
Fish grown to enormous size

By 3,000 million years ago — microscopic one-celled life forms
From about 1,000 to 800 million years ago — soft-bodied animals like worms and jellyfish in the seas

Devonian Period
408-360 million years ago
The Age of Fish
Early types of sharks
The first land animals, such as millipedes and insects
The first vertebrate land animals, amphibians,
evolved from fish

Carboniferous Period
360-290 million years ago
(Sometimes divided into Lower Carboniferous or Mississippian
Period and Upper Carboniferous or Pennsylvanian Period)
Swamps of huge ferns and horsetails covering much of the land
Giant dragonflies and other insects
The Age of Amphibians
Large, fierce amphibians
The first lizardlike reptiles

Permian Period
290-248 million years ago
Many different groups of reptiles spread over the land
Mammallike reptiles very common

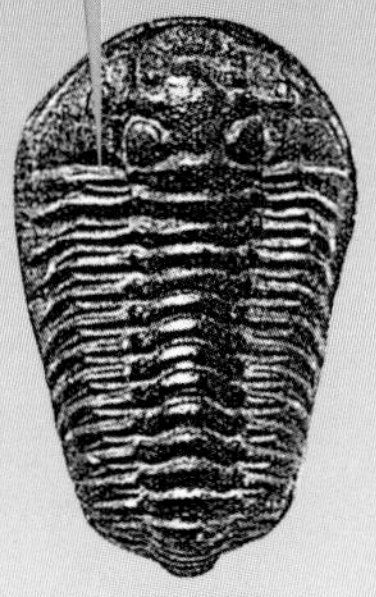

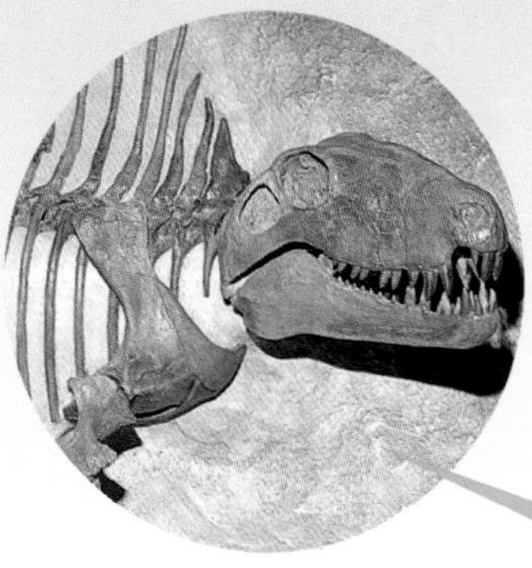

Myths about dinosaurs

Time in the rocks

The eras and periods make up what is known as the geological timescale. It is based on rocks – the various types and layers of rocks that have formed though the ages. Certain types or layers of rock contain fossils of the animals and plants that thrived at the time the rocks were formed (see page 24). So, the further we dig down into the rocks, the more ancient are the fossils of animals and plants we discover. Doing this shows us how life has changed, or evolved, through time (see page 29).

The Age of the Dinosaurs

Humans have lived on earth for two or three million years. Dinosaurs were around for more than 50 times longer – over 160 million years. Most of this time was during the Mesozoic Era, which lasted from about 248 to 65 million years ago. The Mesozoic Era was truly "the Age of the Dinosaurs." Yet even this is a short part – only about one-twentieth – of the entire history of life on earth and less than one-thirtieth of the history of the earth itself.

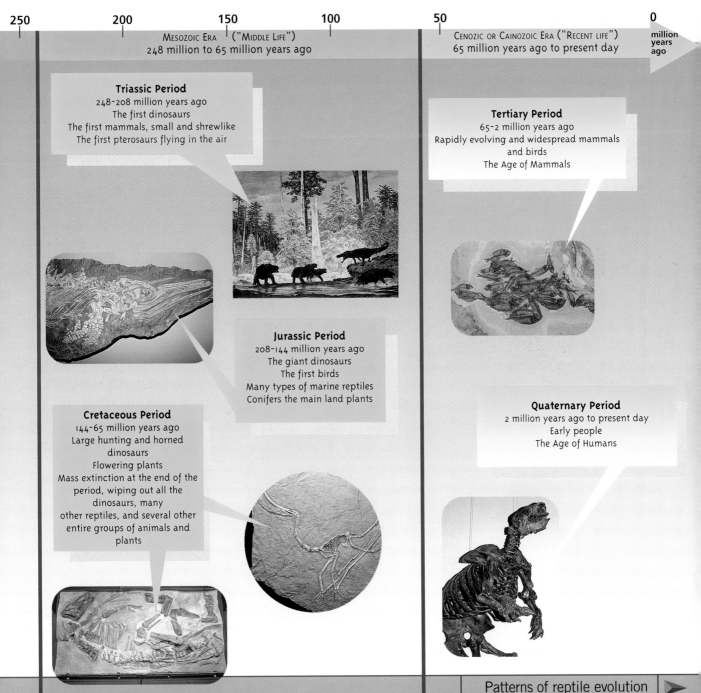

| 250 | 200 | 150 | 100 | 50 | 0 |

MESOZOIC ERA ("MIDDLE LIFE")
248 million to 65 million years ago

CENOZIC OR CAINOZOIC ERA ("RECENT life")
65 million years ago to present day

million years ago

Triassic Period
248-208 million years ago
The first dinosaurs
The first mammals, small and shrewlike
The first pterosaurs flying in the air

Tertiary Period
65-2 million years ago
Rapidly evolving and widespread mammals and birds
The Age of Mammals

Jurassic Period
208-144 million years ago
The giant dinosaurs
The first birds
Many types of marine reptiles
Conifers the main land plants

Cretaceous Period
144-65 million years ago
Large hunting and horned dinosaurs
Flowering plants
Mass extinction at the end of the period, wiping out all the dinosaurs, many other reptiles, and several other entire groups of animals and plants

Quaternary Period
2 million years ago to present day
Early people
The Age of Humans

⇒ Patterns of reptile evolution

Fossils show that soon after the reptiles evolved from amphibians more than 300 million years ago, they became very varied and widespread with many different groups.

Dinosaurs may be the most famous group of prehistoric reptiles. But many other reptile groups came and went even before the dinosaurs appeared – and while the dinosaurs were alive – and after they had become extinct.

Holes in skulls

One way of grouping reptiles is by holes in their skulls. This may sound odd, especially for present-day reptiles. But it has the advantage for long-extinct animals that skulls are found quite often as fossils. Also, the holes or openings in their skull bones are relatively easy to identify compared with other features in other bones.

Euryapsids

In the euryapsids the skull had one pair of openings, one on each side, in the upper temporal region of the skull. (Synapsids were similar but had the openings lower down.) The euryapsids included seagoing reptiles such as placodonts, nothosaurs, and plesiosaurs. However, they may not be a true evolutionary group. They may be a rag-bag of types that look similar for less important reasons.

Skull holes

Fossils of skulls sometimes show various holes that help group the animals. The temporal region holes in the early lizardlike reptile *Petrolacosaurus* (see opposite) may have been to save the weight of the skull bones. Its fossils have been found in Kansas.

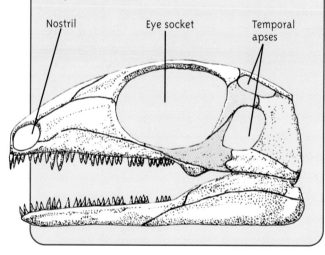

Nostril   Eye socket   Temporal apses

There are many holes in a typical animal skull, such as the sockets for the eyes and the openings for the nostrils. But the holes used for grouping reptiles are in the temple region of the skull, on each side of the head behind the eye. They are called apses, meaning "arched recesses." (See also panel on page 113.)The general position of the apse is important. So are the various bones that form its edges, since the skull itself is made up of many separate curved

bones joined tightly together. There are four types or patterns of apses, as follows.

Anapsids

"Anapsid" means "without apses." Some of the earliest reptiles had no temple holes, including *Hylonomus* from the Late Carboniferous Period. One fossil find from Canada shows *Hylonomus* inside a tree stump that has also fossilized. The small, lizardlike reptiles may have been sheltering there or feeding on insects, worms, and other small animals in the rotting wood, when they were overcome by a sudden flood.

Hylonomus had a slim body, long legs and tail, and small, sharp, insect-grabbing teeth. It was a cotylosaur or captorhinid, also known as a "stem reptile." This name refers to the early and basic reptiles from which other groups branched off or evolved.

Anapsid reptiles are still around as the turtle and tortoise group, chelonians. They first appeared in the Late Triassic Period some 200 million years ago, already fully equipped with

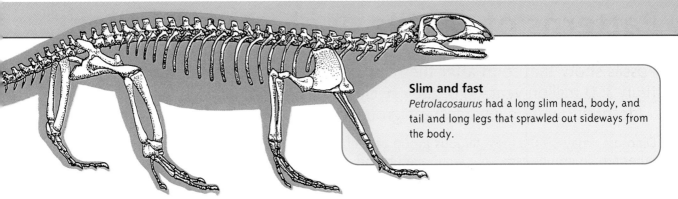

Slim and fast
Petrolacosaurus had a long slim head, body, and tail and long legs that sprawled out sideways from the body.

protective domed body shells. They have hardly changed since.

Synapsids

The synapsids were among the earliest groups to evolve from the anapsids. They had one hole on each side in the lower temporal (temple) region of the skull. They included the mammallike reptiles, which became the ancestors of the mammals.

Diapsids

Another group of early descendants from the anapsid "stem reptiles" were the diapsids. They had two holes on either side of the skull's temporal region.

One of the first diapsids was *Petrolacosaurus* from North America. It was an agile, long-legged, insect-eating, lizard-shaped creature about 16 inches (40 centimeters) in length. Other early diapsids included further small, lizardlike creatures such as *Heleosaurus* and *Coelurosauravus*, which lived in southern Africa.

More diapsids

About 250 million years ago, as the Permian Period changed into the Triassic, the diapsids gave rise to more reptile groups. One evolved and branched off into the majority of modern reptiles – lizards, snakes, the tuatara, and crocodiles (see below). It also gave rise to lizard cousins called mosasaurs, which were huge, fierce, sharp-toothed predators of Late Mesozoic seas.

Another group of diapsid reptiles that appeared around this time were the protorosaurs. *Protorosaurus* itself lived in the Late Permian deserts of what is now Germany. It was about 6 feet (2 meters) long, like a large lizard, with a long neck and long legs tucked under its body. It could probably run fast after small animals.

Yet more diapsids

Triassic protorosaurs were a very varied group. *Tanystropheus* of Asia and Europe was an amazing creature with a body and tail shaped like a lizard's, about 4 feet (1.2 meters) long, and a thin neck almost 6 feet (1.8 meters) long! It may have fed on small animals along the shore, darting its head into rock pools or the shallows.

Slightly later came *Hyperodapedon*, also from Asia and Europe. It was a rhynchosaur about 4 feet (1.2 meters) long. It had a barrellike body and stout legs and ate plant food. Its fossils are very common. Rhynchosaurs must have been dotted about the landscape, munching plants much like "reptilian sheep."

The protorosaurs also gave rise to the group that contained the dinosaurs – the archosaurs.

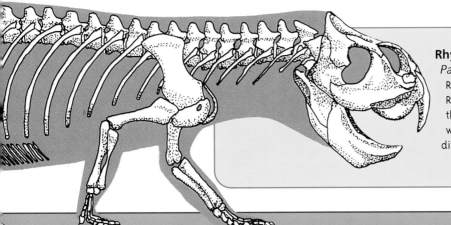

Rhynchosaur skeleton
Paradapedon was a herbivorous Rhynchosaur about 5 feet (1.5 meters) long. Rhynchosaurs were tusked, piglike reptiles that lived in the Late Triassic Period. They would have been preyed upon by early dinosaurs such as *Herrerasaurus*.

→ The ruling reptiles

Dinosaurs belonged to a larger group of reptiles called the archosaurs, or "ruling reptiles." The archosaurs would dominate life during the Mesozoic Era – on land, in water, and in the skies.

The archosaurs are well named as the "ruling reptiles." Most groups of archosaurs, like the dinosaurs, are extinct as described below. One main group survives today, the crocodiles and alligators. The main archosaurs were:

- thecodontians
- dinosaurs
- pterosaurs
- crocodiles.

However, there may be a fifth group. Many experts believe that birds evolved from dinosaurs (see chapter 5 in this book) and that they did so without changing any of the essential archosaur features. If so, birds are also archosaurs. In that case, birds are not a separate group or class equivalent to reptiles. They are part of the reptile group and are "feathered reptiles."

Early archosaur skull
This is the skull of an early thecodontian, *Chasmatosaurus* (also known as *Proterosuchus*). It shows the archosaur feature of an opening just in front of the orbit or eye socket, the anteorbital fenestra ("window").

Nostril   Eye orbit   Temporal openings

Anteorbital fenestra

Archosaur features

The archosaurs have features of their group that are not present in other reptiles. In the bones and teeth, which are important because they are usually the only parts preserved as fossils, they include:

- two openings on each side of the skull in the temple region behind the eye - the diapsid feature (see page 17);
- an anteorbital fenestra, a usually triangular opening in the skull just in front of the eye socket;
- a fourth trocanter, or ridge, in addition to the usual three on the thighbone;
- recurved (back-curved), flat-sided teeth.

Archosaur tendencies

Other general features are shown by most archosaurs, but not all. If these general features are not fully present, they may be partly present or hinted at in the bones, teeth, and other fossils. Or they may be present but then fade and become lost in later stages as evolution continues. These types of general or partial features are known in evolutionary terms as "tendencies." For the archosaurs tendencies include:

- more openings in the skull in the region

just in front of the eye in addition to those mentioned above;
- a row of horny or bony plates or armor along the back of the animal;
- back legs that were larger and more powerful than the front legs and that were held directly below the body like upright pillars, rather than sprawled out to the sides of the body and then angled down at the elbows and knees, as in other reptiles.

Upright walking

The last tendency produced what is called the "erect gait" – walking with the rear legs directly below the body, as we do. The hips, knees, and ankles swing the legs forward and backward. Most other reptiles have a quite different walk, a waddling gait. The upper parts of the limbs (upper arms and thighs) stick out sideways from the body, and the body itself swings from side to side like the movements of a swimming fish.

The erect gait

Other Triassic reptiles

During the Late Permian and Early Triassic Period the thecodontians were spreading across the world. But on land the dominant large creatures were the herbivorous dicynodont reptiles such as *Dicynodon*, *Kennemeyeria*, and *Lystrosaurus*. They were members of the mammallike reptile group. They were mostly between 3 and 10 feet (1-3 meters) long and heavily built. They spread over the landscape and munched the vegetation like prehistoric reptilian versions of today's cows and sheep.

The dicynodonts were pursued by other types of mammallike reptiles, the carnivorous cynodonts such as *Thrinaxodon* and *Cynognathus*. They were reptilian versions of lions, hyenas, and wolves. The cynodonts were among the most successful group of mammallike reptiles and continued to the Jurassic Period, well into the Age of Dinosaurs.

Later in the Triassic Period the plant-eating dicynodonts faded. Some smaller cynodonts evolved as plant-eaters. The reptiles called rhynchosaurs (see page 17) were also very numerous. But their success was brief and they had died out by the end of the Triassic Period.

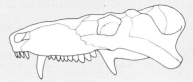

Cynognathus skull

Dicynodon skull

may have been one of the main reasons for the success of the dinosaurs and other archosaurs. However, it may have developed in different ways in different groups of archosaurs. The upright gait meant major changes in the limbs, not only in the shapes of the bones, but also the angles at which the bones came together in the joints and the design of the joints themselves. Also, the muscles that moved the bones to work the joints had to adapt. At each stage of evolution from a sprawling posture to an upright one, the posture would have to be successful for the animal that had it at the time. A version that did not work properly would soon be weeded out by natural selection.

The socket-teeth

The first main group of archosaurs appeared by 250 million years ago at the end of the Permian Period. They were the thecodontians (thecodonts). The name means "socket tooth" and refers to the way that the teeth fit into pits or sockets in the jawbone.

The thecodonts rapidly evolved into several main groups. Three of them resembled crocodiles. They were the proterosuchians, phytosaurs, and rauisuchians. A fourth group, the aetosaurs, also looked generally like crocodiles but ate plants. The fifth group were the ornithosuchians or pseudosuchians and contained smaller, more lightly built creatures such as *Ornithosuchus* and *Lagosuchus*. They raced along on their back legs using the erect gait, hunting insects and other creatures. It was probably from the ornithosuchians that the dinosaurs evolved.

▼ Parallel with dinosaurs

Ornithosuchus was a large and very dinosaurlike thecodontian reptile. It could probably run on its longer back legs, as shown in the lifelike reconstruction (below), and also walk on all fours, as in the composite skeleton view (left). This creature lived at a time when dinosaurs were already evolving and spreading rapidly, during the Late Triassic Period. It is described more fully on pages 28-29.

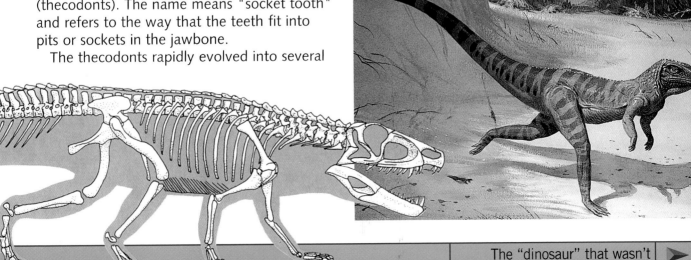

The "dinosaur" that wasn't

Dimetrodon was one of the first large, fully land-based predators. It is often mistaken for a dinosaur. But it was not. It was a pelycosaur, one of the mammallike reptiles.

The early archosaur reptiles gave rise to the dinosaurs, crocodiles, and many other important groups. But well before they had appeared, another important group of reptiles ruled the land. They too would leave various descendants. They were the mammallike reptiles.

The mammallike reptiles appeared at the end of the Carboniferous Period, not long after the very first of all the reptiles. They were synapsids (see page 17) and became widespread and common during the next period, the Permian. (It was in the period after that, the Triassic, when the first dinosaurs evolved.)

Three phases of success

In a sense, the mammallike reptiles had three phases of success.

- The first phase was during the Permian Period, as described here, with the subgroup known as the pelycosaurs. They appeared before the dinosaurs.
- The second phase was during the Middle and Late Triassic Period, with the subgroup called therapsids or advanced mammallike reptiles. It included cynodonts and dicynodonts (see page 19), which lived alongside the early dinosaurs. The first mammals probably evolved from cynodonts. In the fossil record it is difficult to tell during the Triassic Period when the mammallike reptiles ended and mammals began.
- The third phase was after the dinosaurs, during the Tertiary Period, and continues today. Strictly, this was not a time of success for the mammallike reptiles themselves, which had all died out, but for their descendants, the mammals.

Permian success

The first heyday of the mammallike reptiles was during the Permian Period around 290-250 million years ago. Their first main subgroup, the pelycosaurs, became the dominant large land creatures, with both meat-eating and later plant-eating types.

One of the best-known pelycosaurs was *Dimetrodon*. It was about 10 feet (3 meters) long. In some ways it resembled certain dinosaurs, being a large, fierce, meat-eating reptile with sharp teeth. But its legs splayed out to the side as in most reptiles, rather than being directly under the body as in the dinosaurs.

Why the sail?

Why did *Dimetrodon* have such a large yet flimsy sail on its back? In a battle between predator and prey, the sail would be one of the first casualties. To outweigh this disadvantage, it must have been very useful.

One possibility is that the skin of the sail was colorful or even changed color. This would help *Dimetrodon* to signal to others of its kind, perhaps to possible mates at breeding time or to rivals that intruded into its territory.

Camouflage is a very unlikely explanation. Why evolve such a large structure in the first place if its purpose was to become colored for concealment or disguise?

The sailback

The most obvious feature of *Dimetrodon* was the large "sail" or "fin" along its back. This was probably made of a thin layer of muscle and connective tissue sandwiched  between two layers of skin. It was held erect by long spines of bone, which were extensions of the vertebrae (backbones) along the animal's back. The middle part of the sail was about 3 feet (1 meter) tall.

This type of fishlike fin or back sail has cropped up several times since then in various other groups of reptiles. The large meat-eating dinosaur *Spinosaurus*, a cousin of *Tyrannosaurus*, had one. So did the plant-eating dinosaur *Ouranosaurus*, which was in the same group as the well-known *Iguanodon*.

Cold blood

Another reason may be body temperature control. Reptiles today are cold-blooded. That is, their body temperature is the same as their surroundings, rather than being kept constantly high as in warm-blooded mammals and birds. However, reptiles can control their body temperature to some extent. If they sunbathe in a place sheltered from the wind they warm up. In a shady, breezy place they cool down.

Warm and cool

The sail of *Dimetrodon* probably had a rich supply of blood vessels. If *Dimetrodon* stood side-on to the full glare of the sun, the large area of the sail absorbed heat, and the blood spread it around the body. If *Dimetrodon* became too hot it would seek shade and turn its body side-on to the wind. So the sail worked as a solar panel to take in heat or as a radiator to lose it.

This type of behavior would allow *Dimetrodon* to become warmer and therefore active sooner in the day. It would gain an edge over its cool-bodied, sluggish prey.

▶ **Sailed predators and prey**
Several plant-eating *Edaphosaurus* in the background eye the two *Dimetrodon* in the foreground. All of these were pelycosaur reptiles.

Warmer faster

Scientists have made models of *Dimetrodon* and tested the temperature control idea for the sail with calculations. These suggest that *Dimetrodon* could raise its body temperature from a sluggishly cool 79°F (26°C) to an actively warmer 90°F (32°C) in only about one and a half hours with the back sail. Without the sail, it would take three and a half hours.

Dimetrodon could seize victims in its long, sharp-pointed canine teeth and then cut up their bodies with its strong, shearing cheek teeth. A formidable predator - but still not a dinosaur!

DATA BASE

Name *Dimetrodon*
Pronounced DIE-mee-TROE-don/Die-MEE-troe-don
Meaning "two kinds of teeth"

What it ate
Meat-eater, preying on other large animals

Length (nose - tail-tip) 10 feet (3 meters)
Maximum head height 2 feet (60 centimeters)
Weight 440 pounds (200 kilograms)

When it lived Early Permian Period 280 million years ago
Where it lived U.S. (Oklahoma, Texas)

Order Pelycosauria (sail reptiles)
Suborder Sphenacodontidae

⇒ Definitely dinosaur

What makes a reptile into a dinosaur rather than a member of another reptile group? There are various features. Some are general, others are more detailed.

When does just any prehistoric reptile become a dinosaur? It is sometimes very difficult to decide. It is especially difficult for the earliest dinosaurs in the Middle and Late Triassic Period at the beginning of the Age of Dinosaurs. Not only dinosaurs but many other reptiles were evolving from one kind into another in various parts of the world. Also, many of the fossil remains from that time are scarce and fragmentary, so it can be hard to work out the details. And new fossils regularly come to light that contradict older views. This is one reason why it is so difficult to point to one specimen and say, "That is the first dinosaur."

◄ Walking tall
Mammals share an upright posture with dinosaurs. This is especially obvious in tall, spindly mammals like the giraffe, where there is a vertical leg under each corner of the body.

Features lost again
But then, as evolution went on, some groups of dinosaurs lost the ability for bipedal locomotion. They included the sauropods like *Diplodocus* and horned dinosaurs such as *Triceratops*. They stood and walked on all fours, known as quadrupedal locomotion.

Characteristics came, changed, and went like this over long periods of time. So it becomes even harder to draw up a list of features that all dinosaurs had but that no other animals had. Usually we have to look at a collection of features, known as a "suite" or a "constellation," for each candidate. The suite of features will take into account evolutionary relationships and trends that were happening at the time the animal lived.

Features gained
We can say with confidence that *Diplodocus*, *Stegosaurus*, *Triceratops*, and *Tyrannosaurus* were definitely dinosaurs. The dinosaur group in time became well established. Complete and plentiful remains of many types have been found. Many of the evolutionary relationships between types can be worked out.

However, continuing evolution complicates things. For example, one of the main features of the early dinosaurs, such as those on the following pages, was that they could rear up and run on their back legs, which were longer and stronger than the front legs. At the time, in the Middle-Late Triassic Period, no other reptiles – indeed no other animals of any kind – could do this. So, the feature of standing and running on two back legs, known as bipedal posture and locomotion, helps identify a dinosaur.

General features
The features used to diagnose a dinosaur must be based mainly on

bones. The fossil bones, teeth, and other preserved parts are the main evidence we have for dinosaurs. Below are some of the general features of dinosaurs. *Lagosuchus* already showed several important features that were found in dinosaurs. Two of the main ones were bipedal posture and fully upright gait. Others include:

Skull and spine
- The skull had two openings, or windows, in the temporal region behind the eye, that is, it was diapsid (see page 16).
- Each side of the snout had a long bone called the vomer, which reached to the opening in front of the eye.

Front limbs
- The upper end of the humerus (bone in the upper arm) fitted into a socket, called the glenoid fossa, in the shoulder blade (scapula). The glenoid fossa faced backward.
- The humerus had a ridge along its outer side called the deltopectoral crest (named after the muscles anchored there).
- There were four or fewer fingerbones, phalanges, in the fourth finger (counting the thumb as the first finger).

Hips
- The spinal column was linked to the hipbones, or pelvic girdle, by three of its backbones (vertebrae).
- The femoral head was inturned (see previous page).

▶ Standing tall
Like mammals and dinosaurs, birds have the fully erect posture. And as in mammals, it is seen most clearly in tall, thin birds such as waders like flamingoes. But unlike mammals, in birds it may have been inherited from their distant ancestors — dinosaurs.

- The hipjoint socket, or acetabulum, was perforated.

Rear limbs
- There was an extra small bump or ridge on the shaft of the thighbone known as the fourth trochanter.
- The knee had an in-line joint that could be fully straightened.
- The shinbone in the front of the lower leg, the tibia, was thicker and sturdier than the calfbone at the back of the lower leg, the fibula.
- There was a groove or notch in the base of the tibia for an upward projection of the upper ankle bone, the astralagus.
- There was a ridge at the front of the tibia near its upper end, the cnemial crest.
- The ankle joint worked as a simple hinge rather than a swivel joint.
- The animal had a digitigrade posture, walking and running on the toes rather than the sole of the foot.

◀ Dinosaur variety
Dinosaurs evolved into such a variety of shapes and sizes that the original features of the group in its early stages became changed or lost or distorted. We can hardly imagine a giant sauropod like *Diplodocus* rearing up on its hind legs to run at speed! Such constant change makes defining a dinosaur quite awkward.

How fossils form ▶

⇒ How fossils form

We know about dinosaurs and other long-dead animals and plants from their fossils. They are the remains of the hard parts such as bones, teeth, horns, claws, and shells, preserved in the rocks and turned to stone.

The "fossil record" consists of millions of fossils in the rocks, which trace the history and evolution of life on earth. The fossils we have actually discovered, dug up, identified, and studied make up just a tiny fraction of the fossils that must exist buried in rock layers all over the world. And only a tiny fraction of the animals and plants that ever lived have left fossils behind. The great majority of living things left no traces at all. So the fossil record is very far from complete. It is exceptionally selective, patchy, and fragmentary, and what we have found has often turned up just by chance.

The fate of living things

Most animals today die and eventually leave no trace. They may be eaten by other animals, the predators. If not, their soft parts such as flesh and guts soon rot away. Even hard bones are crunched up by strong-jawed scavengers. If not, the bones are eventually worn down and crumbled to dust by hot sun, rain, wind, frost, and other forces of nature. The same must have happened to dinosaurs.

Stages in fossil formation

However, a chance series of events may lead to fossilization. A typical scenario runs something like this:

- A dinosaur dies (1). After its soft parts have rotted or been eaten, the hard parts such as bones are left.
- Before they can be broken or worn away, they may be covered by sediments (2). A sediment consists of small particles such as sand, mud, or silt.
- For example, a dinosaur may die on a riverbank. The river then floods and washes along sand, which settles on the skeleton. Or the dinosaur's bones are swept into a lake or the sea, where they settle on the bottom and become covered by mud. Or the dinosaur dies in a sandy area like a desert, and wind blows sand grains over it (3).
- Over a very long time more sediments pile up, burying the bones deeper.
- Minerals dissolved in the water around the particles of sediment seep into the bones. They begin to replace the once-living, or organic, tissues with inorganic substances. This process is known as permineralization (4 left). The whole bone may be replaced by inorganic materials, called petrification (4 right).

- The particles of sediment become squashed and pressed by the weight of the sediments above them. As the water is squeezed out and drains away, the minerals dissolved in it become solid once again.
- In the end, these processes compact and cement the particles into solid rock (5). Rock formed in this way is called sedimentary rock

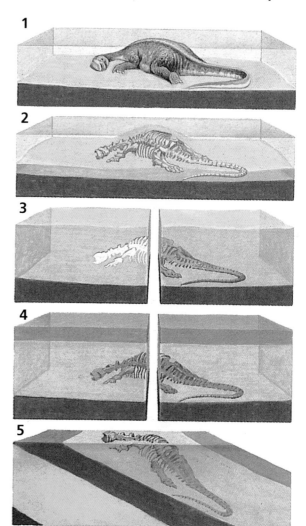

1

2

3

4

5

▲ Sedimentary rock

Snow, ice, rain, frost, wind, plant roots, and other forces of nature crack and wear rock into pieces from large boulders to tiny grains of silt. They are rolled and swept by wind, rain, and rivers into lakes and seas, where they settle in layers (strata), go hard and solid, and become sedimentary rocks.

(see above). Embedded in the rock are the fossils. They are the shapes of the original bone, but now turned to stone.

Molds, casts, and mummies

Some fossils are just empty spaces. They are holes in the rock that were originally occupied by a bone, tooth, or similar body part. As the sediments over them turned to stone, the body part dissolved away to leave an empty place with its shape. Empty-space fossils are called mold fossils.

Another type of fossil is the cast fossil. It forms when water carrying a lot of dissolved minerals fills a mold fossil. The water eventually seeps away, leaving behind the minerals, which become solid and gradually fill

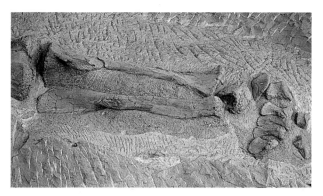

the gap. They form a lump of rock in the same shape as the original body part and also different from the surrounding rock.

Another fate could happen when the dinosaur died but did not completely rot away. If it died in a very dry place, such as a desert cave, its body would dry out (desiccate) very fast. Without water, the microbes that encourage decay cannot survive. This fast-drying process is known as mummification. It can preserve soft parts of the body like skin.

Why fossils form in certain rocks only

There are three main kinds of rocks at the surface of the earth.

- Igneous rocks were once so hot that they were molten — melted and liquid or runny. They exploded out of volcanoes or oozed out of cracks as lava. Quickly or slowly, they cooled and went solid.
- Metamorphic rocks are any type of rock that is changed physically and chemically by great heat and immense pressure, usually deep below the surface of the earth. If the heat is too great, the rock melts and becomes igneous rock.
- Sedimentary rocks were once mud, sand, or other rock particles. They form as shown on the left.

Only sedimentary rocks contain fossils, because melting or metamorphosis destroys any fossils in the rock.

◀▲▼ Rocks of ages

The age of a sedimentary rock determines which types of fossils it may harbor. The skeleton (above) is not dinosaurian; it is a prehistoric dolphin from the Tertiary Period, dated at about 23 million years old. The part-excavated leg- and footbones (left) are in Jurassic sandstone. The Jurassic was the heyday of the sauropods, and these are indeed sauropod remains, being those of *Diplodocus*. The rocks of the excavation site (below) in the Pyrenees Mountains are Late Cretaceous, and they have yielded many fossils of ankylosaurs and titanosaurs.

Rebuilding a dinosaur ▶

Rebuilding a dinosaur

A few fossil dinosaur bones dug from the ground are only the beginning. It can take years to rebuild them into a skeleton and then recreate the dinosaur as it may have looked in life.

Herrerasaurus is one of the best-known of the early dinosaurs. Fossils of nearly all parts of its body have been found. They include the skull, teeth, neck, backbone, limbs and toes, claws, and even the tail down to its tip. And not just from a single specimen of *Herrerasaurus* but several. So we can compare the same bones in different individuals, and where some bones are missing in one specimen, they can be "filled in" from another.

A long road

For scientists to have so many fossils is a luxury. It is much more usual for fossils to be bent, broken, and fragmented, with various parts of the skeleton missing. The bones are usually mixed together and jumbled up (disarticulated). The restored skeletons in displays and museums, where the bones are neatly joined together and arranged as in life (articulated), are the result of years of careful, painstaking work. The process of digging up fossils from the ground and cleaning them ready for reassembly is described in chapter of this book.

Scientific comparisons

The restored skeleton of a dinosaur is the basis for a reconstruction of the whole creature. One of the major skills involved here is comparative anatomy. The word "anatomy" means both the structure of a living thing and the study of that structure. The anatomies of different creatures can be compared to reveal similarities and differences and to gain a greater understanding of the way the parts develop and work, and also how the different animals are related. One of the first great comparative anatomists was Georges Cuvier (see panel opposite).

Working forward and backward

The fossil bones, teeth, and other hard parts of dinosaurs can be compared with the equivalent parts in living animals. The closest living cousins of dinosaurs are crocodiles and birds, and their body parts are often used. So are those of other reptiles like lizards and turtles and the "living fossil" tuatara, and even of mammals.

Then the soft parts of these living animals can be used as a basis to build the muscles, guts, and other soft parts of a dinosaur on and around its skeleton. In this way anatomical knowledge from the present can be used to reconstruct the past.

Flesh on the bones

Living bones have roughened areas where the muscles that pull them are strongly anchored

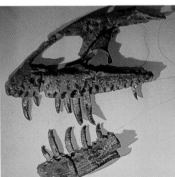

◄▲ Three fossils into one
Fossils found near each other at Sandown, on the Isle of Wight, southern England, build up a picture. A footprint (above left) shows the typical three-toed foot of a theropod, or meat-eating dinosaur. The skull and teeth (above right) confirm this identification, and the single vertebra from the backbone (left) helps to fill out the picture.

Georges Cuvier

French Baron Georges Cuvier (1769–1832) was the leading comparative anatomist of his time. He studied many vertebrates (animals with backbones), including various reptiles and mammals. He was also involved in one of the first scientific namings of a dinosaur, *Iguanodon*, even before the name "dinosaur" had been invented (see volume 7 of this series).

Cuvier saw how the bones of various creatures were shaped differently to carry out their tasks and resist stresses and strains. Yet the skeletons of these widely differing animals all had the same basic parts, such as a single bone in the upper leg (thigh) but two bones in the lower leg (shin). Likewise, the muscles of different animals were also varied in shape and size, but they too corresponded to a general plan. The similarities applied to many other parts of the body.

Cuvier lived at a time before the process of evolution by natural selection was described by Charles Darwin (see page 48). Cuvier saw the comparisons and parallels between different animals as evidence of God's work and grand plan.

▲ Very complete
The pelycosaur (mammallike reptile) *Dimetrodon* left several sets of fairly complete fossils, allowing a full reconstruction of its skeleton. This meat-eater lived in the Permian Period before the dinosaurs.

into the bone tissue. These rough patches or muscle scars remain after death when the muscles have rotted away. They may even remain after fossilization. So, the sizes and positions of these anchorage scars on a fossil dinosaur bone show how it was moved by muscles and in which direction and with how much power. Estimates of the size and weight of the head, neck, backbone, limbs, and tail also help to show the muscle power needed to move these parts.

Clothed in skin

In this way, the dinosaur is rebuilt from its skeleton outward, layer by layer. The position and size of the lungs and heart can be guessed at from the structure of the ribcage. The stomach and intestines are added in, again using modern reptiles as a guide.

The outermost layer is the skin. It seems a reasonable guess that dinosaurs, being reptiles, would have scaly skin like modern reptiles. In rare cases, actual specimens of fossil dinosaur skin have been found. Indeed, they show patterns of scales similar to the scales of some modern reptiles.

What color were dinosaurs?

The final but missing element is the color of the skin. Fossil dinosaur skin is made of stone and so it is the color of stone. Its color in life cannot be determined (see chapter 12 for discussion of advances in technology). So, the lifelike reconstruction of a dinosaur can be painted in any color, even yellow with pink spots, and no one could say it was wrong! However, most reconstructions have colors and patterns based on good guesses involving the colors of similar animals today such as crocodiles and lizards.

◄ Adding layers
Several skilled scientific disciplines converge in the process of adding muscles and other soft tissues to bones, then covering the whole body with skin, as here for the very well-known dinosaur *Iguanodon*.

⇒ The Age of Dinosaurs begins

By the end of the Triassic Period the Age of Dinosaurs was truly under way. These reptiles were spreading across the world and evolving into many different shapes and sizes.

As the Triassic Period reached its close, the dinosaurs were becoming established around the world as the dominant land animals. Why? Perhaps because the new carnivorous dinosaurs could walk and run more effectively than their sprawling prey and rivals. They became efficient killers of the old-style reptilian herbivores. The animals that had until now preyed on these same reptilian herbivores were the nondinosaur reptilian carnivores. Once the dinosaurs starting taking their prey, the nondinosaur reptilian carnivores began to starve. Soon they too became victims of the dinosaurs.

Evolution back in balance

Meanwhile, with the old-style reptilian plant-eaters on the way out, some early dinosaurs took their place and became vegetarian. Their upright stance allowed them to escape easily from the nondinosaur carnivores, adding another nail to the latters' coffin. However, the new dinosaur plant-eaters found it less easy to run from the rapidly evolving dinosaur meat-eaters.

After a time of rapid change the balance was restored. Dinosaur plant-eaters and meat-eaters developed together, each trying evolutionary tricks to get ahead but soon being caught by the other. *Coelophysis* was one of the early carnivores known from very plentiful fossil remains (see chapter 8). Meanwhile, some herbivores remained relatively small and agile, such as *Pisanosaurus* and *Technosaurus*. Prosauropod herbivores such as *Plateosaurus*, *Melanorosaurus*, and *Riojasaurus* evolved to a greater size,

A new era

One of the most exciting new lines of reptile evolution during the Triassic Period involved the winged pterosaurs like *Eudimorphodon* (skull shown here). It seems that within a few million years these creatures were soaring and flapping through the skies. Pterosaurs share many features with dinosaurs and may have evolved from an early type of dinosaurs, or the dinosaurs and pterosaurs both shared their ancestors.

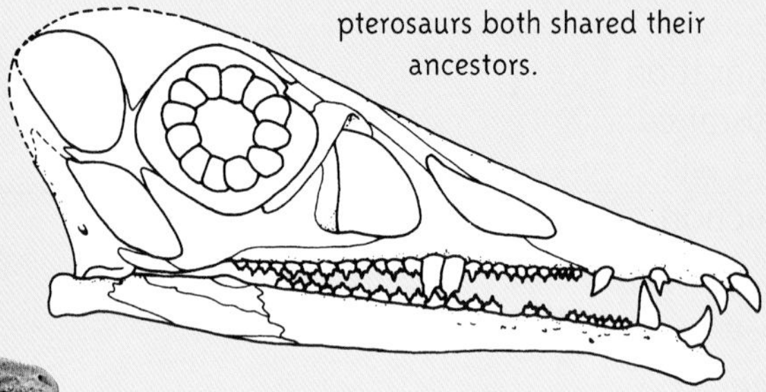

although not yet as big as the giant sauropods of the following Jurassic Period.

Dinosaurs and evolution

To understand the possible reasons for the rise of the dinosaurs, it helps to understand evolution itself. The idea of evolution was set out by the English naturalist Charles Darwin in 1859 in his book *On the Origin of Species.* Darwin had sailed around the world in the survey ship HMS *Beagle*. He explored new lands and studied and collected the plants and animals. While in the rainforests of South America, he was struck by the amazing color and activity of

◄ Bigger
One of the earliest "experiments in evolution" of the dinosaurs involved increasing size. It was exceptionally successful. Triassic prosauropods like *Plateosaurus* gave way to the giant Jurassic sauropods, the largest dinosaurs and the biggest of land animals.

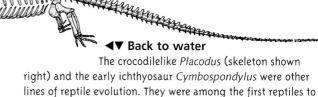

the wildlife.

On the Galapagos Islands in the Pacific Ocean Charles Darwin noticed how each island had its own species of certain animals, such as finches. Yet all of the finch species were quite similar to each other. It seemed to him that one original species had lived on all the islands and had changed to suit the particular conditions on each island, thereby giving rise to different species.

How evolution happens

The theory of evolution says that living things change, or evolve, through time. Each living thing has a struggle to survive in its environment. It must find food and shelter and avoid predators and danger. It must also breed, otherwise its kind may not carry on generation after generation. It is as though the natural conditions choose who will perish and who will survive. This is known as "natural selection."

If a living thing is well suited to its conditions, it has a better chance of surviving and breeding. This is known as "survival of the fittest."

As time passes on earth, conditions change. The climate becomes wetter or drier and hotter or colder. Sea levels rise and fall. Ice ages come and go. To keep up with changing conditions, living things have

◀▼ Back to water
The crocodilelike *Placodus* (skeleton shown right) and the early ichthyosaur *Cymbospondylus* were other lines of reptile evolution. They were among the first reptiles to take to the water from where their distant amphibian ancestors had crawled millions of years ago.

evolved through the ages. This is perhaps why the dinosaurs rose to prominence and why life continues to evolve today.

Reptiles galore

Toward the end of the Triassic Period, reptile success was also happening in the air and sea. The early winged reptiles, or pterosaurs, such as *Eudimorphodon* flapped through the skies. In the oceans were small-headed, long-necked nothosaurs such as *Nothosaurus* with its paddlelike limbs. There were also the early dolphin-shaped ichthyosaurs such as *Cymbospondylus* and *Shonisaurus*, and placodonts like *Placodus*, which resembled giant newts. The Mesozoic Era was not just the Age of Dinosaurs, it was truly the Age of Reptiles.

◀▲ Darwin's journey
Charles Darwin (upper picture) was overwhelmed by the color, variety, and activity of tropical forest life (lower picture) compared with the quiet English countryside. As an older naturalist who liked peace and privacy , he brought the theory of evolution into modern science.

⇒The start of an era

Around 230 million years ago a new group of creatures began to appear on earth. They would become one of the most successful types of animals ever and rule the land for more than 150 million years. They were the dinosaurs.

Fossils are the bones, teeth, claws, horns, shells, and other hard parts of living things, buried and preserved in rocks and gradually turned to stone. The fossil record reveals how life has changed on earth during tens and hundreds of millions of years by the process of evolution. Fossils show that the first of the animals we call dinosaurs appeared some 230-220 million years ago during the timespan known as the Middle to Late Triassic Period.

▲ **Prehistoric view**
A long-range view of the Middle Triassic landscape shows rolling hills, forests of trees, rivers and lakes, beaches and cliffs along the coast — in fact, much like today's countryside.

The Age of Dinosaurs

The Age of Dinosaurs really got under way as these first kinds of dinosaurs began to spread across the world and evolve during the Late Triassic period around 230-210 million years ago. At that time, the map of the world looked very different from the map we know today

▼ **Swampy scene**
Closer to, the view reveals many differences between the Triassic Peirod and today. There were no flowers or blossom trees, no grasses or reeds, no mammals or birds. The trees were conifers and large ferns and cycads.

What is a dinosaur?
A dinosaur is, or rather was, a type of animal called a reptile. Features of a typical reptile include:
- A bony skeleton built around a backbone, or vertebral column. (This means reptiles are vertebrate animals, along with fish, amphibians, birds, and mammals.)
- A cold-blooded body, unlike the warm-blooded bodies of birds and mammals.
- Four limbs (except for snakes and a few lizards).
- Skin covered with hard scales.
- Reproduction by laying eggs that hatch into young forms of the adult, rather than by giving birth to babies.

Several groups of reptiles survive today. They include:
- Snakes (ophidians) and lizards (lacertids).
- Turtles, terrapins, and tortoises (chelonians).
- Crocodiles, alligators, and caimans (crocodilians).

Like the dinosaurs, many other groups of reptiles have appeared on earth and then become extinct. Some are mentioned in this book, such as rhynchosaurs. The group of living reptiles that is most closely related to the dinosaurs is probably the crocodilians.

(see page 12). All the major landmasses or continents were joined into one great supercontinent, Pangaea. So the dinosaurs - which all lived on dry land - had no ocean barriers to prevent their spread to almost every part of the supercontinent. When Pangaea broke up, and the continents drifted into their present shapes and locations on the earth's surface, various groups of dinosaurs went with them.

As the Triassic Period gave way about 208 million years ago to the next major timespan, the Jurassic Period, dinosaurs were firmly established as the main large land animals.

A time of change

The origins of the dinosaurs and a few of the very first kinds of dinosaurs are described in chapter 1. This chapter covers the time from

▲ Dominant plants
Towering conifer trees such as *Araucarioxylon* (which grew nearly 200 feet or 60 meters tall) dominated the Triassic land. Primitive reptiles such as the newtlike *Procolophon* would soon be ousted by early dinosaurs.

the Middle-Late Triassic Period to the Early Jurassic Period, broadly from about 220 to 180 million years ago.

It was a very exciting time for dinosaur evolution. The basic dinosaur body plan, which had given them their initial success, was showing its adaptability. Different types of dinosaurs were evolving rapidly to take advantage of the many available food sources. This process of speedy evolution, as a new group of living things quickly becomes more diverse, numerous, and widespread, is known as adaptive radiation. It has happened many times through the immensely long history of life on earth. But few other adaptive radiations of a single animal group have had such a lasting effect as the

spread of those early dinosaurs.

Plants and animals

The probable ancestors of all dinosaurs were small, slim, darting hunters of little creatures such as insects. Some of the early dinosaurs remained much like these ancestors. Others developed into larger, fierce-fanged predators. Some became medium-sized browsers of leaves and other vegetation. Still others evolved into giant plant-eaters, as big as any land animals the world has seen before and since. This process was so rapid in terms of the timescale of evolution that within 30 million years, nearly all of the major groups of dinosaurs had appeared.

▼▶ A successful dig
On the right a paleontologist scrapes away earth to reveal the femur (thighbone) of a *Massospondylus*. The skull of the dinosaur (below) was dug up at the same site in South Africa.

Reptiles then and now
Turtles (left) were becoming established during the Triassic Period over 300 million years ago. However, other groups of reptiles such as snakes, were still well in the future. The snakes did not begin to appear until the Middle to Late Cretaceous Period less than 100 million years ago.

⇨ The Late Triassic world

The world at the time of the Late Triassic Period some 220-210 million years ago was very different from our world today. The landmasses and oceans were in different positions.

Living things change or evolve in response to their changing surroundings or environment. The environment includes temperature, rainfall, seasons, and other aspects of climate; rocks, soil, water, and other features of the nonliving world; and the living world of plants, animals, and microscopic life around them. As these factors alter, so do living things, driven by the struggle for existence and the battle to survive. Some do not make it and become extinct.

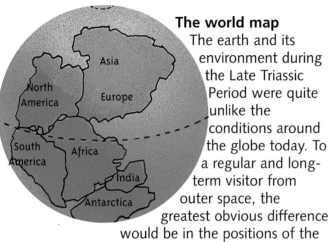

The world map

The earth and its environment during the Late Triassic Period were quite unlike the conditions around the globe today. To a regular and long-term visitor from outer space, the greatest obvious difference would be in the positions of the major landmasses or continents. North and South America, Europe, Africa, Asia, the Indian subcontinent, Australia, and Antarctica were not where they are today. They were all gathered into one vast and continuous landmass, the supercontinent of Pangaea. It was surrounded by an even greater single ocean, Panthalassa.

▼ Ever-changing world
We see forces of nature such as coastal erosion at work today. The sea relentlessly wears away cliffs, while in other areas land takes over from sea. Such processes must have happened through earth's history

Drifting continents
Since our planet began its landmasses have been pushed around its surface by the enormous forces, tremendous pressures, and incredible temperatures deep within the earth. The movement of the landmasses is known as continental drift.

The idea of continental drift was put forward as a serious theory by German scientist Alfred Wegener in 1912. He noticed that the various continents seem to fit together like pieces of a jigsaw puzzle. The close fit is particularly obvious in places such as the east coast of South America and the west coast of Africa.

The idea was rejected at first. But the discovery of similar fossils on landmasses now far apart, such as South America and Africa, added support to the theory. In the 1960s scientists began to examine the notion in more detail. Today it is an accepted idea.

Drifting continents
Pangaea had existed for many millions of years through the last part of the Paleozoic Era. This was the time before the Mesozoic Era - the era that consisted of the Triassic, Jurassic, and Cretaceous Periods and that roughly corresponds to the Age of Dinosaurs. As the Age of Dinosaurs went on, Pangaea began to split up as the continents drifted, often by only a few inches each year, to their present locations.

For most of the Triassic Period Pangaea was still more or less intact and stable. The early dinosaurs could still move freely from one part of the supercontinent to another. So, there were no great geographical differences between the various types of dinosaurs. These differences occurred later, as continents and islands became separate, and their dinosaurs evolved in isolation.

Currents and winds
The sea levels during the Triassic Period were slightly higher than they are today. So the

▲ Warmth-carriers
Ocean currents spread or distribute warmth from the sun around the planet. Today the Gulf Stream beings warmth from the tropical west Atlantic to the northeast Atlantic, making the climate milder.

lower-lying areas were flooded, and less dry land was exposed. Since the oceans were completely different in shape from today, their great currents were also different. Seawater absorbs much of the sun's warmth, and ocean currents have an enormous effect in distributing this around the world. Ocean currents also affect wind patterns around the world, as do the sizes and positions of sea and land areas, especially mountain ranges.

Winds, in turn, largely determine cloud and rainfall. So, continents, oceans, currents, and winds all contributed to the climate of the Triassic Period, as described on the next page.

What drives continental drift?
How can great landmasses slide around the surface of the planet? The answer lies in the idea of plate tectonics. The earth's surface is not one ball-shaped unit. It is made up of about 12 major curved pieces called lithospheric plates. They do, indeed, fit together like a giant spherical jigsaw.

From the deeper layer of the earth called the mantle, molten rock wells up under the middle of the oceans at chains of submerged mountains called mid-oceanic ridges. The molten rock hardens and adds to the edge of its lithospheric plate. This pushes the plate sideways. Its other edge rams into a neighboring plate. The two may crinkle and buckle, throwing up folds, which become mountains. Or one may slide below the other and melt back into the earth's depths.

In this way the lithospheric plates slide about on the molten mantle, carrying the continents about the globe. The energy to drive the process comes from the tremendous heat at the center of the earth. The whole process is known as the mechanism of plate tectonics.

▼ Seasonal change
In places such as temperate North America and Europe we are used to four seasons, spring, summer, fall (autumn) and winter, as signified by changing broad-leaved or deciduous trees. During the Triassic Period such seasons were probably much less marked, with perhaps just wet and dry phases.

⇒ Early variety

Dinosaurs are divided into two main groups, saurischians and ornithischians, based on the structure of their hipbones. Almost from the beginning, there were representatives of both groups.

In the study of dinosaur fossils the position of a small bone called the pubis in the hip has major importance (see panel opposite). In some dinosaurs it sloped forward, as in lizards today. They are known as the saurischian, or lizard-hipped, dinosaurs. This bone sloped rearward parallel with another hipbone, the ischium, in the ornithischian, or bird-hipped, dinosaurs. Which group came first? From almost the earliest dinosaurs both groups are represented in the fossil record.

The saurischians – prosauropods

The first group of dinosaurs to undergo the rapid evolution called adaptive radiation was the prosauropods. They were forerunners of the sauropods, or "lizard feet," the great long-necked, barrel-bodied dinosaurs of the Jurassic Period such as *Diplodocus* and *Apatosaurus*.

The prosauropods took over from the reptiles called dicynodonts, such as *Lystrosaurus*, which were the main large land-dwelling plant-eaters during the Early Triassic Period. The prosauropods appeared very quickly across the globe in every continent except Antarctica. They included slender plant-eaters like *Massospondylus*, *Anchisaurus* from North America and Africa, and larger, heavier plant-

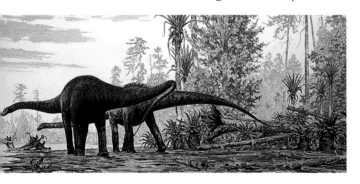

◄ ▼▲ New reptiles on the scene
The dicynodonts were cat-to-pig-sized plant-eating reptiles of the Late Permian and Triassic Periods. *Lystrosaurus* (above) is well known from abundant fossils. But the group died away as the early dinosaurs evolved along various pathways, such as the huge tree-browsing Jurassic sauropods (left) and the small, darting Late Triassic hunters known as coelurosaurs (below).

eaters like *Plateosaurus* from Europe, *Lufengosaurus* from China, and *Riojasaurus* in South America.

They were the first animals on earth that were large enough to browse on tree leaves several feet above the ground. They were very successful, and some became extremely abundant. They are described on later pages, starting with *Plateosaurus* on page 36.

The saurischians – theropods
Prosauropods were early plant-eating saurischian dinosaurs. The early meat-eating saurischians were known as theropods, or

Two types of dinosaurs

There were two great groups of dinosaurs. They were the Saurischia, or "lizard-hips," and the Ornithischia, or "bird-hips." These two groups of dinosaurs are distinguished by the bone called the pubis in the hip between the rear limbs.

- In some dinosaurs the pubis sloped down and forward, as in lizards today. They are known as saurischian, or lizard-hipped, dinosaurs.
- In others the pubis sloped down and backward, below another hipbone, the ischium, as in birds today. They are known as the ornithischian, or bird-hipped, dinosaurs.

It may seem odd to base the groupings of dinosaurs on such a small and apparently unimportant feature. But the position of the pubis is very significant in terms of evolution (see pages 44-45). When unfamiliar fossils of a new kind of dinosaur are discovered, examination of the hipbones (if they are present) helps identify it as a saurischian or ornithischian. At once this cuts down the options and points toward its closer relations.

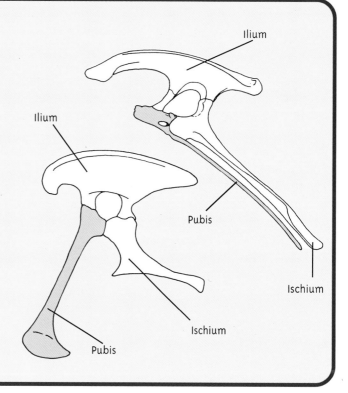

Ilium

Ilium

Pubis

Ischium

Ischium

Pubis

"beast feet." They were small, fast-moving carnivores that had little armlike front limbs and ran on their two larger rear limbs.

Some of the best-known early theropods are the slim, lightweight *Staurikosaurus* from the Late Triassic Period, which lived in Brazil, and the heavier *Herrerasaurus* mentioned in chapter 1).

Slightly later examples are *Coelophysis* (see chapter 8) and *Syntarsus*. *Syntarsus* – the name means "fused ankle" – was about 10 feet (3 meters) long. Its remains have been found in Early Jurassic rocks in South Africa, Zimbabwe, and Arizona.

The ornithischians

By the Late Triassic Period the ornithischian dinosaurs, which were all plant-eaters, had already become very successful.

The early types were small, lightweight animals that ran on their two larger rear limbs. They grabbed and manipulated plant food with their front limbs, which were like short arms with five-fingered hands.

One of the first was *Pisanosaurus*, "Pisano's lizard," which lived in Argentina in the early part of the Late Triassic Period. This dinosaur, which was about 3 feet (1 meter) long, was possibly a heterodontosaur (see page 49).

◀ **Early prosauropods**
Anchisaurus (left) and *Plateosaurus* (center and right) lived in different regions but were both plant-eaters.

Dinosaurs diversify

Plateosaurus was the first sizable dinosaur and probably the first of all animals to reach the leaves high in trees.

The best-known of the sauropods from its plentiful fossils is *Plateosaurus*, the "flat lizard." Its remains were first found in Germany in 1837. Dozens of specimens were uncovered between 1911 and 1932 also in Germany, and more were unearthed in France and Switzerland.

The main site for *Plateosaurus* fossils is Trossingen, near Stuttgart, Germany. It has yielded 35

Mass grave or chance collection?

The Trossingen fossils were at first believed to be the mass grave of a migrating *Plateosaurus* herd that had been overcome by some sudden disaster. This would be evidence that prosauropod dinosaurs lived in groups and showed social and migrating behavior.

Of course it may just be that skeletons of individuals that had died in separate places over several years happened to get washed into the same small area by flash floods. The floodwaters ran along otherwise dry channels, swishing and sweeping any remains in their way. The waters then disappeared into the ground at the same place each time, as floods do in the desert, leaving more carcasses or bones piled together. Methods of interpreting such evidence are described on pages 40-41.

The body of *Plateosaurus*

Plateosaurus was some 23 feet (7 meters) long. It is one of the first really sizable dinosaurs known from the fossil record and the first big land animal of any kind. It had the standard prosauropod shape: small head, a long and fairly flexible neck, a bulky, rounded body, and a very long, deep, tapering tail. The tail could have been held up off the ground for balance.

The rear legs of *Plateosaurus* were almost twice as long as the front legs and very strongly built. Like other prosauropods, *Plateosaurus* could probably walk on all fours or rear up on its two hind limbs.

What did *Plateosaurus* eat?

Plateosaurus had many small, thin, almost leaf-shaped teeth. They had wavy, or serrated, edges, which meshed together as the jaws worked up and down. The design seems ideal for shredding and chopping leaves and other vegetation. But there were no broad, flat-topped teeth for crushing and chewing. So *Plateosaurus* probably relied on stomach stones in its "gastric mill" gizzard to grind and further pulverize its food. Rounded pebbles have been found in the ribcage or gut regions of several fossilized *Plateosaurus* specimens.

▶ **The first large dinosaur**
Plateosaurus was the first large dinosaur, growing to more than 26 feet (8 meters). It could stand on its hind legs or on all fours and with its long neck probe for food over a wide area.

Being common is a clue

Another clue to the diet and lifestyle of *Plateosaurus* is the fact that so many of its fossils have been found, compared with other dinosaurs of the time. In natural habitats today, plant-eaters are always more numerous than meat-eaters. For example, there are more zebras, and wildebeest than there are lions and leopards. That is because the carnivores must feed on the herbivores. So, they cannot have a greater biomass – the overall weight of their living tissues – than the herbivores or outnumber them. If they did, the carnivores would be making their biomass out of nothing. Taking the chance and randomness of finding fossils into account, remains of *Plateosaurus* are more common than the remains of meat-eaters from its time. This is an ecological reason for presuming *Plateosaurus* was a plant-eater.

Cousins of *Plateosaurus*

Plateosaurus may be the ancestor of the sauropods, the truly giant dinosaurs that flourished during the Jurassic Period. Later, during the Early Jurassic Period prosauropods similar to *Plateosaurus* lived in other regions.

- *Lufengosaurus*, "Lufeng lizard." Its fossils were located in 1941 in Early Jurassic rocks of the Lufeng Basin in southwest China. This medium-sized prosauropod differed from *Plateosaurus* mainly in its distinctive skull bones. About 30 preserved specimens are known.
- *Yunnanosaurus*, "Yunnan lizard." Another Chinese prosauropod, it was found in 1942. It was also named from the place where its fossils were found — Yunnan Province. It was slightly smaller and less heavily built than *Plateosaurus*. It had a typical prosauropod skeleton, but its teeth were more like those of sauropods — like flattened pencils or spoons, with chisellike top edges that sharpened themselves during use.
- *Atlasaurus*, a possible forerunner of the great brachiosaurs. Its fossils were discovered in the late 1990s in Morocco, Africa, and date to 165 million years ago.

▼ Ambling along beside the river

Plateosaurus probably lived in herds. When the herd had stripped an area of tasty plants, it would have to wander off in search of more food. Here a herd ambles along a riverbank.

A well-known European

The first remains of *Plateosaurus* were described in 1837. Since then parts of this dinosaur have been collected from over 50 sites in Europe. So, its structure is well known.

Plateosaurus skull

The skull of *Plateosaurus* was small for the overall body size, long and pointed when seen from above, and deep from top to bottom when viewed from the side. A ridge on the lower jaw anchored strong jaw-closing muscles, and there were probably fleshy cheek pouches to retain food in the mouth.

▼ **A strong, balanced structure**
The back and tail of *Plateosaurus* were long, helping balance the front of the body. The front legs were short but strong enough to assist in weight-bearing when the dinosaur toppled or leaned forward.

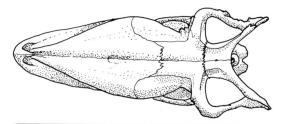

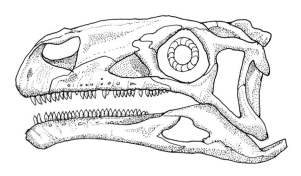

Whose teeth?

Stronger, blade-shaped teeth have been found near certain *Plateosaurus* skeletons. It has been suggested that they belonged to *Plateosaurus* itself and indicate a more mixed diet. However, the teeth could well have come from the mouth of a scavenger feeding off the *Plateosaurus* carcass. Overall, the comparison of *Plateosaurus* teeth with those of herbivorous lizards today and the position of the *Plateosaurus* jaw joint right at the lower rear of the head suggest a diet of plant leaves and stems.

Plateosaurus in place

Plateosaurus dates from the beginnings of dinosaur evolutionary radiation (see page 31). It lived at a time when a range of dinosaur body shapes and sizes was beginning to appear. We can imagine small herds of *Plateosaurus* wandering across arid Triassic plains, always looking for new food to graze or browse. If predators appeared, *Plateosaurus* could use its thumb-claws to defend itself and also a new feature - its sheer size, weight, and power.

Feet and toes

The front feet of *Plateosaurus* had five toes, the first three being quite long. The first toe or "thumb" had a massive claw. The outer two toes of each foot were much shorter than the others. The front foot could be weight-bearing with the toes bent backward and splayed out and the thumb-claw held off the ground. It could also be grasping. The thumb-claw may have been used to grab or hook cycads, conifers, and other foliage toward the mouth. Possibly it was also a self-defense feature.

Each rear foot had three long middle toes, with a shorter first toe and a much reduced fifth toe.

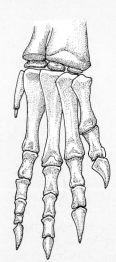

DATA BASE

Name *Plateosaurus*
Pronounced PLAT-ee-oh-SORE-us
Meaning "flat lizard"

What it ate
Plant-eater, especially fibrous leafy plants such as ferns

Length (nose - tail-tip) 23 feet (7 meters)
Standing height 10 feet (3 meters)
Weight nearly 1 ton (1 tonne)

When it lived Late Triassic Period
220 million years ago
Where it lived Europe (England, Germany, Switzerland, France)

Order Saurischia
(lizard-hipped dinosaurs)
Sub-order Sauropodomorpha
Family Plateosauridae

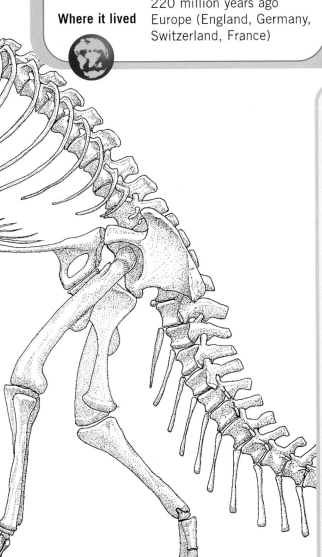

Why increasing size?

Any change in size has both payoffs and drawbacks in evolution. The balance of these in a particular habitat and time determines whether an animal group will adopt the trend or not. Advantages include:

- Protection from predators, using size, strength, and bulk in self defense. Also, only large predators can singly tackle large prey, and there were few large predators about in Triassic times.
- A large animal has more body volume compared with body surface area than a small animal. Heat is retained in body volume, but lost or gained through body surfaces. So, greater size leads to stability of the internal body temperature, making the animal more independent of ups and downs in the outside temperature.
- Moisture is also lost mainly through body surface, even through the scaly skin of reptiles. So, large size also reduces the risk of drying out in a dry climate.
- Large animals in general need less energy for their bulk than small ones. This would be especially important for herbivores living on an energy-poor diet.

Disadvantages include:

- A long period of growth and therefore vulnerability before adulthood is reached. This can be offset by parental care or herding behavior to protect the young.
- Growth puts a great strain on body chemistry, or metabolism.
- Huge amounts of energy are needed to move a large weight, and speed of reactions and agility are lost.
- Large herbivores put a great strain on the environment. They can strip an area of almost every green scrap of food. Then they have to move on, and the area takes much time to recover. This has occurred in Africa today where elephants have been confined to small park areas, and they have devastated the landscape.

Why piles of fossils ➤

Why piles of fossils?

Does a pile of *Plateosaurus* fossils mean that the animals lived and died together as a gregarious herd, or is it just a chance accumulation caused by natural forces such as floods?

Taphonomy is the scientific study of collections, gatherings, and accumulations of objects, and how, when, where, and why they occur. We can perhaps think of it as "the laws of burial."

Taphonomy is a growing science and is being applied to fossils, including dinosaur fossils, with increasing success. It is detective work that can find out how the animals died, and how and why they became buried and fossilized. It can also reveal how the animals lived and behaved in life, for example:

- Were they gregarious and group-dwelling or solitary?
- Did various ages and different sexes live together?
- Did they breed or nest alone or in colonies?
- Did the young leave the nest on hatching or stay for parental care?
- Were they predators or plant-eaters?
- Which other animals lived alongside them?

▲ **Two jaws**
A simple example of an articulated fossil is a skull with its lower jaw still in position as in life, like this *Plateosaurus* example., Many other specimens are skull and upper jaw only.

Whole and partial skeletons

The position of the bones in a fossil skeleton and the skeleton's completeness can reveal a lot. If the bones are separated and jumbled, it indicates that the skeleton was moved after the connecting joints between the bones had rotted away.

An articulated skeleton is one where the bones are positioned next to their neighbors, as they were linked in life. It suggests that the carcass was buried while the body was still in one piece, before scavenging or disintegration took place. Often, the stringlike tendons that hold the neck and tail stable contract after death. This pulls the head and neck backward over the shoulders or makes the tail curl up over the hips. Changes likes these are seen in many fossil articulated skeletons, including (famously) those of the first known bird, *Archaeopteryx*.

Missing bits in bone fragments or bones with gnaw marks indicate that the carcass was attacked by scavengers after death.

Associated remains

The fossils and debris near the fossil dinosaur can also yield many clues. The size of the rock pebbles or grains indicates whether the carcass lay at the bottom of a fast river or on the still, muddy bottom of a lake or sea.

From other fossils, especially shellfish and other invertebrates, and also from plants we can tell what kind of water was around them – salty or fresh, stagnant or fast-moving, sea or lake, swamp or river. Microfossils of plant pollen are especially numerous and useful in this respect.

Fossils of other large animals reveal the species that lived in the same area. That tells us about the type of habitat, such as a desert, wood, or swamp. Sometimes the relative positions of these fossils show if a creature was caught and died in the act of attacking prey or defending its young. In this sense the relative positions of the fossil remains represent "frozen behavior."

Search for the truth

Sometimes different people interpret fossil accumulations in different ways. A collection of the remains of one type of animal, such as the dinosaur *Plateosaurus* (see previous page), may indicate:

Elephant graveyards

For centuries in Africa and Asia there have been tales of "elephant graveyards." An old or sick or injured elephant that knows its end is near will make a final pilgrimage to a traditional and mystical site. The site is known to all elephants in the region and has been used by the herds since the mists of time.

Here the animal lies down among the massed bones, tusks, and other remains of its ancestors and dies peacefully. The lucky explorer who finds such a graveyard will also find a vast fortune in money — by selling the ivory of the tusks. At least, that is what used to happen when the ivory trade was at its height.

There have indeed been finds of several elephants that have died together rather than split up their herd. Also, bones and tusks have been found washed into the same area by floodwaters. But the idea that elephants make a special trip to a mystical graveyard site in order to die is not at all likely.

- a herd that was overcome by some catastrophe, such as a flood or volcanic fumes, when the members all died together;
- isolated carcasses that all found their way to the same place but at various times, because of water movements such as flash floods;
- a particular hazard at one site, such as a patch of quicksand or sinking mud, that repeatedly trapped individuals.

Further work may reveal the most likely interpretation. For example, fossils encased in certain fine-grained rocks could represent a bend in a river or an estuary, where the water's flow rate suddenly slows down, and particles that have been floating in the water settle on the bottom.

Improving techniques

Evidence useful in taphonomy was often ignored or lost in fossil excavations carried out in the past. The people involved did their digging in less time and did not keep such careful records, sketches, and photographs. So, valuable clues to the lives of the animals were lost.

However, methods have steadily improved. Fossils are now dug out with great care, and detailed grid drawings are made and photographs taken at each stage, as the layers of rocks are removed. The rocks around the fossils are not thrown away but are analyzed for bone fragments and microfossils. In addition, the modern and sophisticated science of forensics, developed especially for police work, is applied more and more to fossils. It will doubtless yield fascinating results in the future.

▶ **Associated evidence**

In addition to the dinosaur fossils themselves, many other rocks and fossils are excavated from the site. They are scrutinized back in the laboratory where conditions are more suited to work and there are plenty of equipment reference books and other fossils at hand for comparisons.

Big baby dinosaurs! ▶

⇒ Big baby dinosaurs?!

Since the 1970s Argentina has provided some of the most exciting fossil dinosaur discoveries. They include some of the smallest of all known dinosaur specimens – babies just 8 inches (20 centimeters) long.

In 1979 a group of tiny and almost perfectly preserved dinosaur hatchlings (babies just hatched from their eggs) were found in Argentina. They date back to the Late Triassic Period and each was no more than 8 inches (20 centimeters) in total length from nose-tip to tail-end. They were found in a nest alongside two similarly tiny unhatched eggs just 1 inch (2.5 centimeters) long, smaller than a hen's eggs. They are the smallest dinosaur specimens so far discovered. Because they were so tiny they were given the name *Mussaurus*, "mouse lizard." However, the fully grown adult would have been far larger.

Baby features

How do we know that these specimens were young and not fully grown individuals? The new babies of almost all vertebrate animals, including most fish, amphibians, reptiles, birds, and mammals, have certain "baby features" that we can recognize. They are mostly concerned with the sizes and proportions of their various body parts, such as:
- a large head relative to the body;
- a small or short face relative to the overall size of the head;
- large eyes relative to the size of the face;
- a small snub or flattened nose or snout;
- a short, thin neck;
- a chubby body;
- thin, often long but spindly limbs.

We can see these features in new toadlets, young crocodiles, bird chicks, and baby mammals from horse foals to puppies, kittens, and human beings. The *Mussaurus* fossils also had these features.

Clues from growth

There are other clues in the way that an animal body grows, especially the bones of its skeleton. A bone's shape forms first as cartilage or gristle – the softer, slightly more flexible version of bone. Only later does the shaped object that is cartilage gradually ossify, or turn to bone. It fills itself with the hard chemicals of calcium, phosphate, and other minerals to form true bone tissue.

This ossification process does not happen all over the bone at once. It usually begins in the middle of a bone and spreads along to the ends. This allows the bone to grow and shape itself quickly in the cartilage form during development and then harden and strengthen into its final shape as mature bone tissue.

In the *Mussaurus* specimens, the growing end regions of the fossil bones show that they

◀ Bursting into life

In this interesting reconstruction a model baby dinosaur hatches from its egg. The size of the egg is based on the fossil remains in the foreground.

▲ Still new to self-defense

A young *Maiasaura* tries to escape from an *Albertosaurus*. Like all youngsters, they still have a lot to learn about self-protection.

were still cartilage. They had not yet formed into true bone tissue. That is evidence of their youth or immaturity.

Clues from size

There is also the evidence of size. No other dinosaurs have been discovered that are anywhere near the tiny size of the specimens of *Mussaurus*, especially among the prosauropod or sauropod group. Some of the *Mussaurus* skulls were only about 1 inch (less than 3 centimeters) long, smaller than a human thumb. The next-largest well-known dinosaur came from an entirely different group. It was the Jurassic meat-eating theropod *Compsognathus*, with a total length of 70-80 centimeters and a head and body about the size of a chicken.

Two types of dinosaurs ▶

⇒ Two types of dinosaurs

There were two great groups of dinosaurs. They were the saurischians, or "lizard-hips," and the ornithischians, or "bird-hips" (see also page 35).

▲ Cousins face to face
A large predator or carnosaur faces a sauropod — two very different dinosaurs, but both with a saurischian hip structure.

Saurischians
- The small, lightly built, early dinosaurs called coelurosaurs such as *Coelurus* (see page 34).
- The very long-legged and swift "ostrich dinosaurs," or ornithomimosaurs, like *Struthiomimus*.
- The dreaded pack-hunting dromaeosaurs, or "raptors," such as *Deinonychus* and *Velociraptor*.
- The largest and fiercest of meat-eating dinosaurs, the carnosaurs such as *Allosaurus* and *Tyrannosaurus*.
- The prosauropods and sauropods, which were the biggest of all dinosaurs, with small heads, long necks, bulky bodies, pillarlike legs, and long tails, including *Diplodocus*, *Apatosaurus*, and *Brachiosaurus*.

Ornithischians
- The ornithopods, a very large and varied group, which consisted of the fabrosaurs such as *Lesothosaurus*, heterodontosaurs (see page 46), hypsilophodonts such as *Hypsilophodon*, dryosaurs and camptosaurs, iguanodonts like *Iguanodon* and *Ouranosaurus*, and the hadrosaurs or "duckbilled" dinosaurs such as *Parasaurolophus*.
- The plated dinosaurs or stegosaurs such as *Stegosaurus*, with upright plates of bone along their backs.
- The armored dinosaurs, or ankylosaurs, like *Euoplocephalus*, with massive bony plates like shields in their skin.
- The bone-headed dinosaurs, or pachycephalosaurs, with thick crests or helmets of bone on their heads.
- The horned dinosaurs, or ceratopsians, such as *Triceratops*, with long horns on their heads and bony frills over their necks.

▲ Big teeth
A facial view of a great carnosaur such as *Allosaurus* or *Tyrannosaurus* shows the most fearsome of saurischians and of all dinosaurs.

◄ Bird-hip
Triceratops may not resemble a bird. But its dinosaur group, the ornithischians, had a basically birdlike structure to their hipbones. This seems even stranger when we consider that the first birds probably evolved from small theropods or meat-eating dinosaurs, the "raptors" — which have the lizard-like rather than birdlike hip pattern.

Saurischian features

The main feature of a saurischian dinosaur is, as the name suggests, its hipbone arrangement. The part of the hip called the pubic bone jutted downward between the legs and also forward (see illustration on page 35). In many saurischians this bone also developed a hook- or footlike end at right angles to the main shaft for extra muscle anchorage. Many saurischians also had long necks with elongated neck bones.

This group included both herbivores, such as the prosauropods and sauropods, and carnivores, such as the various types of theropods.

Ornithischian features

In the ornithischian dinosaur hip, the pubic bone jutted down and also backward. However, in some groups this bone developed an additional forward-pointing part, like a rod or spike. At first glance this part, the prepubis, resembles the forward-pointing pubis of a saurischian dinosaur, and it can lead to confusion. However, a saurischian dinosaur lacked the true pubis bone projecting down and back below the other bone in the hip, the ischium.

Many ornithischians also had a predentary bone at the tip of the lower jaw, which was often toothless and covered by a horny "beak." Another feature was bony tendons along the backbone, forming a trellis arrangement to link the individual bones, or vertebrae, for added support. All ornithischian dinosaurs, as far as is known, were largely or totally herbivorous.

Hips and guts

The arrangement of the hipbones affected the position of the dinosaur's digestive system.

- In a saurischian, the forward-pointing pubic bone made the dinosaur's guts sit further forward in the belly. In large carnivorous saurischians such as *Tyrannosaurus* this was not a problem, since the guts were fairly straight and simple, and food passed quickly through. But in the larger herbivores like the sauropods, the weight of the guts to the front of the body meant that they had to stay on all four legs.

- In an ornithischian, the backward-pointing pubic bone allowed the guts to be further back in the abdomen, so that their main bulk was between the hind legs. This helped the balance of large bipedal dinosaurs – those that walked and ran on their two rear legs. The bipedal herbivore body design became very common among ornithischian dinosaurs, including most of the ornithopods, the group including *Iguanodon* and the hadrosaurs.

▲ Small teeth
The prosauropods and sauropods had small teeth shaped like leaves or pegs or pencils, for snipping and raking plant food. Compare this view with the carnosaur teeth opposite!

◀ Steps in time
Clues about the size, weight, posture, and moving speeds of dinosaurs come from fossils of their footprints. These were made by a saurischian dinosaur, probably a meat-eater; or theropod. Note how the feet are "pigeon-toed" and turn in slightly – the print in the foregound (at the bottom of the picture) is a right foot.

→ Struggle for survival

Many reptiles today become inactive and "sleep" through bad conditions, such as a drought. It saves energy and valuable reserves of body fluids. Could some of the early dinosaurs have done the same?

Lesothosaurus was a small, slim, lightweight, fleet-footed, plant-eating dinosaur. Along with *Heterodontosaurus* shown on the following page, it was possibly one of the earliest members of the large and varied dinosaur group called ornithopods (see page 44).

Lesothosaurus was hardly larger than a pet cat of today. It moved about mainly on its larger, stronger back legs, its body tilted slightly upright, its small front legs dangling like arms, and its long, stiff tail held out horizontally behind.

The head of *Lesothosaurus*, low and long-mouthed, resembled that of some modern lizards. At the front the mouth was narrow and pointed and perhaps covered in horn during life to form a "beak" for pulling, snipping, and cropping leaves and other food.

At the dawn of the Jurassic

Lesothosaurus lived about 207-205 million years ago, at the very start of the Jurassic Period, in southern Africa and possibly also in Venezuela, South America. Its fossils, reconstruction, and lifestyle, and its possible confusion with another small early dinosaur named *Fabrosaurus*, are described in chapter 7 of this book. Here we examine the fascinating fossil find of two *Lesothosaurus* skeletons that were curled up together.

The puzzle of the teeth

The two preserved *Lesothosaurus* specimens each had a full set of new-looking, unworn teeth. But there were worn teeth of the same type scattered around their remains.

What had happened? One suggestion is that these two small dinosaurs were aestivating. Aestivation is similar to hibernation, but it is a way of surviving heat and dryness rather than cold. It is a response to drought conditions in which there is very little food available.

The rocks and fossils of the area show that the land at the time was dry scrub and semidesert, probably with

The skull of *Lesothosaurus* (right, above) is compared with that of *Pisanosaurus* (right, below) which has stronger, sturdier teeth for bettter food-grinding.

A reptilian gazelle?

Gazelles, large and small, feed on the African plains today. Perhaps in its day *Lesothosaurus* was the equivalent of a gazelle. It was small and very light, built for speed, as shown by the very long shin and toe bones in its back legs. The front legs were short but strong, with five stubby, fingerlike toes. *Lesothosaurus* would feed on low plants, looking up to scan for danger with its large eyes, ready to dart away at the slightest disturbance. This dinosaur was among the earliest with a definite "birdlike" hip structure that identifies one of the two great groups of dinosaurs, the ornithischians.

seasonal rains and then long dry spells. Perhaps the two *Lesothosaurus* were sleeping out the hottest, driest part of the year, inactive in a cool burrow. During this time they shed their old, worn teeth and grew a new set, ready to feed immediately after they woke up, when conditions were more favorable and their plant food was growing.

Close-fitting choppers

Humans have only two sets of teeth, the baby (milk or deciduous) teeth and the adult (permanent) set. Most living reptiles shed their teeth and grow new ones to replace them all through their lives. Fossils show that dinosaurs probably did the same.

The cheek teeth of *Lesothosaurus* were like wedges or arrowheads, ridged and with grooved edges. The upper and lower teeth of *Lesothosaurus* fitted together and intermeshed

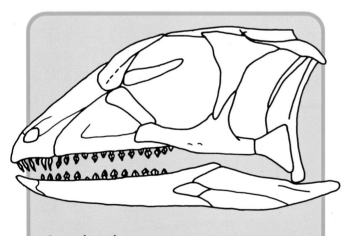

Spaced teeth
The fossil skull, jaws, and teeth of *Lesothosaurus* show how the teeth were widely spaced. Those at the very front of the upper jaw may have pressed down on a horny pad at the front of the lower jaw supported by the predentary bone, to crop food in the manner of sheep today (see page 48).

Light-boned runner

The lifelike picture of *Lesothosaurus* (opposite) is reconstructed around the fossil bones of the skeleton shown here. Animals today that have shins longer than their thighs are very fleet of foot, and the same probably applied in dinosaur times. The bones themselves are very slim, and the skull is "reduced" from plates and slabs to thin struts. This structure would also save weight at the front end and allow the dinosaur to dart and flick its head about at speed, perhaps to peer at predators or snap off leafy food.

A Texan *Lesothosaurus*?
"*Technosaurus*" is the preliminary name for a dinosaur known from fossils found in Texas. These remains suggest a creature very like *Lesothosaurus*, an early ornithischian and perhaps one of the early ornithopod dinosaurs. It was small, slim, and light, and ran on its two longer back legs. It lived during the Late Triassic Period.

closely as the jaws closed. The jaw joints allowed only up-and-down cutting movements, not side-to-side grinding motion.

New teeth for old

Eating would become tricky if a few teeth were being lost here and there all the time at random. It would be easier for the animal if all its teeth were lost and replaced at once. And it would be convenient if this happened during aestivation because then the animal would not be eating.

⇨Teeth and feet

Teeth are very hard and make good fossils. They also give clues to what their owner ate. *Heterodontosaurus* and *Pisanosaurus* were among the early dinosaurs that left fine fossils of their teeth.

Teeth are so important and revealing in the fossil record that some dinosaurs have been described and named on the basis of just one preserved tooth specimen. Not *Heterodontosaurus*. It has left many fossils of its teeth and jaws and other parts of its skeleton.

Also, a typical reptile has teeth that are all much the same size and shape. This also applies to most dinosaurs. Again, not *Heterodontosaurus*. It had three distinct types of teeth in its mouth, hence its name, which means "varied-toothed lizard."

Types of teeth

From front to rear the tooth types of *Heterodontosaurus* were:

- A few small, sharp, almost spiky teeth in the front of the upper jaw. They bit against the standard ornithopod horny beak covering the predentary bone at the front of the

long, tusklike teeth. Possibly they belonged to one sex, perhaps females, and it was the males that had the teeth. Suggested uses for such teeth include mating battles or fights with rivals, mating displays to partners, self-defense, and digging or grubbing in the ground for food.

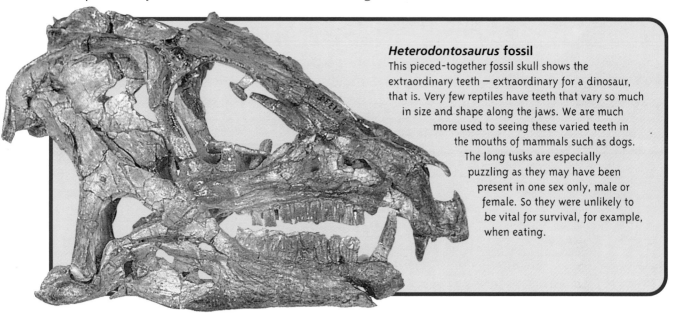

Heterodontosaurus fossil

This pieced-together fossil skull shows the extraordinary teeth — extraordinary for a dinosaur, that is. Very few reptiles have teeth that vary so much in size and shape along the jaws. We are much more used to seeing these varied teeth in the mouths of mammals such as dogs. The long tusks are especially puzzling as they may have been present in one sex only, male or female. So they were unlikely to be vital for survival, for example, when eating.

lower jaw and were for snipping and cropping.

- A pair of extraordinary fang- or tusklike teeth in both upper and lower jaws. They were like the large canine teeth of today's dogs. As the mouth closed, the lower teeth fitted into socketlike grooves in the opposing jaw.
- A row of around 12 close-packed, chisel-sharp, high-crowned cheek teeth on either side of both the upper and lower jaws. They were for grinding and pulping food.

Some fossil skulls lacked any trace of the

The discovery of *Heterodontosaurus*

Heterodontosaurus was about 3-4 feet (1-1.2 meters) in total length. It was a small dinosaur, slightly larger than *Lesothosaurus* shown on the previous page and more heavily built. It lived at about the same time as *Lesothosaurus*, the Early Jurassic Period, and in the same region, southern Africa.

The first fossils of *Heterodontosaurus* were found by experts from South Africa and from the University of London, England. This dinosaur was named in 1962 from a fossil skull. Since then more specimens have been discovered, including a virtually complete skeleton. *Heterodontosaurus* browsed on low-growing vegetation, snipping off the leaves and chewing them thoroughly.

An early bird-foot

Some of the bodily features of *Heterodontosaurus* place it as one of the earliest members of the ornithopod group (see page 44). The ornithopods were a very varied and successful group of dinosaurs that included hypsilophodonts, dryosaurs, camptosaurs, iguanodonts, among them the famous *Iguanodon*, and hadrosaurs or "duckbills," which flourished near the end of the Age of Dinosaurs.

"Ornithopod" means "bird-foot." *Heterodontosaurus* had the typical ornithopod foot structure of three long, forward-pointing toes on each foot – like many modern birds. The bones of its lower leg, ankle, and upper foot were also firmly joined together, again as in birds.

Pisano's lizard

Another early ornithischian dinosaur and possibly one of the earlier ornithopods like *Heterodontosaurus* was *Pisanosaurus*, "Pisano's lizard." It lived during the Late Triassic Period in Argentina, South America. It was a plant-eater, similar in general size and shape to *Lesothosaurus* and *Heterodontosaurus*. It may have made a good meal for the meat-eater *Herrerasaurus*, which lived at the same time and in the same region (see chapter 1 in this book).

Missing evidence

However, the fossilized remains of the pelvis, or hipbone, of *Pisanosaurus*, which is the main bone used to determine membership of the ornithischian group (see page 35), are fragmentary. So we cannot yet be sure about the exact identity of *Pisanosaurus* and its

▲ Creeping among the giants
A small *Pisanosaurus* walks warily among the tangled roots of conifers, cycads, and tree ferns in the Late Triassic Period. Dinosaur evolution was occurring rapidly at this time as the main groups became established across the supercontinent of Pangaea.

relationship with other dinosaurs. But it did leave fossils of its low, triangular-crowned teeth, which could grind food effectively (shown on page 46). They are characteristic of the later ornithopods and similar ornithischians and are arranged in same way. *Pisanosaurus* may also have had fleshy cheek pouches, another ornithopod feature.

⇨ Introduction to the carnosaurs

The most feared and fearsome of all dinosaurs belong to the group called carnosaurs – the "flesh-eating lizards." The world has not seen such big, powerful meat-eating land animals before or since.

Picture a dinosaur in your mind. Is it a fierce meat-eater with a mouthful of sharp teeth? Does it have a large head relative to its body, with big, beady eyes and a thick, strong neck? How about an upright body posture, smaller armlike front limbs, and larger, longer back limbs like our own legs? A long powerful tail? And a hungry, knowing look, as though it is figuring out what to do? It may even be ready to pounce at once and tear its victim to bits...

From the king downward

Above is the description of a typical carnosaur. It applies perfectly to *Tyrannosaurus rex* itself, among the biggest of the group, king of the dinosaurs, and one of the most famous animals that ever existed. Other carnosaurs were very similar to *Tyrannosaurus* in body shape and plan, but smaller in size.

This chapter describes the main members of the dinosaur group Carnosauria, "flesh-eating lizards." It has between 20 and 30 well-known members. They lived at various times through almost the entire Age of Dinosaurs, from about 185 million years ago to the great extinction of all dinosaurs 65 million years ago.

Today's carnivores

Think of a carnivorous or flesh-eating animal today. Maybe a lion or tiger, perhaps a wolf, or a smaller hunter such as a mink or weasel. It shows the bodily features needed by a creature that preys on other animals — agile and fast movements, strength with stealth, sharp teeth and claws, and keen senses both to detect victims and to try and remain unnoticed by them until the last moment.

◄ **Kings of yesterday and today**
Tyrannosaurus was one of the biggest carnosaurs and one of the last of all dinosaurs. On the left is one of today's largest carnivores, a lion.

The ultimate predators?

The fossil bones (see page 61) and other parts of carnosaurs show that they had strong, flexible skeletons, sharp teeth and claws, and large eye sockets and other features suggesting keen senses. The carnosaurs may have been some of the most effective killers that the animal world has ever produced.

Putting the evidence together

Fossils are solid evidence of the bones, teeth, horns, claws, and other hard parts of dinosaurs and other living things from prehistoric times.

Putting a collection of dinosaur fossils together to form a skeleton requires some informed guesswork, especially when parts are missing.

Reconstructing the animal's muscles and other soft parts, its skin, and outward appearance needs more guesswork.

And trying to reconstruct the dinosaur's behavior and daily life requires yet another series of guesses, including knowledge about related living animals.

It is possible to determine whether the fossils of a dinosaur came from a male or female animal if certain bones are preserved. The main one is the ring-shaped pelvis, or hipbone. As a female reptile lays its eggs, they must pass through the large hole in the middle of the pelvis, known as the pelvic opening, on their way from the egg tube, or oviduct, to the outside. So female reptiles tend to have proportionally wider and more rounded pelvic openings than males of the same species.

What were the carnosaurs?

The dinosaurs known as carnosaurs (Carnosauria) were part of a much larger group of dinosaurs — the Theropoda (theropods), or "beast-feet." Other members of the Theropoda included:

- The small, lightly built, early dinosaurs called coelurosaurs.
- The very long-legged and swift "ostrich dinosaurs," or ornithomimosaurs.
- The dreaded pack-hunting dromaeosaurs, or "raptors," such as *Deinonychus* and *Velociraptor*.

In turn, the Theropoda belonged to an even bigger group of dinosaurs, the Saurischia, or "lizard-hips."

Dinosaurs

Saurischians   Ornithischians

Sauropods   **Theropods**

Carnosaurs   **Coelurosaurs**   **Ornithomimosaurs**   **Dromaeosaurs**

The early carnosaurs

From almost unknown origins carnosaurs evolved rapidly. By the middle of the Jurassic Period they were the main predatory dinosaurs.

Among the earliest of all dinosaurs were the small, lightly built, slim-limbed coelurosaurs (see chapter 2). They appeared around 210-200 million years ago. One of the best-known is *Coelophysis*, about 10 feet (3 meters) long and standing 5 feet (1.5 meters) tall on its back legs. It lived in western North America almost at the beginning of the Age of Dinosaurs. Huge numbers of its fossilized skeletons have been found in New Mexico.

◀ **Ancestor of the carnosaurs?**
Coelophysis was almost certainly a meat-eater. It probably ate small victims such as insects, lizards, amphibians, and fish. Its teeth were numerous, but not large or strong enough to tear flesh from large prey.

Stouter, stronger, and heavier

Quite possibly, a creature such as *Coelophysis* may have been the ancestor of the first carnosaurs, which appeared millions of years later. The overall body shape and posture needed only small changes during the process of evolution from coelurosaur to carnosaur.

The main differences were that coelurosaurs were more lightly built than carnosaurs, with slimmer limbs, front legs almost as big as back legs, a narrower, longer neck, and a relatively smaller, slimmer head. The individual bones of the skeleton were very light in coelurosaurs, with hollowed-out cavities, thin walls, and additional weight-saving "windows." Most early carnosaurs had larger, stronger, heavier, more solid bones.

But this is only informed guesswork. *Coelophysis* lived around 210 million years ago. Apart from one notable exception, shown on the next page, the earliest fossils of large carnosaurs date back to around 170-160 million years ago. Good fossil evidence for the change from coelurosaur to carnosaur through the timespan in between is lacking.

The rise of the carnosaurs

The earliest large carnosaurs date from the Middle Jurassic period. They include *Eustreptospondylus* from what is now England, *Gasosaurus* from China, and *Piatnitzkysaurus* from South America. They show the developing carnosaur features of larger overall size, thicker and heavier bones, shrinking front legs, and enlarging back legs, each with three or four big-clawed toes. They probably walked with the body held horizontal to the ground, the head and neck at the front balancing the thick tail behind.

Why predators are rare

Nature's food chains and webs move in one direction. Plants grow using the sun's light energy and soil nutrients. Herbivore animals eat plants. Carnivore animals eat herbivores. Top carnivores eat herbivores and other carnivores. As all this happens, food nutrients and energy pass from plants to herbivores to carnivores to top carnivores.

But at each link in the chain there are losses. Some plants and animals die and rot without being eaten. Animals lose energy and nutrients in their droppings. They also use energy for their own life processes such as moving, feeding, and breeding. So at each stage or link energy and nutrients become less and support fewer animals.

This is why today herbivores are the most common animals, and top carnivores are rarest. Presumably the same principles of ecology

applied to dinosaurs. Carnosaurs, being top carnivores, would be naturally rare compared with the plant-eating dinosaurs. By the laws of chance rare animals would leave fewer fossils. This may be one reason why carnosaur fossils are so scarce and fragmentary. (See also page 59.)

A creature before its time?

The earliest large carnosaur known from good fossil evidence is *Dilophosaurus*. In fact, it is the earliest big meat-eating dinosaur of any kind. It roamed western North America and China about 200-185 million years ago. It was not as heavily built as the later carnosaurs and could probably outrun most other creatures of its time. Also, its jaws were not as wide and powerful as later carnosaurs, nor its teeth as long and daggerlike. They were more like the jaws and teeth of a modern crocodile, set in a long, slim mouth. So this hunter may have grasped and killed smaller prey with its very sharp toe claws, then ripped off flesh with the teeth, rather than biting victims to death. *Dilophosaurus* is described in more detail on the next page.

▼ More than 200 million years old

This fossil skeleton of *Coelophysis* has been preserved almost complete. The bones are still in position next to each other, as they would be in life, rather than jumbled up as in most fossil finds. They show the long, slim head and neck and the base of the very long, thin tail.

⇨ The megadinosaur

Megalosaurus, a powerful and thick-set Jurassic carnosaur, is only vaguely known from scarce and scattered fossils. Yet it is famous as one of the first dinosaurs to be given an accurate scientific description and name.

In centuries past people wondered at the solid stone lumps dug from the ground and shaped like bones, teeth, and horns. Now we know them as fossils. But back then there were many fanciful explanations about their origins — animals that had died in a Great Flood, fakes fashioned by the Almighty to test our faith, even the remains of great dragons and other mythical beasts.
In the early 1800s scientists began to take a more studied interest in these lumps of rock. The idea arose that they could be the remains of great creatures that thrived long ago but survived no more.

The first named dinosaur

In 1824 the English naturalist, geologist, anatomist, and clergyman William Buckland (1784-1856) wrote a scientific article describing some of these remains. They were from a quarry at aptly named Stonesfield in

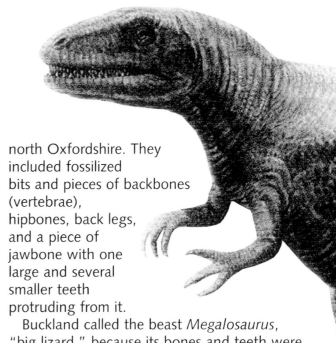

north Oxfordshire. They included fossilized bits and pieces of backbones (vertebrae), hipbones, back legs, and a piece of jawbone with one large and several smaller teeth protruding from it.

Buckland called the beast *Megalosaurus*, "big lizard," because its bones and teeth were so huge compared with those of other known animals of the time. This was how *Megalosaurus* became the first dinosaur to receive a formal scientific name.

However, at the time no one knew that *Megalosaurus* was a dinosaur. This was because the name "dinosaur" had not been invented. It was coined in 1841 by Richard Owen (see panel).

How dinosaurs got their name

Richard Owen (1804-92) was an eminent British anatomist and eventual superintendent of the Natural History Museum in London. In about 1839-40 he recognized the similarities between *Megalosaurus* and two other lizardlike beasts also named from their fossils, *Iguanodon* and *Hylaeosaurus*. Owen realized that they were reptiles but not from the lizard group. He also acknowledged their great size. And so he invented a new group of reptiles for them. He called it Dinosauria — "terrible lizards."

A confusion of *Megalosauruses*

For many years after the official naming of *Megalosaurus* various other fossils that were even only vaguely similar were given the same name. This resulted in great confusion, which persists even today. An example involves remains found in Arizona in 1942. In 1952 they were said to be *Megalosaurus*. But further study and more discoveries showed that they were from a different carnosaur, and in 1970 they were renamed as *Dilophosaurus* . Other examples concern *Eustreptospondylus* and *Altispinax*.

A typical carnosaur?

Despite its important place in the scientific study of dinosaurs, *Megalosaurus* remains a little-

▲ **Parts and whole**
Remains of *Megalosaurus bucklandi*, displayed at Oxford University Museum, England.

Killer with its claws?
Megalosaurus probably had very strong fingers and toes, with large claws. It may have attacked victims by kicking and slashing them, inflicting deep wounds that bled profusely. The carnosaur then followed its prey as it weakened from loss of blood. Fossilized footprints found in southern England, if made by *Megalosaurus*, show that it walked on its back legs.

known carnosaur. Its fossils range from Middle to Late Jurassic times and have been found in England, France, possibly Morocco, and probably Australia. They suggest a carnosaur about 23 to 30 feet (7 to 9 meters) long, around 13 feet (4 meters) tall, and weighing 1-2 tons (tonnes).

In overall body proportions *Megalosaurus* was similar to, although larger than, *Eustreptospondylus*. It probably had a powerful, short neck and a large head with strong jaws. The rest of this dinosaur was like a typical carnosaur. At least, that is the assumption. Very few fossils of the body, arms, legs, or tail have been firmly identified.

→ The great Jurassic carnosaur

Allosaurus was one of the biggest and most powerful of all meat-eating dinosaurs — and its fossils are unusually common.

When asked to picture a big, meat-eating dinosaur, many people imagine *Tyrannosaurus* (see page 60). Yet 80 million years earlier another huge and powerful predatory dinosaur, similar to *Tyrannosaurus*, stalked the land on its two strong back legs, ready to sink its dozens of bladelike teeth into a likely victim.

It was *Allosaurus*, one of North America's best-represented carnosaurs. Thousands of its fossilized bones, teeth, and claws have been uncovered at various sites, including huge piles of the remains of more than fifty *Allosaurus* at the Cleveland-Lloyd Dinosaur Quarry in Utah.

▲ Face down
Two *Allosaurus* size each other up in the Jurassic fern and frond forest. Each is at the edge of its territory, ready to resist the other's intrusion. However, the confrontation probably ended without a fight – neither wanted to risk being wounded.

A widespread beast

Allosaurus is the biggest carnosaur yet discovered from the Jurassic period around 200-144 million years ago. It had an overall length of some 36 feet (10.9 meters) and weighed 2 tons (2 tonnes) or more.

The first fossils of *Allosaurus* were dug up in 1870 in Colorado. The dinosaur's name, meaning "strange lizard," reflects the confusion surrounding the identity of these remains when they were first studied. Fossils have since been located in many other U.S. states, including Utah, Montana, New Mexico, Oklahoma, South Dakota, and Wyoming.

More recently remains of *Allosaurus* — or a very similar creature — have been found at Mtwara in Tanzania, East Africa. And yet more fossils come from the Dinosaur Cove region near Melbourne, in the state of Victoria, Australia. These fossils represent a smaller

Well-engineered design

The steel frame of a skyscraper is designed to use the minimum materials for maximum strength. Girders, struts, and plates are placed at certain positions and angles to withstand the stresses and strains imposed on the whole structure. The skull of *Allosaurus* shows similar design principles, shaped by the natural process of evolution. There are struts and plates of bone to withstand precisely the shocks and stresses of catching, tearing up, and eating a kicking, struggling victim. Where strains are less, there are gaps, or "windows," to save on raw materials and weight.

version of *Allosaurus*, perhaps because of this dinosaur's geographical variation.

Wide mouth

Another fascinating feature of *Allosaurus* was its jaws. They ran almost the entire length of the head. The lower jawbone was nearly as long as the main skull above it, and the main jaw hinge joints between the two were at the rear. When *Allosaurus* opened its mouth, it seemed that the upper part of its head almost detached from the lower part to produce an enormous top-to-bottom gape.

Even more frightening for prey, the mouth could become wider too. The bones of the skull were loosely attached to each other and to the jaws, so they could splay outward, increasing the distance between the left and right sides of the jaws. Also, there were joints midway along the lower jaw bones that could flex outward even further.

The combination of these various features meant that *Allosaurus* had a truly vast mouth and could certainly "open wide"!

Strong body

Allosaurus had the typical carnosaur body plan, with small front "arms," a stout body, long and strong back legs for walking and running, and a thick-based tail that was almost the same length as the head and body together. Although small, the arms were far from useless, since the three fingers on each hand were equipped with long, curved claws, like grappling hooks. The claws on the three main toes of each foot were wider and straighter, with a small fourth toe and claw facing rearward.

Big head

One of the most impressive features of *Allosaurus* was its head — very large in relation to its body size and held above its shoulders rather than in front of them on a stout, almost upright neck. The skull was more than 3 feet (1 meter) long, with large snout and eyebrow ridges, yet lightly built, with many weight-saving spaces and holes. There was a small, lumplike "horn" on the forehead just in front of the eyes and also a bowl-shaped hollow above each eye. This may have been a recess for some type of body gland that removed excess salt from body fluids. (Many living reptiles and birds have these "salt glands.")

▲ Well-balanced mover

As with many bipedal (walking on two legs) dinosaurs, the whole body of *Allosaurus* was balanced over the rear limbs. The head, arms, and front torso counterbalanced the hips and large tail at the rear.

⇨ Battle of the Jurassic giants

Allosaurus was a worthy predator of the largest land animals of all time — giant Jurassic sauropod dinosaurs such as *Apatosaurus* and *Brachiosaurus*.

How did *Allosaurus* spend its days and nights? Probably resting, looking for and eating food, and occasionally breeding – as with most animals. But what was its lifestyle? Was this huge beast an active hunter that rapidly pursued prey or a slow skulker that ambushed the sick and dying or scavenged their dead carcasses?

Fossil evidence for the anatomy (body structure) of *Allosaurus* is relatively plentiful. Experts can glean many clues about lifestyle from such evidence. But there are conflicting viewpoints about

The skulking scavenger

Some experts believe that this dinosaur was heavily built and fairly sluggish and clumsy. So it probably fed on the larger, slower herbivores of its time and place, such as *Stegosaurus* and *Camptosaurus*, and sauropods like *Apatosaurus* (formerly "*Brontosaurus*"), *Camarasaurus*, and *Diplodocus*.

Allosaurus may have finished off the slow and sick, or sniffed out carrion, or used its bulk to drive away smaller carnivores that had actually made the kill. It could prevent a struggle by biting its ailing prey and ripping out the guts. Its teeth were certainly up to this task, being a combination of meat hook and steak knife – almost 4 inches (10 centimeters) long, recurved (backward-pointing) so the victim could not escape, with a daggerlike shape, and serrated (saw-edged).

The speedy hunter

Another expert viewpoint, which has gained ground in recent years, is that *Allosaurus* was a rapid, agile pursuer. Otherwise, the weight-saving skeleton, especially the "windowed" skull, would be of little practical use.

The large accumulations of *Allosaurus* fossils suggest that it may have lived in groups and worked in packs to bring down

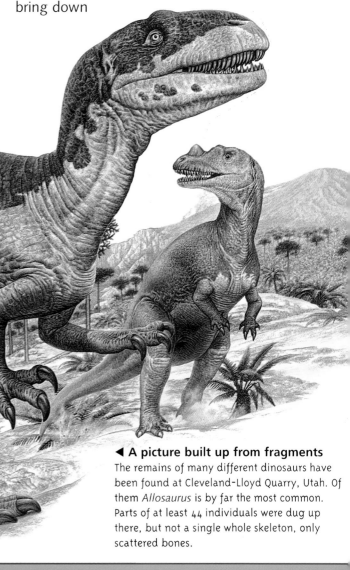

◀ **A picture built up from fragments**
The remains of many different dinosaurs have been found at Cleveland-Lloyd Quarry, Utah. Of them *Allosaurus* is by far the most common. Parts of at least 44 individuals were dug up there, but not a single whole skeleton, only scattered bones.

DATA BASE

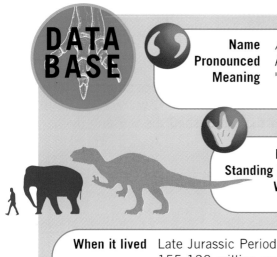

Name	*Allosaurus*
Pronounced	ALLO-sore-us
Meaning	"strange lizard"

What it ate Meat-eater, probably an active hunter of other large, herbivorous dinosaurs

Length	(nose - tail-tip) 36 feet (11 meters)
Standing height	15 feet (4.6 meters)
Weight	2 tons (2 tonnes)

When it lived	Late Jurassic Period 155-130 million years ago
Where it lived	Midwest U.S. (various sites), Tanzania in East Africa

Order	Saurischia (lizard-hipped dinosaurs)
Suborder	Theropoda (beast-footed)
Family	Allosauridae

large prey or even ambushed speedier prey such as *Camptosaurus*. *Allosaurus* could move its jaw backward, forward, and sideways under the main skull above to shear off chunks of meat.

A recent study of the fossil ribs of one *Allosaurus* specimen revealed a pattern of fractures – that is, broken ribs. The fractures could have been caused by perhaps tripping and bellyflopping onto hard ground while the animal was running at speed. If so, it is more evidence that *Allosaurus* was a fast and active creature. And details of the fractures show that they had healed during life, so the animal must have survived its fall. There are further details about carnosaur activity levels and running speeds on pages 62-63.

More hunters than hunted?
In nature predators are usually less common than their prey. At least, the living weight of their combined bodies, known as predator biomass, is less than the equivalent prey biomass. However, some American fossil sites have yielded far more remains of *Allosaurus* specimens than of its possible prey.

According to the principles of ecology and energy transfer, it is not possible for predator biomass to exceed prey biomass (see page 53).

So, the reason for the high frequency of *Allosaurus* remains may be elsewhere. How and when animals and plants become fossilized – especially in large numbers within a small area – is a process riddled with chance. Perhaps *Allosaurus* rested in places where fossilization was more likely, such as sandy riverbanks prone to flash floods. How and why accumulations, collections, or groups of objects are formed is the subject of a study known as taphonomy.

A likely meal
Evidence that the huge sauropod dinosaur *Apatosaurus* succumbed to *Allosaurus* is relatively strong. Fossil bones of *Apatosaurus* have been found in western North America, with teeth marks and scrapes on them that match the teeth of *Allosaurus*. Also, some *Apatosaurus* remains were surrounded by broken fragments of *Allosaurus* teeth.

King of the dinosaurs

Star of museum displays and movies, *Tyrannosaurus rex* was one of the biggest, most fearsome land predators that the world has ever seen.

Hold out one of your hands, fingers together and straight. Your whole hand is about the size of one tooth from the massive mouth of *Tyrannosaurus rex*, one of the most fearsome of all dinosaurs. *Tyrannosaurus* had more than 50 of these teeth. It could have swallowed a ten-year-old child in one gulp — if there had been any humans around at the time!

Main features of *Tyrannosaurus*

Tyrannosaurus had the typical carnosaur body plan. Its huge head had a wide mouth, big eyes for hunting by sight, and a large nose for sniffing out victims. Its body was short and strong, and the tail was thick at the base. The rear legs were extremely powerful, with big muscles for rapid walking and running (see page 62). These are all usual carnosaur features, but *Tyrannosaurus* was much bigger and stronger than the usual carnosaurs.

Too tiny to be useful

One puzzle is why *Tyrannosaurus* had such tiny forelimbs, or "arms," compared with the rest of its body. They were only about the size of our own arms! Other carnosaurs also had microsized arms, like *Carnotaurus*, *Tarbosaurus*, and *Albertosaurus*. They were too short to reach the dinosaur's head, so they could not be used to hold food and pass it up to the mouth. The "hands" had sharp claws, which may have been used for scratching and tearing at attackers. Alternatively they may have been used to hold a mating partner or as aids to standing up

The terrible teeth

The teeth of *Tyrannosaurus* were about 7 inches (18 centimeters) long and pointed for stabbing and ripping flesh. Each tooth had two ridges, like a dagger or double-bladed knife, and the ridges had wavy serrations, like a saw blade or steak knife.

Tyrannosaurus probably fed by opening its mouth wide, lunging forward, and clamping its jaws onto the victim's body. Then it would pull, twist, and shake its head, using its powerful neck muscles to make its teeth "saw" through skin, muscle, and gristle. This action would slice off a great mouthful, probably for swallowing in one gulp — *Tyrannosaurus* had no chewing teeth. However,

◀ **Hunter or scavenger?**
Some pictures show *Tyrannosaurus* tearing flesh from the carcass of another dinosaur. Feeding on dead things is called scavenging. However, most experts now think that *Tyrannosaurus* could also run fast to chase and kill its own prey. So it may have been more of an active predator than a scavenger.

recent evidence from newly discovered
Tyrannosaurus fossils challenges this idea and
also fuels the debate about the speed with
which this great dinosaur could run (see pages
62 and 64).

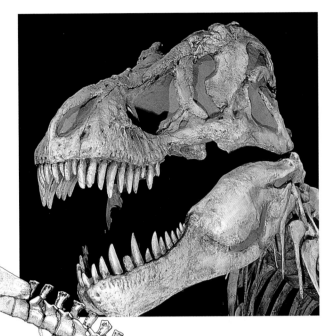

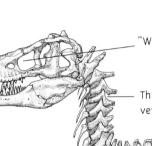

"Windows" in skullbone

Thick, strong neckbones (cervical
vertebrae)

Extra front ribs
(gastralia)

Thigh bone (femur)

Three large, clawed, forward-
facing toes

Tiny fourth toe

◀▲ *Tyrannosaurus* skeleton

Tyrannosaurus was a huge and powerful creature, yet its
skeleton was lightly built. Its skull had large gaps, or
"windows," in front of and behind the eyes. In life they would
have been filled in by skin. This design meant less heavy
bone and so saved weight. The neckbones were especially
strong. Perhaps *Tyrannosaurus* charged straight at victims and
plunged its teeth into them, so the neck had to absorb the
jarring shock of a head-on impact.

DATA BASE

Name	*Tyrannosaurus rex*
Pronounced	Tie-RAN-owe-SORE-us RECKS
Meaning	"king of the tyrant lizards"

What it ate Meat-eater, swift hunter possibly tackling smaller prey, also probably scavenger

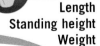

Length	(nose - tail-tip) 44 feet (13.4 meters)
Standing height	18 feet (5.5 meters)
Weight	6 tons (6.1 tonnes)

When it lived	Late Cretaceous Period 68-65 million years ago
Where it lived	U.S. (Colorado, Montana, New Mexico, South Dakota, Wyoming), Canada (Alberta, Saskatchewan)

Order	Saurischia (lizard-hipped dinosaurs)
Suborder	Theropoda (beast-footed)
Family	Tyrannosauridae

Could carnosaurs run fast? ▶

⇨ Could carnosaurs run fast?

How can we know the running speeds of animals that died out millions of years ago? Combine amazing fossil finds of skeletons and footprints with studies of living animals and get a mathematician to help!

There have been hundreds of scientific studies on the way animals move and on their walking and running speeds. In all of the creatures studied, maximum running speed can be predicted by a mathematical relationship or calculation. This relationship involves the length of the animal's leg and the length of one of its strides or steps. The calculations are complicated but relatively accurate whether the animal is a reptile, bird, or mammal.

Legs and feet

No one has ever seen a dinosaur, let alone watched one run and measured its speed. Fortunately, we have the evidence of fossils. Preserved limb bones show the length of a dinosaur's legs. Preserved footprints or trackways show the length of a dinosaur's stride. If the limb bones and footprints can be identified with reasonable certainty as coming from the same type of dinosaur, we can use the mathematical calculations for living animals to estimate how fast it could walk or run.

General dinosaur speeds

2.5-3.75 miles per hour (4-6 kms per hour)
Sauropods (massive, long-necked plant-eaters) such as *Diplodocus*

3.75-5.25 miles per hour (6-8.4 km per hour)
Large, nontyrannosaur carnosaurs such as *Megalosaurus*

10 miles per hour (16 km per hour)
Medium-sized carnosaurs such as *Dilophosaurus*

25 miles per hour (40 km per hour)
A lower estimate for smaller theropods such as the "ostrich dinosaurs" like *Struthiomimus*

30 miles per hour (48 km per hour).
This upper estimate for *Tyrannosaurus* has caused enormous debate. The arguments for and against these results are discussed on the following pages.

Using the standard methods, the calculations for the approximate running speeds of dinosaurs work out as shown here. However, there are many other conflicting versions of this chart.

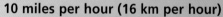

Top speeds

The world's fastest land animal today is the cheetah (right). This big cat, with its long, rangy legs and lean, flexible body, can sprint in bursts of about 70 miles per hour (112 kilometers per hour).

This compares with about 45 miles per hour (72 kilometers per hour) for an ostrich (center), 37 miles per hour (59 kilometers per hour) for a wildebeest, and 25 miles per hour (40 kilometers per hour) for a champion human sprinter.

Big but fast

Animals that have heavy bodies and stumpy legs do not look particularly rapid. Yet some of them are capable of surprising bursts of speed. A 2-ton (2-tonne) rhino (left) can charge over a short distance at 32 miles per hour (51 kilometers per hour), and a 4-ton (4-tonne) elephant at 24 miles per hour (39 kilometers per hour).

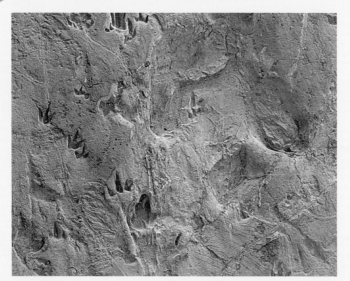

Following footsteps

Many thousands of fossilized footprints from prehistoric times are known around the world. Many hundreds have been identified as dinosaur footprints, or trackways, from evidence such as the print shapes, the age of the rocks, and fossils of the actual dinosaurs and their feet in the area. One set of trackways from southern England has been identified as made by a carnosaur, probably the otherwise poorly known *Megalosaurus* (see page 54). They show that the dinosaur walked on two legs, slightly pigeon-toed, its long tail swinging from side to side. The lengths of the strides help with calculations of running speed, while the depths of the prints linked to the type of mud they were made in give an idea of the animal's weight.

⇒ Slow bus or sprinter

The debate about carnosaur running speeds has centered around *Tyrannosaurus* and its possible lifestyle.

Until the 1980s many dinosaur experts thought that *Tyrannosaurus* was so big and heavy that it could not run at speed. It must have waddled or lumbered slowly, head held up and tail dragging along the ground.

But more fossil finds have provided new information. Around 1990 two almost complete fossilized *Tyrannosaurus* skeletons were found in South Dakota and Montana. In fact, the 67-million-year-old Montana specimen, nicknamed "Sue," is not so much fossilized as mummified — preserved by desiccation, that is, very thorough drying out.

As fast as an athlete!
The new finds show that *Tyrannosaurus* probably walked and ran with its head, body, and tail all held level. The head, neck, and front legs were balanced by the long and heavy-based tail over the powerful back legs.

This body position meant that *Tyrannosaurus* may have been able to run quite fast — at speeds of more than 25 miles per hour (40 kilometers per hour). This is about the same speed as world-class human sprinters! The evidence is supported by the calculation method from leg and stride lengths (see previous page). So *Tyrannosaurus* may have been able to pursue other creatures and hunt them down for food.

Evidence from cracked ribs
Fossils of carnosaurs such as *Allosaurus* have been found with cracked ribs (see page 59). They appear to have broken and healed again while the animal was alive and then been

What one print can tell
Further evidence for the running speed of *Tyrannosaurus* comes from a fossil footprint — just one. It was made in soft mud, and it has about 10 feet (3 meters) of undisturbed ground in front of it, lacking other prints from later strides. This means a minimum stride length of 10 feet. It suggests that the dinosaur was traveling at least 7.5 miles per hour (12 kilometers per hour).

preserved after death. The ribs could have been broken when the animal was running fast and tripped and fell on hard ground.

Recent research on fossil *Tyrannosaurus* skeletons has revealed broken ribs that also healed in life. It is unclear whether these breaks were due to falls onto the chest while the animal was running.

One view is that if the ribs were cracked by a fall at speed, then the speed was probably not very fast, less than 15 miles per hour (24 kilometers per hour). With an animal as heavy as *Tyrannosaurus*, a fall at greater speed would have crushed the chest and been fatal.

Still under debate

But analyzing the same fossil evidence in another way brings a different view. It contends that *Tyrannosaurus* could have reached speeds of about 22 miles per hour (35 kilometers per hour) before a fall would be likely to cause the animal's death.

More debate centers around studies on the strengths of dinosaur legbones. One view is that these bones in *Tyrannosaurus* were too weak for fast running. At speeds above 15 miles per hour (25 kilometers per hour) they would have cracked under the shocks and stresses caused by the great weight of the creature. However, another view is that *Tyrannosaurus* had large, shock-absorbing lumps of cartilage (gristle) in its leg joints. They cushioned the stresses and so allowed faster running.

Such disagreements among experts are a normal part of paleontology and of the reconstruction of dinosaurs and their lifestyles.

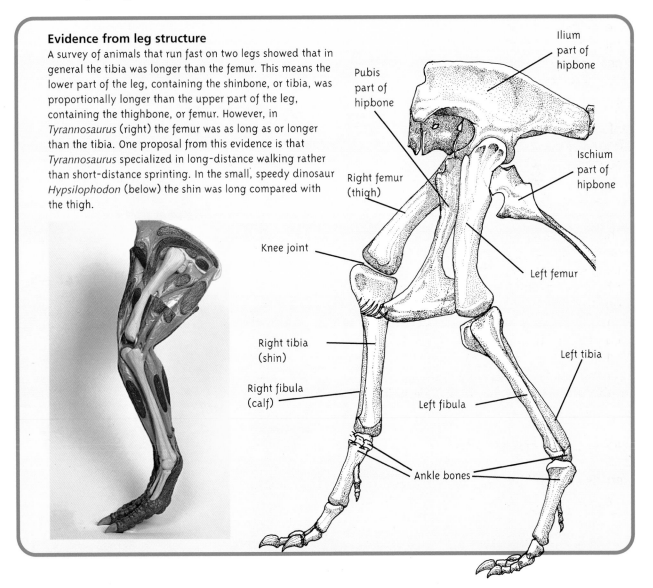

Evidence from leg structure

A survey of animals that run fast on two legs showed that in general the tibia was longer than the femur. This means the lower part of the leg, containing the shinbone, or tibia, was proportionally longer than the upper part of the leg, containing the thighbone, or femur. However, in *Tyrannosaurus* (right) the femur was as long as or longer than the tibia. One proposal from this evidence is that *Tyrannosaurus* specialized in long-distance walking rather than short-distance sprinting. In the small, speedy dinosaur *Hypsilophodon* (below) the shin was long compared with the thigh.

Pubis part of hipbone

Ilium part of hipbone

Ischium part of hipbone

Right femur (thigh)

Left femur

Knee joint

Right tibia (shin)

Left tibia

Right fibula (calf)

Left fibula

Ankle bones

⇨ Carnosaur hunting methods

How did carnosaurs find, catch, and eat their food? Fossils of many kinds, especially from *Tyrannosaurus*, help build up a possible picture of the hunt.

Some of the body features of *Tyrannosaurus* suggest that this huge predator was really a specialized scavenger. The evidence comes from endocast fossils. They are lumps of rock that form inside the cavity of a bone or similar item, taking up the shape and contours of the cavity as they do so, as a cast forms in a mold.

Endocast fossils from the interior of the cranium, or braincase, are virtually fossils of the brain itself. In *Tyrannosaurus* they show that the brain had very large olfactory lobes. These are the parts of the brain that deal with smell. The olfactory lobes are similarly large in modern scavenging birds such as turkey vultures. They are used for smelling dead, rotting meat at great distances.

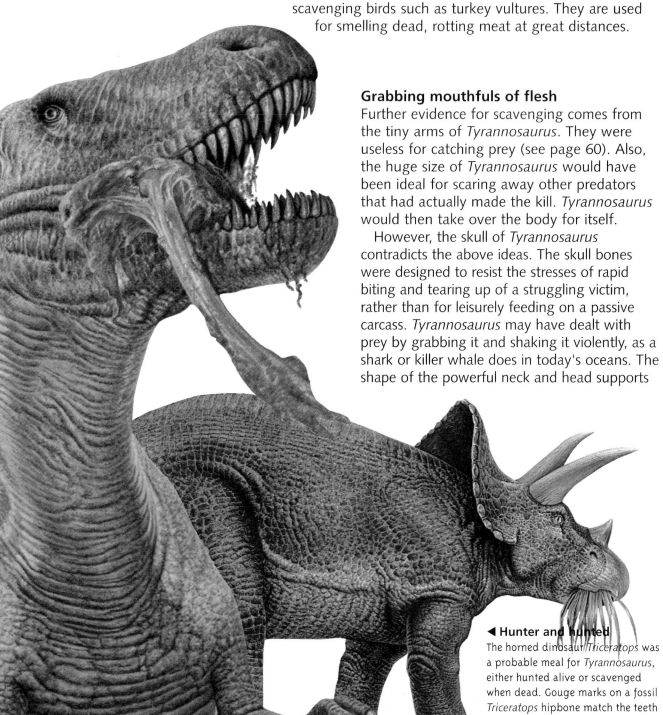

Grabbing mouthfuls of flesh

Further evidence for scavenging comes from the tiny arms of *Tyrannosaurus*. They were useless for catching prey (see page 60). Also, the huge size of *Tyrannosaurus* would have been ideal for scaring away other predators that had actually made the kill. *Tyrannosaurus* would then take over the body for itself.

However, the skull of *Tyrannosaurus* contradicts the above ideas. The skull bones were designed to resist the stresses of rapid biting and tearing up of a struggling victim, rather than for leisurely feeding on a passive carcass. *Tyrannosaurus* may have dealt with prey by grabbing it and shaking it violently, as a shark or killer whale does in today's oceans. The shape of the powerful neck and head supports

◀ **Hunter and hunted**
The horned dinosaur *Triceratops* was a probable meal for *Tyrannosaurus*, either hunted alive or scavenged when dead. Gouge marks on a fossil *Triceratops* hipbone match the teeth of *Tyrannosaurus*.

Bite power

In 1996 scientists reported the results of "bite rig" experiments. The bite rig machine measured the force that the teeth of various meat-eating animals could produce on the bone of a typical victim — a cow. The teeth came from the dead bodies of living carnivores, from a human, and from a dinosaur — *Tyrannosaurus* — using metal models of its fossil teeth.

To make the marks found in the fossil hipbone of *Triceratops* (below), *Tyrannosaurus* would have needed to exert 3,000 pounds of force (13,400 newtons), equivalent to the weight of a pickup truck on each tooth!

Animal	Biting force of cheek teeth (pounds of force/newtons)
Labrador dog	45/200
Human	90/400
Wolf	315/1,400
Shark	315/1,400
Orangutan	360/1,600
Lion	900/4,000
Alligator	2,920/13,000
Tyrannosaurus	3,000/13,400

this notion. The serrated teeth would saw and shear off a great chunk of flesh, ready to be swallowed, while further wounding the victim.

A fossilized victim

Triceratops was a horned dinosaur, or ceratopsian, about 30 feet (9.1 meters) long, which lived at the same time and place as *Tyrannosaurus*. One fossil pelvis or hipbone of *Triceratops*, from Montana, has about 80 deep gouges and furrows in it. The pelvis had been ripped from the rest of the body, and there were puncture marks near the spine and long furrows suggesting that flesh had been gnawed from bone. The teeth of *Tyrannosaurus* fit these marks perfectly.

The pattern of these tooth holes indicates that *Tyrannosaurus* fed by "puncture-and-pull" bites. It snapped its jaws shut with crushing power, forcing its teeth through skin and muscle down to the bone. Then it pulled back without releasing its grip, so ripping out a large chunk from the *Triceratops*.

The end products

Trace fossils are preserved remains and signs of a living thing other than from its actual body.

They include eggshells, footprints, tail drags, nests, burrows, tooth marks — and droppings.

Fossilized lumps of dung are called coprolites. Being fossils, they have become solid rock, so they are not squishy and smelly! Coprolites can be broken or cut open to reveal the bits, pieces, and undigested remains of the animal's recent meals.

Bare bones

A huge coprolite about the size of a football was dug up recently in Saskatchewan, Canada. It was dated at 68-65 million years old. Bone fragments made up about half of its volume. So it probably came from a big carnivore, most likely *Tyrannosaurus*.

But the presence of so many pieces of bone is unexpected. It indicates that *Tyrannosaurus* did not simply strip pieces of juicy flesh from its meal, leaving the hard parts behind. Instead, the carnosaur ate bones as well. Perhaps it was forced to, since it was scavenging a carcass, and the soft meat had already been eaten by others.

The bones were either sheared and chopped by teeth in the mouth of *Tyrannosaurus* or ground up in the dinosaur's powerful, muscular stomach or both.

Warm- or cold-blooded killers? ➤

→ Warm- or cold-blooded killers?

Today's reptiles are cold-blooded. Their body temperatures are largely at the mercy of the surroundings. Were dinosaurs cold-blooded too? Carnosaurs are at the center of the debate.

Since the 1980s a great debate has centered around carnosaurs and other predatory dinosaurs, especially the smaller "ostrich dinosaurs" and similar theropods (see chapters 5 and 8 in this series). It concerns whether some dinosaurs were cold-blooded like present-day reptiles or warm-blooded like mammals such as ourselves.

   This debate goes much wider than warm or cold blood. It affects our ideas about the way these dinosaurs moved, lived, and hunted, the ecology of the prehistoric world, how dinosaurs evolved, their relationships with other animal groups including birds and mammals, and even whether we are correct to divide the animal kingdom into these great groups.

   First, however, terms such as "cold-blooded" should be made clear.

What is "warm blood"?
We are warm-blooded. More accurately, we are endothermic. This means our bodies make their own heat inside by chemical processes. A warm-blooded body stays at a constant temperature that is usually higher than the temperature of the surroundings. Human body temperature is about 98°F (37°C) day and night, winter and summer.

What is "cold blood"?
In the animal kingdom only mammals and birds are endothermic. All other creatures, including reptiles, are cold-blooded, or ectothermic. Their bodies cannot make heat within by "burning" food. Warmth must be taken in from the sun or the surroundings. So ectothermic animals tend to have body temperatures that are similar to their surroundings. In cold conditions they are cold. On a hot day they are hot.

Fossil bone chemicals
The exceptionally well-preserved *Tyrannosaurus* skeleton found in Montana in 1990 gave scientists a unique opportunity. More than 50 tiny samples were taken from various parts of the skeleton and analyzed for certain chemicals. These chemicals were two forms of the substance oxygen, called O-16 and O-18. (Oxygen is one element in the crystals called carbonates that give hardness to bone tissue.)

◀ **Never mind the cold**
In the Siberian snow a tiger bounds actively after prey. In subzero temperatures a reptile would be far too cold to move.

Why is body temperature important?

What are the advantages of being warm- or cold-blooded?

- Warm-blooded animals such as lions (right) can be active at any time, even in cold conditions. When a cold-blooded animal becomes too cool, its muscles cannot work properly. It becomes slow and sluggish, or torpid, and at the mercy of predators.
- But high body temperature has a price. The heat is produced by chemical changes fueled by the energy in food. So warm-blooded animals must eat more food than cold-blooded creatures. A meal that lasts a lion two days might last a crocodile two weeks.

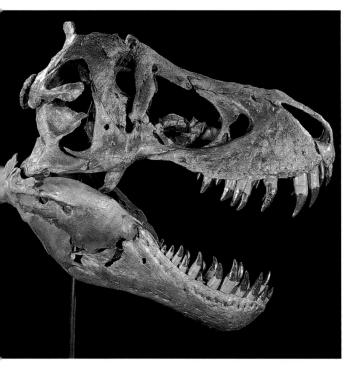

◄ Fossils hide the truth

If this skull of *Tyrannosaurus rex* was real bone, rather than stone, microscopic analysis of the bone tissue could reveal warm- or cold-bloodedness.

A heated debate

In practice cold-blooded animals are not totally at the mercy of their surroundings. They can move into shade to cool down if they get too hot. They can sunbathe to warm up if they become too cold. These actions, which help a cold-blooded animal partly control its body temperature, are called thermoregulatory behavior.

What about dinosaurs? They were reptiles. All living reptiles are cold-blooded, or ectothermic. But supporters of the "warm-blooded dinosaurs" theory point to various strands of evidence that suggest that *Tyrannosaurus* and similar carnosaurs were not cold-blooded. And if they were not, were they truly reptiles?

Studies on modern animals show that the cooler a bone, the more O-18 is present in relation to the amount of O-16. So, if there is lots of O-16 and little O-18, even in a dead and preserved fossil bone, then the bone was warm in life.

This method is not absolute. It does not give an actual temperature for the bone during life. But it does allow the different bones of a single skeleton to be compared, showing which were warmest or coolest in the living animal.

What happened to the carnosaurs? ➤

What happened to the carnosaurs?

The carnosaurs survived through most of the Age of the Dinosaurs. But they could not withstand the mass extinction that wiped every dinosaur off the face of the earth.

The carnosaurs include some of the biggest, fiercest, most exciting predatory dinosaurs yet discovered, such as *Allosaurus* and of course *Tyrannosaurus*. The group showed continuing evolution through the Age of Dinosaurs, some kinds dying out and new types appearing. Right to the end, the carnosaurs were evolving into new and ever more specialized forms.

What killed the dinosaurs?

Suggested causes of the mass extinction include:

- A huge meteorite crashed into earth, throwing up clouds of dust that blotted out the sun and brought sudden global cooling. Lack of warmth and light killed many plants, affecting the food chains, and lower temperatures affected cold-blooded animals too.
- A massive series of volcanic eruptions covered the planet with smoke, ash, and choking poisonous fumes.
- The drifting of the continents around the globe caused rapid changes around the world in climate, wind patterns, and sea currents.
- Epidemics of disease broke out, which affected only selected groups of living things.
- Competition arose from increasingly successful mammals and birds, which perhaps ate the eggs and young of much bigger creatures.
- Genetic "staleness" may have set in. It occurs when the same group of living things has been evolving for a very long time and runs out of genetic variation or biodiversity to cope with changing conditions.
- Large amounts of dangerous rays, heat, and light reached the earth from outer space, such as solar explosions on the sun, storms of meteorites or comets, or even a vast passing mist of dust known as a GMC, giant molecular cloud.

The mass extinction

However, even the great carnosaurs could not survive the huge catastrophe that brought the Age of Dinosaurs to a relatively sudden end 65 million years ago. This mass extinction at the end of the Cretaceous Period affected not only all the dinosaurs but also the flying reptiles called pterosaurs, the swimming reptiles such as plesiosaurs and ichthyosaurs, various other kinds of animals, and certain types of plants too.

These causes and possible combinations of them are discussed in detail in chapter 12 of this book.

Bigger than the biggest!

Giganotosaurus probably had a similar body shape to *Tyrannosaurus*, but it was slightly larger all over. For example, its skull is about 6 feet (1.8 meters) long, compared with the 4-foot (1.2-meter) skull of *Tyrannosaurus*. Its teeth are also slightly bigger than those of *Tyrannosaurus*. The fossilized upper jaw and teeth of *Giganotosaurus* are shown right.

Overall, *Giganotosaurus* may have been about 46 feet (14 meters) long and 8 tons (8.1 tonnes) in weight.

Giganotosaurus lived earlier than *Tyrannosaurus*, in the mid-Cretaceous period about 100 million years ago. It probably fed on huge sauropod dinosaurs such as *Rebbachisaurus*.

▶ Star trek

Star of stories and movies, *Tyrannosaurus* is the dinosaur we love to fear. Few land predators have come anywhere near its size.

In at the death

The huge carnosaur *Tyrannosaurus* was present at the death of the dinosaurs. Its fossils are dated to 65 million years ago, right at the end of the Cretaceous Period.

Since its discovery in 1902 *Tyrannosaurus* has held the record as the largest predatory (hunting) animal ever to walk on the earth.

That record held until the early 1990s, when fossils of an even bigger predator were discovered in western Argentina, South America. Like *Tyrannosaurus*, it was a carnosaur – *Giganotosaurus carolinii*. It was first described in a scientific report in 1995 (see panel above).

The future of carnosaurs

The carnosaurs are long gone. But we continue to dig up their fossils, reconstruct their skeletons and bodies, discover better ways of studying them, and make better guesses about how they lived, fed, bred, and died. A new find such as *Giganotosaurus* can rewrite the record books and change our ideas about some of the most exciting creatures ever to live on earth.

◀ Largest meat-eater

Paleontologists hold the fossilized thighbone of *Giganotosaurus*, the biggest carnivorous dinosaur unearthed to date. It is more than 100 million years old.

Introduction to the sauropods ➤

Introduction to the sauropods

The sauropod dinosaurs, with their immensely long necks and tails, were the largest animals ever to walk on earth. Today's biggest land animals, such as elephants, rhinos, and hippos, are small by comparison.

Picture a dinosaur in your mind. It may be a fierce meat-eater like *Tyrannosaurus rex*. Or it may be a far bigger beast with a small head, an extraordinarily long neck, a barrel-shaped body, four pillarlike legs, and a tapering tail like a long, twitching whip. This dinosaur's head, with a little mouth bearing blunt, peg-shaped teeth, seems far too small to eat enough food for such a gigantic body. And the brain inside the head is so tiny, compared with the creature's vast bulk, that this dinosaur must have been one of the most stupid animals that ever existed.

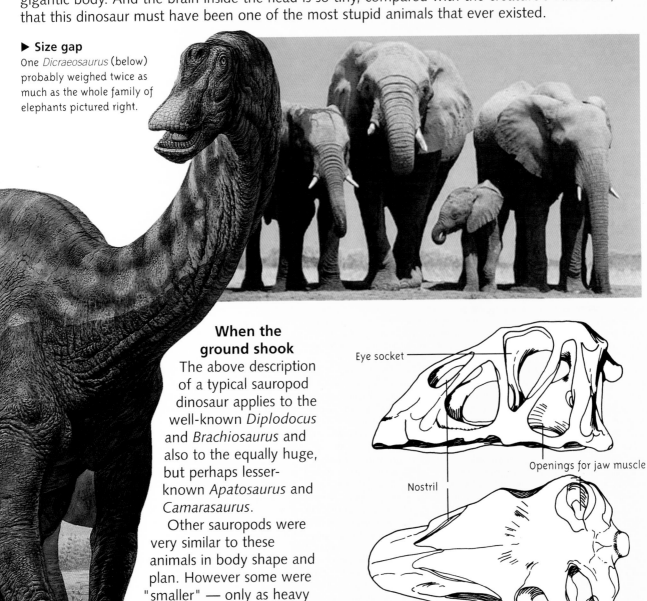

▶ **Size gap**
One *Dicraeosaurus* (below) probably weighed twice as much as the whole family of elephants pictured right.

When the ground shook
The above description of a typical sauropod dinosaur applies to the well-known *Diplodocus* and *Brachiosaurus* and also to the equally huge, but perhaps lesser-known *Apatosaurus* and *Camarasaurus*.

Other sauropods were very similar to these animals in body shape and plan. However some were "smaller" — only as heavy as a few elephants! We cannot imagine how such

Eye socket

Openings for jaw muscle

Nostril

▲ *Omeisaurus* **skull**
The sauropod skull was generally small and low. However, the skull of *Omeisaurus* was taller and more wedge-shaped. This sauropod was about 65 feet (20 meters) long and lived in China during the Jurassic Period.

vast animals moved across the land. Today the only animals that reach a similar size to the sauropods are the great whales in the sea.

Sauropod heyday

This book describes the main members of the dinosaur group Sauropodomorpha, "lizard-feet shapes." It has between 30 and 40 well-known members and about the same number of lesser-known types. They lived at various times through almost the entire Age of Dinosaurs from about 210 million years ago to the great extinction of all dinosaurs 65 million years ago. However, the sauropod heyday was the Late Jurassic Period about 160 to 144 million years ago.

What were the sauropods?

The dinosaurs known as prosauropods and sauropods made up the group Sauropodomorpha. In turn, they were a subgroup of a much larger group of dinosaurs – the Saurischia, or "lizard-hips." The other main group of saurischians besides the Sauropodomorpha was the Theropoda, or "beast-feet." They included:

- the small, lightly built, early dinosaurs called coelurosaurs;
- the very long-legged and swift "ostrich-dinosaurs," or ornithomimosaurs;
- the dreaded pack-hunting dromaeosaurs, or "raptors," such as *Deinonychus* and *Velociraptor*;
- the largest and fiercest of meat-eating dinosaurs, the carnosaurs such as *Allosaurus* and *Tyrannosaurus*.

The Saurischia were one of the two biggest groups of dinosaurs. The other was the Ornithischia, or "bird-hips." Together, the Saurischia and Ornithischia made up the group of reptiles we call Dinosauria, dinosaurs.

Sauropods probably evolved from small,

▲ Spread of the sauropods

During the Jurassic Period sauropods were spread all over the globe. Those with spatulate (spoon-shaped) teeth were found everywhere, while peg-toothed sauropods were probably missing from Asia.

1	*Lapparentosaurus*	11	*Euhelopus*
2	*Volkheimeria*	12	*Omeisaurus*
3	*Baraparasaurus*	13	*Mamenchisaurus*
4	*Patagosaurus*	14	*Brachiosaurus*
5	*Cetiosaurus*	15	*Tornieria*
6	*Rhoetosaurus*	16	*Dicraeosaurus*
7	*Shunosaurus*	17	*Diplodocus*
8	*Amygdalodon*	18	*Barosaurus*
9	*Haplocanthosaurus*	19	*Apatosaurus*
10	*Camarasaurus*		

meat-eating dinosaurs, the early therodpods, by way of the group known as prosauropods, which were also members of the Sauropodomorfpha group.

Profile of a sauropod

Brachiosaurus was a giant animal, even by sauropod standards. It showed off the main features of the group, and its kind lasted an exceptional time – about 30 million years.

One of the best-known sauropods and one of the most famous of all dinosaurs is *Brachiosaurus*. Not only was it a vast animal, but it was also very widespread around the world. Fossils have been found in North America, Europe, and North and East Africa. And its kind survived for tens of millions of years with hardly any changes. In terms of success in evolution "biggest was best" at the time of *Brachiosaurus*.

Twice as tall as a giraffe
This sauropod's scientific name, *Brachiosaurus*, means "arm reptile." It refers to the immense arms, or forelimbs, considerably longer than the hind limbs. They raised the shoulders and neck of the beast so that the head could reach more than 40 feet (12.2 meters) above ground – high enough to look into a window on the fifth floor of a building.

The tallest animal today, the giraffe, has similarly long forelimbs. Like *Brachiosaurus*, its body slopes down from the shoulders to the hips. But a giraffe can reach barely 20 feet (6.1 meters) into the air, less than half the height of *Brachiosaurus*.

▼ Peaceful giants
Brachiosaurus probably spent much of its life quietly feeding in small herds. It browsed on tall ferns, conifer trees such as pines and firs, and other leafy plants. Many of the trees we know today, such as oak, beech, maple, birch, and willow, had not evolved when this dinosaur was alive. Neither had flowers or grasses on the ground. These plants did not appear until the Middle Cretaceous Period.

How long was *Brachiosaurus*?

The fossils of *Brachiosaurus* were first discovered in Colorado in 1900. Further remains turned up in 1907 in Tanzania, East Africa. The most massive complete skeleton of any animal ever found consists of fossil *Brachiosaurus* bones from Tanzania, dug up around 1909-12. They are now on display in the Humboldt Museum in Berlin, Germany.

Several other sets of *Brachiosaurus* fossils have been unearthed. From these various fossils the length of this sauropod is estimated at between 70 and 80 feet (21.3 and 24.4 meters). This is not the longest of the dinosaurs (see *Diplodocus* on pages 82-83).

How heavy was *Brachiosaurus*?

However, the enormous thickness of fossil *Brachiosaurus* bones suggests that it was an extremely heavily built animal. Estimates of its weight range from less than 30 to more than 80 tons (30-81 tonnes).

So, *Brachiosaurus* is the heaviest dinosaur and the largest ever land animal known from fairly complete remains.

There are scattered fossils that suggest some dinosaurs were even larger than *Brachiosaurus*, as shown on page 87. But these skeletons are not complete enough to make accurate estimates of their size.

▲ Jurassic forest confrontation

A meat-eater, *Ceratosaurus*, confronts *Brachiosaurus*, which swings its head to enormous height to assess the danger. A flock of pterosaurs, *Rhamphorhynchus*, flap away from the possible battle.

Great dinosaur versus great whale

A reasonable guesstimate for the size of *Brachiosaurus* is 80 feet (24.4 meters) in length and perhaps 50 tons (51 tonnes) in weight. Although truly huge, this is not quite as big as the largest animals ever to live on earth, which are the blue whales. From the 1920s onward mass commercial whaling killed off the biggest blue whales. Before this time some blues reached perhaps 100 feet (30.5 meters) long and well over 150 tons (153 tonnes) in weight. Living in water helps support the blue whale's mammoth body.

More about *Brachiosaurus* ➤

⇒ More about *Brachiosaurus*

This giant among giants had both primitive and advanced features. It represents an intermediate stage in sauropod evolution.

In evolution "primitive" does not necessarily mean old-fashioned and out-of-date. Similarly, "advanced" does not need to imply the latest, improved, best version. These terms refer mainly to time. Primitive was earlier; advanced came later. So a primitive feature in an animal or plant has been around for a longer time, while an advanced feature has evolved more recently.

Continuing evolution

Sometimes the primitive feature is simpler or less sophisticated in its structure or function than the advanced equivalent that replaces it. But not always.

The dinosaur *Brachiosaurus* shows a mix of both primitive and advanced features. They show how sauropod bodies evolved in their early stages and gradually continued to change as more advanced features appeared – probably in response to the changing world around them.

Primitive features

- Later sauropods tended to have peglike or sticklike teeth, some almost as thin as pencils. *Brachiosaurus* had broader, wider teeth, shaped like spatulas, or flat spoons. They could probably deal with tougher vegetation than the peg-shaped versions.

▼ Long vertebra

A neck vertebra from *Brachiosaurus*. It measures 35 inches (89.5 cm) from left to right. Notice the deeply gouged-out sides and heavy scarring where muscles were attached.

- The skull of *Brachiosaurus* had large nasal openings high up on the top of the head. These openings allowed air to flow in and out of the windpipe and lungs. In life the large openings would be covered with skin. The exact size and position of the air openings in the skin, commonly known as nostrils, is difficult to pinpoint.
- Why did *Brachiosaurus* have such large nasal openings? Perhaps it had an exceptionally keen sense of smell to locate its food. Or it may have had a fleshy addition or appendage on the nasal area, such as a small trunk or a balloonlike, inflatable flap of skin.

Advanced features

- *Brachiosaurus* had very long front legs and an exceptionally long neck.
- The great length of the neck was due not to extra numbers of neck bones (cervical vertebrae) but to the extra length of each neck bone. This meant the joints between the neck bones, which allowed the neck to bend, were further apart. So, in spite of its length, the neck was not especially flexible.
- In other types of long-necked dinosaurs the joints between the neck bones have beveled (sloping) edges, allowing more movement in

DATA BASE

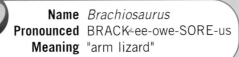

Name *Brachiosaurus*
Pronounced BRACK-ee-owe-SORE-us
Meaning "arm lizard"

What it ate Plant-eater, probably browsing in the highest treetops for leaves and other vegetation

Length (nose - tail-tip) 80 feet (24.4 meters)
Standing height 41 feet (12.4 meters)
Weight Up to 50 tons (51 tonnes)

When it lived Late Jurassic to Early or Middle Cretaceous Period 150-120 million years ago
Where it lived U.S. (Colorado, Utah, Wyoming, Arizona), Portugal in Europe, Algeria and Tanzania in Africa

Order Saurischia (lizard-hipped dinosaurs)
Suborder Sauropodomorpha
Family Brachiosauridae

▼ The dinosaur bridge

The backbone of *Brachiosaurus* was an excellent example of engineering design. The head and neck at one end and the tail at the other end both act as counterbalances for the body, using the two pairs of legs as dual supports. It is similar in design to a modern cantilever bridge. The many separate bones, or vertebrae, link to form what is now called an I- or H-section girder, giving stiffness with strength. The general principles of sauropod skeletal design are shown on the next page.

each joint. But sauropods had sharper-edged neck bones, which could not move or engage with each other so well. This is another piece of evidence that the neck may not have been very flexible.

Why did *Brachiosaurus* have such a greatly elongated neck? And how was the blood pumped along it up to the head? These questions are discussed on pages 38-39.

Slow growth

Despite its great neck and forelimbs, the tail of *Brachiosaurus* was relatively short compared with that of other sauropods. Each foot had five toes. There was probably one claw on the first (inner) toe of each front foot and three claws on each rear foot. Evidence from growth rates of reptiles alive today, such as lizards and crocodiles, suggests that *Brachiosaurus* took about one hundred years to reach its immense size.

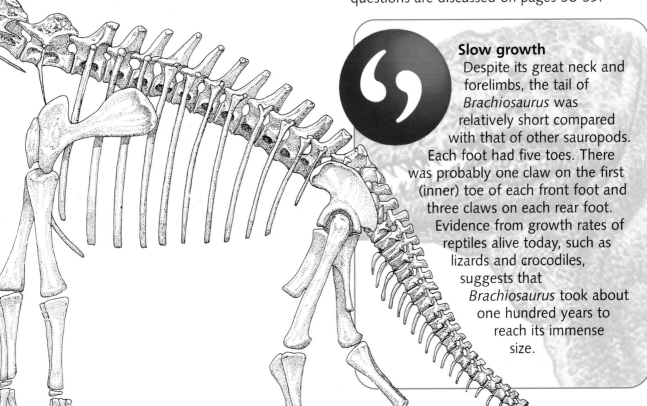

→ Sauropod construction

The vast skeleton of a sauropod was an excellent example of engineering design principles brought to life.

Throughout their time sauropods showed conservative evolution. This means they changed relatively little in their basic body structure, or anatomy, even over immense periods of time. Other animal groups that have shown conservative evolution and still survive today include crocodiles, turtles, sharks, and starfish. These animals are much the same today as they were hundreds of millions of years ago. It's as though nature came up with a successful design first time around, and the design needed little modification, even in a changing world.

Neck
- Hugely lengthened, in some cases (such as *Mamenchisaurus*) forming half the length of the entire animal.
- Increased neck length is due to increased length of individual neck bones (cervical vertebrae), not to more bones.
- Large spine- or flangelike extensions (neural spines) along the tops of the neck bones for attachment of muscles and ligaments to support and move the neck.
- Ligaments ran over V-shaped notches in the neural spines of each neck bone (except in brachiosaurs), like guy ropes or stabilizing cables to save energy and muscle use.
- Joints between neck bones designed mainly for strength, perhaps at the expense of flexibility.

Main backbone
- Spinal or vertebral column is similar in cross-section to an engineering H-girder or I-beam. It provides stiffness over a great length.
- Huge body weight is hung from the main backbone like a suspension bridge.
- Individual bones (vertebrae) have air-filled cavities (pleurocoels) within them to reduce weight.
- Thicker ridges of bone developed only along stress lines for strength with minimum weight.
- In the hip region several vertebrae (up to six) are fused or joined solidly together for strength, where the rear legs take the great weight of the massive body.

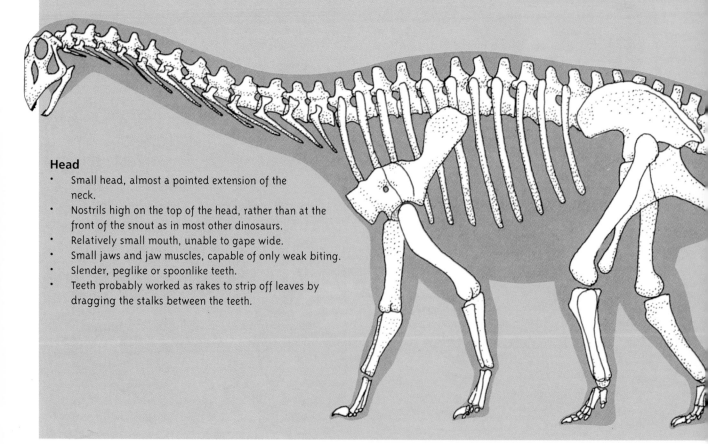

Head
- Small head, almost a pointed extension of the neck.
- Nostrils high on the top of the head, rather than at the front of the snout as in most other dinosaurs.
- Relatively small mouth, unable to gape wide.
- Small jaws and jaw muscles, capable of only weak biting.
- Slender, peglike or spoonlike teeth.
- Teeth probably worked as rakes to strip off leaves by dragging the stalks between the teeth.

More about *Brachiosaurus*

◀ ▼ **Suspension bones**
Bones of a sauropod found on the Isle of Wight, southern England. The vertebrae (below) were the main support for the great weight of the body.

Body

- Very deep, barrellike body to contain the huge digestive organs where plant material was crushed and fermented.
- Rounded, polished stones called gastroliths, often found within fossil sauropod skeletons, may have been swallowed to help grind food.
- Rib cage is narrow and deep.
- Rib bones have air-filled cavities within them to reduce weight.
- These cavities may have contained air sacs as extra "lungs" to increase breathing efficiency (as in birds).

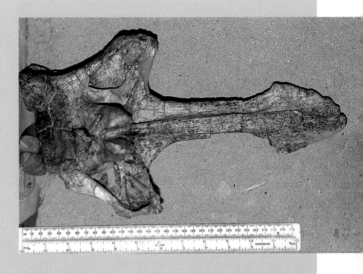

Tail

- Very long tail, tapering to a narrow whiplash end (some types had a club-ended tail, such as *Shunosaurus*).
- Joints between tail bones designed mainly for strength, perhaps at the expense of flexibility.
- Ligaments ran over V-shaped notches in the neural spines of each tail bone like guy ropes or stabilizing cables to save energy and muscle use.
- Bones at the end of the tail lack flanges and projections, being simple cylinders.
  - Tail tip may have simply been dragged or flexed by the rest of the tail like a whip's end, rather than able to twitch on its own.

▼ **Club-ended tail**
A reconstructed skeleton of *Shunosaurus*. The long tail narrowed to a club end.

Limbs

- Four sturdy, pillarlike limbs.
- Hind legs usually longer than the front legs, brachiosaurs.
- Wide, elephantlike feet with soft, plate-shaped soles, five splayed toes to spread the huge weight.
- Claws or hooves on some toes supported by wedges of padding.
- Claws may have been used for defense or digging.

Early sauropods

The earliest recognized subgroup of sauropods was the cetiosaurs, named after *Cetiosaurus* – the first sauropod to be discovered in fossil form and described for science.

In the 1830s several huge fossil bones from quarries around Oxford, England, were examined by William Buckland (1784-1856). In 1824 this eminent naturalist, geologist, anatomist, and clergyman had already described and named *Megalosaurus*, "big lizard," which was the first dinosaur to receive a formal scientific name.

Buckland realized that the finds in his current batch were from an even larger animal. He called in Georges Cuvier. At the time Cuvier was the world's foremost scientist in the area of animal fossils and comparative anatomy. He believed that such massive fossils were probably from some great whale that swam in the prehistoric oceans.

Whale to crocodile to dinosaur to sauropod

In 1841 another English scientist, Richard Owen, invented the term dinosaur (see page 17). He also questioned Cuvier's idea that the fossil bones in question were from a whale. Owen suggested instead that they belonged to a giant marine reptile like a huge crocodile. So he named the beast *Cetiosaurus*, "whale lizard."

In 1848 further fossil-hunting turned up a thighbone that could have been from the same animal. This showed it was definitely a walker, not a swimmer. Then in 1869-70 a fairly complete fossil skeleton was dug from the same layer of Middle Jurassic Period rocks in Oxfordshire. Beyond doubt, *Cetiosaurus* was a dinosaur.

In the 1900s a similar sauropod, *Haplocanthosaurus*, was found in Colorado. The mystery was over. *Cetiosaurus* was identified as a sauropod. Thanks to Richard Owen in 1841, it had therefore been the first sauropod to receive a scientific name. It was also given its own sauropod subgroup, the Cetiosauridae.

Cetiosaur features

The cetiosaurs were the earliest true sauropods. They were spread out all over the world during the Jurassic Period. They had

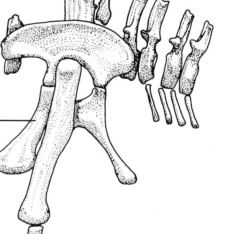

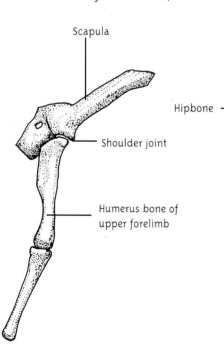

Scapula

Hipbone

Shoulder joint

Humerus bone of upper forelimb

▲ Plant-gathering machine
Cetiosaurus was massively built, with few of the weight-saving features found in later sauropods. Its weight has been estimated at an earthshaking 27 tons (27.4 tonnes) — or as little as 10 tons (10.2 tonnes). Its tiny head, equipped with spatulate (spoon-shaped) teeth, must have been busy most of the time gathering plant food to fuel the animal's vast bulk. This partial skeleton comes from Britain.

DATA BASE

Name	*Cetiosaurus*
Pronounced	SEE-tee-owe-SORE-us
Meaning	"whale lizard"

What it ate Plant-eater, probably raking leafy food from tall trees

Length (nose - tail-tip) 60 feet (18.3 meters)
Standing height 30 feet (9.1 meters)
Weight 20 tons (20.3 tonnes)

When it lived Middle to Late Jurassic Period 180-160 million years ago
Where it lived England (from Yorkshire south to Oxfordshire and Buckinghamshire), Morocco in North Africa

Order Saurischia (lizard-hipped dinosaurs)
Suborder Sauropodomorpha
Family Cetiosauridae

"primitive" (see page 76) sauropod features. They included vertebrae, or backbones, without the hollows (pleurocoels) that would make the structure lighter. In their hips only four of the individual vertebrae were fused together for extra strength, rather than five or even six vertebrae as in later sauropods.

Other cetiosaur features include short but massively sturdy leg bones, stout and broad feet, and a long neck and tail – but not as long as in the later sauropods.

More early sauropods are shown on the following pages. A recent Moroccan discovery is *Atlassaurus*, dating from about 165 million years ago. It weighed some 22 tons (22.4 tonnes) and showed brachiosaur features such as a long neck and front legs, but with a larger head and shorter neck than *Brachiosaurus* itself.

Side view

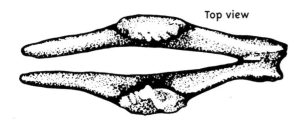
Top view

▲ **Chevrons**
These were V-shaped bones on the underside of the tail of *Cetiosaurus* (shown in position below). They may have worked as skids to enable the middle portion of the tail to slide easily along the ground.

Other cetiosaurs
These sauropods were all very similar to *Cetiosaurus*, around 50-65 feet (15.2-19.8 meters) long, and lived during the Jurassic Period (see page 73).
- *Volkheimeria* from Madagascar, although this may be more closely related to *Brachiosaurus*;
- *Patagosaurus* from the Patagonia region of Argentina;
- *Rhoetosaurus* from Australia;
- *Haplocanthosaurus*, from Colorado and Wyoming. It was one of the longest cetiosaurs, at 70 feet (21.3 meters).
- *Shunosaurus* from China.

The longest dinosaur ➤

⇒ The longest dinosaur

Diplodocus is the longest dinosaur known from relatively complete fossil skeletons, but its neck and tail made up five-sixths of its length.

One of the most famous of all dinosaurs, *Diplodocus* is also well known in structure thanks to several fairly complete skeleton finds. The first fossils of this long but slender sauropod were uncovered near Canyon City, Colorado, in 1877. Further specimens came from Utah, and then in 1899 a more complete skeleton was dug up at Albany, Wyoming.

American millionaire industrialist Andrew Carnegie, who had paid for the Albany expedition, arranged for its fossils to be copied as casts. They were sent to eight museums around the world, thereby spreading the fame of *Diplodocus* (and the good reputation of Carnegie into the bargain).

Light for its length

Despite its great length, *Diplodocus* weighed only as much as about three modern elephants. Its backbones, or vertebrae, had extremely scooped-out hollow sides, known as pleurocoels. This design maintained strength but saved plenty of heavy bone along the animal's great length.

Diplodocus had typical sauropod pillarlike limbs, the rear pair being slightly longer than the front. There were claws on the first toe of each front foot and the first two toes of each rear foot; the other toes had hooves. The tail ended in a whiplash and must have been heavy to balance the animal's long neck.

Why the name?

Diplodocus means "double beam." This refers to the front and rear skilike extensions of the chevrons – the down-projecting parts of the bones (caudal vertebrae) in the middle section of the tail. They seem to form a long beam, or girder. The main parts, or bodies, of the tail bones just above also form a beam.

What were these extensions for? Perhaps they strengthened and protected the underside of the tail's middle section so that it would not bend or crush under pressure. It has been suggested that *Diplodocus* could rear up on its hind legs to feed, resting part of its weight backward onto the "double beams" of the tail chevron bones. If so, the tail was a "fifth leg" and this sauropod could reach an incredible 45 feet (13.7 meters) from the ground.

Other members of the diplodocid family include *Barosaurus*, *Apatosaurus* and *Mamenchisaurus* (shown on later pages), also *Amphicoelias* and possibly *Dicraeosaurus* and *Nemegtosaurus*.

◀ ▼ A walking bridge
The skeleton of *Diplodocus* is often compared with a modern suspension or cantilever bridge. The long neck and tail counter-balanced the main body, concentrating the weight over the columnlike front and rear limbs. The main body mass hung from the backbone between the limbs.

▶ Watching for danger
Like other sauropods, *Diplodocus* possessed a tiny brain for its body bulk. Probably it was not what we would call "intelligent." It also had eyes on the sides of its head, as did other herbivorous dinosaurs and as herbivores do today – from horses to rabbits. This gives good all-round vision, enabling the animal to watch for predators. At the front the head was at a slight angle to the neck. At the rear the long tail had about 73-75 bones (caudal vertebrae) and could whiplash enemies.

DATA BASE

Name *Diplodocus*
Pronounced DIE-plod-OCK-us
Meaning "double beam"

What it ate Plant-eater, probably browsing in high trees or on low, soft vegetation

Length (nose - tail-tip) 89 feet (27.1 meters), some estimates up to 100 feet (30.5 meters)
Standing height 30 feet (9.1 meters)
Weight Up to 12 tons (12.2 tonnes)

When it lived Late Jurassic Period 150-140 million years ago
Where it lived US (Colorado, Utah, Wyoming)

Order Saurischia (lizard-hipped dinosaurs)
Suborder Sauropodomorpha
Family Diplodocidae

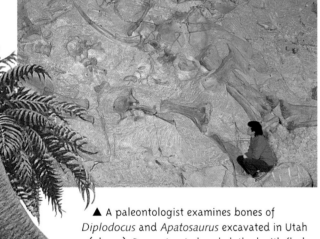

▲ A paleontologist examines bones of *Diplodocus* and *Apatosaurus* excavated in Utah (above). Reconstructed and clothed with flesh and skin, the bones recreate an adult and a baby *Diplodocus* (below).

▼ Weak teeth

The teeth of *Diplodocus* were very slim and pencil-shaped and found toward the fronts of the jaws only. They were probably used to rake or comb vegetation, removing the leaves or fronds from the tougher stalks. In fact, the teeth were so feeble that some experts suggest *Diplodocus* could feed on very soft plants only, such as those growing along riverbanks and lakesides.

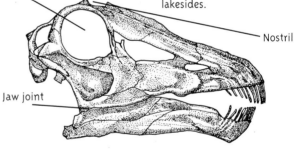

Eye socket

Nostril

Jaw joint

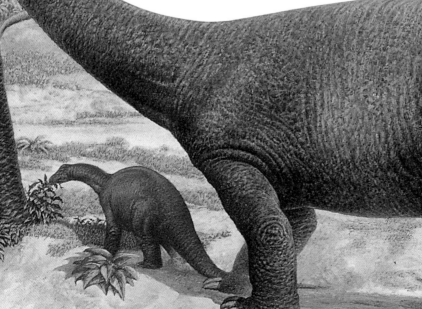

→ The sauropod with three names

Many people have heard of the massive sauropod "*Brontosaurus*," but it is missing from the approved list of scientific dinosaur names. Officially it is known as *Apatosaurus*.

The remains of *Apatosaurus* were first dug up from the fossil-rich Morrison Formation of Colorado in 1877. At the time two rival teams of fossil hunters, led by Othniel Marsh and Edward Drinker Cope, raced to discover the newest and best dinosaur specimens. Cope and Marsh were bitter rivals. The tricks, thefts, and sabotage of their "Dinosaur Wars" make exciting reading (see chapter 10 in this book).

The thunder lizard

Marsh identified some of his great fossils as having come from a long-necked, four-legged plant-eater, which he named *Apatosaurus*. Cope did the same with his specimens but coined the name "*Atlantosaurus*" ("Atlas lizard"). Two years later colleagues of Marsh dug up another enormous fossil skeleton at Como Bluff, Wyoming. Marsh named this one "*Brontosaurus*" ("thunder lizard") because of the earthshaking noise it would make when running.

Growing confusion

In the haste to reconstruct these huge dinosaurs, fossil skulls and other bones were "borrowed" from other sauropods, such as *Diplodocus* and *Camarasaurus*. Over the following years great confusion arose. But gradually more finds and better study showed that *Apatosaurus*, "*Atlantosaurus*," and "*Brontosaurus*" were all one and the same type of dinosaur.

By international agreement, if different official names are given to the same living thing, the first name is the one that is finally accepted. So "*Brontosaurus*" – a catchy name, which had taken the public's imagination – and "*Atlantosaurus*" were dropped, in favor of *Apatosaurus*. When written, these old names are put into quotation marks to show that they are no longer officially accepted.

Getting a new head

Until 1975 *Apatosaurus* did not have its own head. Lacking a good fossil skull linked to the skeleton, this sauropod had been reconstructed with a deep, high-forehead skull similar to *Camarasaurus*. But further study of the records showed that part of a

◀ **Safety in numbers**
Apatosaurus was closely related to *Diplodocus* but shorter and more sturdily built. It was probably twice as heavy too, between 20 and 30 tons (20.3-30.5 tonnes) in weight. It browsed on high vegetation of conifers and tree-ferns, and also on low-growing ferns, cycads, and similar plants. Collections of its fossils and footprints show that it lived in groups, perhaps for protection against huge predatory dinosaurs such as *Allosaurus*.

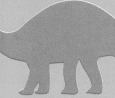

DATA BASE

Name	*Apatosaurus*
Pronounced	Ap-AT-owe-SORE-us
Meaning	"deceptive reptile"

What it ate Plant-eater, probably browsing in high trees or on low, soft vegetation

Length (nose - tail-tip) 70 feet (21.3 meters),
Standing height 25 feet (7.6 meters)
Weight Up to 25 tons (25.4 tonnes)

When it lived Late Jurassic Period 155-140 million years ago
Where it lived U.S. (Colorado, Utah, Oklahoma, Wyoming), Mexico (Baja California)

Order Saurischia (lizard-hipped dinosaurs)
Suborder Sauropodomorpha
Family Diplodocidae

Diplodocus-like skull had been found near one of the *Apatosaurus* skeletons. Also, the rest of *Apatosaurus* was generally more similar to *Diplodocus* than to *Camarasaurus*. So *Apatosaurus* now has a smaller, lower head than it had before 1975!

A shake of the head

A fossil *Apatosaurus* skull found recently has the detailed pathways for nerves and blood vessels preserved on it. They indicate that *Apatosaurus* had a very sensitive snout, using smell to locate food and possibly warn of danger. Also, the skull bones were flexible and could have bent or bowed inward and outward, allowing the head to shake or vibrate. Was this a way of making sound signals for the rest of the herd in the way that elephants trumpet across today's African grasslands?

▲ *Apatosaurus* **in death**
Two *Ceratosaurus* come to the stench of the swollen body of an *Apatosaurus* lying in a swamp. The carcass could provide food for several days — but rival scavengers may soon appear.

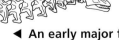

◀ **An early major find**
Apatosaurus bones have many weight-saving cavities, depressions, and hollows. In 1909 a partial *Apatosaurus* skeleton was the first find at the site later designated the Dinosaur National Monument, on the border of Colorado and Utah.

How big were the biggest? ▶

⇒ **How big were the biggest?**

Scientists have made many calculations based on recent finds of fossil dinosaur bones. One of the conclusions is that some sauropods were actually too big to exist!

The sizes of animals and plants can be studied in many ways. There are basic measurements such as length, width, height, weight, and volume. They can be broken down into the weights of different muscles, the densities of tissues such as nerves and guts, the strength of cartilage and bone, the volumes of blood and other body fluids, and so on.

▲ *"Supersaurus"*
The "super lizard" was a huge sauropod from the *Diplodocus* family. Its fossils come from the Late Jurassic Period rocks of Dry Mesa Quarry, Colorado, and were found in the 1970s. Three of the shoulder blades (scapulae) were around 8-9 feet (about 2.4-2.7 meters) long — some 3 feet (1 meter) longer than the same bone in *Diplodocus*. The hipbone (pelvis) was almost 7 feet (over 2 meters) in width and depth.

Estimates of *"Supersaurus"* range from 100 to 130 feet (30 to 40 meters) in length, some 56 feet (17.1 meters) in height, and 100 tons (102 tonnes) in weight.

Theoretical limits
In the 1970s biologists looked at the detailed structure of the biggest animals. In particular, they studied the stresses and strains that arise with increasing size. Is there a size limit, in theory, beyond which animals cannot grow? (This research applies to land animals – see page 89.)

For example, if an animal could grow to twice its normal length, it would not become twice its normal weight. The measure of

weight is based on volume, which is related to the three measurements of length, width, and height. If an animal increased to twice its size in all three of these measurements, it would weigh 8 times (2 x 2 x 2) as much as before.

Increases all over
This leads to the general principle that as animals become longer and wider, their weight increases in proportion far more quickly.

Of course, part of this weight can be extra muscle to provide the power for moving a proportionally heavier body. But other body parts must increase in size too. Larger guts are needed to digest extra food, which is needed to fuel a bigger body. More blood is necessary to distribute nutrients around it. The heaviest

▶ **The great stretch**
Brachiosaurus was unusual among sauropods in that its forelimbs increased in size as it evolved, becoming even longer than the hind legs. Also, its neck became enormously elongated, reaching at least 32 feet 6 inches (10 meters) in length.

body parts, bones, must be still thicker and stronger to support the extra mass.

A limit to muscle power

Eventually size comes up against limits. Muscles have to be so bulky that they cannot move themselves, let alone move the huge bones needed to support their great weight. As a very rough estimate, experts calculated that this limit on weight for a land animal is about 100 tons (102 tonnes). If the animal were any heavier, its legs would be so thick that they would be impossible to move.

Estimating size

The weight of a dinosaur can be estimated by making a scale model of the skeleton. Roughened areas, or "scars," on the fossil bones show where the muscles were attached. Using modeling clay, scaled-down muscles are

Estimated skull size of "*Ultrasaurus*" compared with a human.

▲ *"Ultrasaurus"*
The "ultra lizard" was a vast sauropod related to *Brachiosaurus*. Its fossils date from the Early Cretaceous Period and were discovered in the 1970s in South Korea, in East Asia. The remains are fragmentary, and estimates of size vary. It may have been smaller than *Brachiosaurus* itself or weighed as much as 140 tons (142 tonnes).

shaped onto the bones. The size of each muscle is guessed from the approximate weight it would have to move in the live animal. Then other body parts such as the heart, lungs, and guts are added.

Estimating weight

Finally, the model animal is smoothed to a realistic shape – and immersed in water! The amount of water pushed aside, or displaced, gives the volume of the scaled-down dinosaur. This volume is scaled up to produce the volume of the dinosaur in life. The volume is then compared with the known volume and weight of similar living animals: the crocodiles. By taking into account the relationship between volume and weight, the weight of the dinosaur can now be calculated (see pages 88-89).

Was it great to be big?

⇒ Was it great to be big?

Advantages of being big

- **Defense** A huge animal is powerful and heavy. Its great bulk and weight are deterrents to attackers. It can push, crush, ram, and even roll on enemies!
- **Water needs** Water is essential for life and is lost through the skin, even the tough, scaly skin of reptiles. Compared with a small animal, a bigger animal has less surface area of skin in relation to its body volume. So it loses less water in proportion to its volume. In a dry climate this could help survival.
- **Body temperature control** Warmth, as well as water, is lost through the body surface. If conditions turn cold, a large animal cools down more slowly than a small one. Likewise, in conditions that suddenly become very hot, a large animal is in less danger of overheating. As the outside temperatures fluctuate, the temperature in the interior of a large creature stays much the same, whereas a small creature's will go up and down. The larger animal's body can work more efficiently and withstand greater extremes.
- **Food needs** Of the food an animal eats, more goes toward keeping it alive and less toward supporting size and activity. A 200-pound (91-kilogram) person doesn't eat twice as much as a 100-pound (45-kilogram) person. So a big animal needs less food in proportion to its bulk than a small one.

Disadvantages of being big

- **Absolute food needs** Big creatures need lots of food. They are a huge burden on the local environment, plants, and animals. In many cases they have to move regularly to new feeding grounds.
- **Vulnerable young** The babies take a long time, perhaps tens of years, to grow to huge adult size. When young and small, they are vulnerable to predators.
- **Slow reproduction** Slow-growing animals take years to become mature and breed. This means they cannot respond rapidly if there is a sudden change in conditions, such as food or climate. They cannot build up their numbers quickly after a population crash.

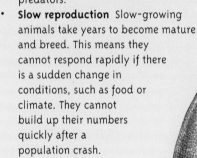

▼ Impossibly big?

Since the 1970s scattered fossils have been found that suggest some dinosaurs were even bigger than *Brachiosaurus*. Three contenders — *Seismosaurus, Ultrasaurus,* and *Supersaurus* — are shown here (left to right). However, the remains are not whole skeletons. So, it is difficult to know if they are from a sauropod that had an unusually large body part, such as shoulders or hips, even though the rest of its body was not quite so gigantic.

▶ *"Seismosaurus"*

The "earth-shaking lizard" was an enormous sauropod from the *Diplodocus* family. It lived during Late Jurassic times in what is now New Mexico. The first remains were uncovered in 1986 and described in a scientific report in 1991. This beast's shoulder blade was 8 feet (2.4 meters) long, and some individual backbones (vertebrae) were 5 feet (1.5 meters) long. Being a diplodocid, it may have had a slender build and so been relatively light. But estimates for its total length are up to 130 feet (40 meters). If so, this is the longest dinosaur yet discovered.

Very variable results

The process of estimating an animal's weight (see page 87) involves several types of guesswork, especially when it comes to the size of the muscles. So, it is not surprising that results vary widely. For example, a "slim" reconstruction of the skeleton of *Brachiosaurus* gave a weight of around 20 tons (20.3 tonnes). Using the same skeleton, a "bulky" reconstruction produced an estimate of 78 tons (79 tonnes).

These estimates also show how weight is drastically affected by the animal's build. The bones of *Diplodocus* are "fine" – relatively narrow and slim, even delicate. Those of *Brachiosaurus* are much thicker and sturdier, and the body is relatively larger. This means that *Brachiosaurus* was shorter in length than *Diplodocus* yet probably five times heavier.

A recent contender for the title of biggest from Oklahoma is *Sauroposeidon*. This 60-ton (61-tonne) brachiosaur may have stood even taller than *Brachiosaurus* itself, perhaps an amazing 57 feet (17 meters). Its preserved neck bones, dug up in 1994, were at first mistaken for fossil tree trunks.

Did sauropods live in water?

When people began to realize how big the sauropods were, many scientists suggested that the animals were too heavy and cumbersome for land. They must have been aquatic, that is, living partly or wholly in water. Water can support great weight (such as ships). The animal's bones would not have had to be so strong or the muscles so powerful.

There are many older pictures of sauropods part-wading, part-wallowing in deep swamps. Some even show these dinosaurs walking along a river or lake bed almost completely submerged (for example, *Brachiosaurus*, right). The long neck was a snorkel, and the nostrils were just breaking the surface to breathe.

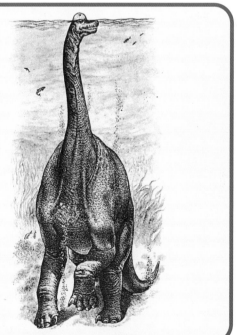

However, the idea of aquatic sauropods has now been rejected. Their body and limb structures show no true aquatic adaptations. There are no webbed toes for swimming nor a flattened tail (like a crocodile's) for propeling the creature through water. The limb bones, backbone, and ribs are adapted to withstand the full pull of gravity felt on land.

The longest-necked dinosaur

Mamenchisaurus had the longest neck of any dinosaur and therefore of any known animal in earth's history.

Even by sauropod standards, the neck of *Mamenchisaurus* was exceptional. It was more than 40 feet (12.2 meters), over half the entire length of the animal. It consisted of 19 cervical vertebrae, or neck bones, itself a record number among sauropods. Each bone was twice the length of an equivalent bone in the creature's chest, a thoracic vertebra. Yet the neck bones were very delicate and light, in some places with walls almost as thin as eggshell.

A stiff neck

The neck structure was reinforced by bony spines, two growing from the back of each vertebra to overlap the one behind. This gave strength but at the expense of flexibility. The only fairly mobile joints were between the head itself and the neck and between the neck and shoulders. So, *Mamenchisaurus* must have swung its stiff neck from the shoulders. It would have been able to tilt its head slightly in a small circle.

Head and tail

Mamenchisaurus is named from the watercourse in China where its fossils were found. There were no complete skull or teeth with the first remains. Some experts believed that this sauropod was peg-toothed, like *Diplodocus*, partly because of its chevron-shaped tailbones. Others had doubts.

Further fragments of skull suggested a taller head than the diplodocids. Also, all other sauropods from the region had spatulate, or spoonlike, teeth. A head found recently shows that *Mamenchisaurus* was indeed a spatulate-toothed sauropod. The rest of *Mamenchisaurus* was typically sauropod, with a huge, bulky body and long, whiplash tail.

A floating plant-rake?

When the remains of *Mamenchisaurus* were first studied, people came up with all kinds of theories about the long neck. Was it too long to be self-supporting? Perhaps the sauropod lived in water and floated its neck on the surface to relieve the strain of holding it up. It could swish the neck from side to side to gather soft water plants.

This theory soon fell into doubt. The teeth were too sturdy, designed for tough, woody vegetation rather than fleshy, easily torn aquatic plants. Also, the neck was obviously built to be extremely light. The joints at the shoulders indicated that the neck bent slightly upward toward the head at this point. If the animal lived in water, the neck would be lifted above the surface (or even the main body!). And the legs were designed for walking, not wading or swimming. The neck of *Mamenchisaurus* is now seen not as an unsolved mystery but as an engineering marvel.

▲ An evening stroll
An adult and young *Mamenchisaurus* paddle across a watercourse as the sky darkens toward evening. They have disturbed small pterosaurs that were fishing in the shallows.

▶ Room for a neck
This specimen of *Mamenchisaurus* in the Natural History Museum, London, was 72 feet (22 meters) long, 13 feet (4 meters) wide, and weighed about 30 tons (30 tonnes). It towers over a stegosaur in the foreground.

DATA BASE

Name *Mamenchisaurus*
Pronounced Ma-MEN-chee-SORE-us
Meaning "Mamenchi [Mamen stream] lizard"

What it ate Plant-eater, probably browsing in high trees and tree-ferns on tough vegetation

Length (nose - tail-tip) 80 feet (24.4 meters)
Standing height 35 feet (10.7 meters)
Weight Up to 25 tons (25.4 tonnes)

When it lived Late Jurassic Period 160-145 million years ago
Where it lived China (including Sichuan, Xinjiang, and Ganshu Provinces), Mongolia

Order Saurischia (lizard-hipped dinosaurs)
Suborder Sauropodomorpha
Family Euhelopodidae or Diplodocidae

Introduction to dinosaurs and birds

Fossil evidence shows us that all dinosaurs died out in a great extinction 65 million years ago. Birds, which were well established by then, did not. Like mammals, they thrived and diversified in the post-dinosaur world. But there are striking similarities between the small theropod dinosaurs and birds. Scientists have therefore come up with many theories about the nature and fate of these reptiles and the origin and evolution of the birds.

Picture the scene about 150 million years ago in the Late Jurassic Period. It is a moist, lush forest of cycads and other ancient trees. A huge dragonfly flits silently past. The main animals in the scene are reptiles – dinosaurs. A herd of house-sized sauropods, similar to *Diplodocus*, rests in the shade. Each has a tiny head, long neck, barrel-shaped body, pillar legs, and a long whiplash tail. On the forest floor small, knee-high dinosaurs called coelurosaurs stand almost upright on their two bigger rear legs, scrabbling in the soil with their long-fingered hands for worms, bugs, and other food.

Color and song

Two features of the forest scene are peculiar. First, the lack of color. Most of the trees and plants are green or brown. There are no flowers. The dinosaurs are also greens, browns, and grays. Second, the lack of sound. Apart from the occasional grunt, the reptiles make little noise.

Suddenly the peace is broken by a splash of bright color and startling sound. A creature squawks raucously and flaps clumsily across a clearing. Its red and yellow body glows in the shafts of sunlight. It is a type of animal that has evolved only in the past few million years. It has feathers. It is a bird.

▶ Fast and agile
Coelophysis was a lightly built coelurosaur (a member of the Coelurosauria, a subgroup of the Theropoda, or "beast-feet") that lived in the Late Triassic Period. In the next period, the Jurassic, small dinosaurs like coelurosaurs or the similar dromaeosaurs (raptors) may have evolved into birds.

Fundamental nature

The above description is based on the evidence of fossils, although the details come from informed guesswork. It relates to one of the most exciting areas in the natural sciences, which is full of questions – especially about the fundamental direction of evolution and classifying such animals as birds and reptiles into groups.

Questions and answers

What features make birds so successful and widespread today? Why were certain dinosaurs, such as the small theropods known as coelurosaurs and raptors, so similar to ancient birds? Did birds evolve from them?

◀ Great survivor
Modern birds, such as this guinea fowl, are descended from birds that survived the mass extinction at the end of the Age of Dinosaurs.

Birds are warm-blooded today, but were they always? If not, were ancient birds truly birds? If so, were the small dinosaurs that evolved into them also warm-blooded? All of today's reptiles are cold-blooded. Are birds "feathered dinosaurs"? Or had those small theropod dinosaurs already moved on from the reptile group to become "scaly birds"? The answers – or at least some of the possible explanations – are in this chapter.

▲ Triassic scene

There is evidence that dinosaurs lived in herds. Here a group of *Coelophysis* make their way through a forest.

There are about 9,000 species of birds in the modern world. They form a class (major group) of animals, Aves, which is one of the great classes of vertebrates. A vertebrate is defined as an animal that has an inner skeleton with a backbone, or vertebral column.

Birds are exceptionally distinctive. They are warm-blooded, have scaly legs, four limbs, and a horny beak, lay hard-shelled eggs, and have a body covering of feathers. There are many theories, past and present, about how and where birds first evolved.

- from thecodonts
- from crocodiles
- from mammals

But lack of evidence makes theories such as these difficult to prove or disprove. Prehistoric bird fossils are extremely scarce and so present a lack of evidence, because

- bird bones are light and delicate and easily destroyed by predators, scavengers, or natural weathering and erosion
- teeth are hard and do not generally rot or crumble — but most ancient birds (and all modern ones) lacked teeth
  - many birds lived in habitats such as forests where the conditions for fossilization were very poor compared, for example, with a lake or the sea.

Similarities and differences

Small theropod dinosaurs and the early birds have numerous and striking similarities, but there are critical differences too.

The many similarities between birds and the small theropod dinosaurs, especially the coelurosaurs and the raptors, are well documented. In 1870 they were listed by Thomas Henry Huxley (1825-95), an eminent zoologist. Huxley strongly supported the theory of evolution by natural selection, as proposed by Charles Darwin in his 1859 book *On the Origin of Species*.

Why so similar?

If we look at the reconstructed skeletons of the earliest known bird, *Archaeopteryx* (shown in detail on the following pages), and a representative small theropod, such as *Compsognathus* or *Ornitholestes*, we see many comparable features.

But are these similarities good evidence for a close link between birds and small theropod dinosaurs? Many "bird" features are general theropod characteristics, shared by the earlier members of the group such as *Ornitholestes* and by bigger and later members such as *Tyrannosaurus*. Some of the features were present even before the first theropods. They were there in the earlier dinosaurs – even in the ancestors of dinosaurs, which may have been types of thecodonts (see chapter 1 in this book).

▼ **Family connections**
The relatively primitive Triassic forms *Coelophysis* and *Syntarsus* are thought to have developed separately from the more advanced late Jurassic coelurosaurs, *Ornitholestes* (below) and

General similarities between small theropod dinosaurs and early birds
• Small body size, about 2-3 feet (60-90 cm) long
• Slim, light build
• Rear legs larger than front legs
• Two-legged or bipedal stance on rear legs

Head
• Long, low, narrow shape
• Large eyes
• Long, narrow jawbones
• Many small, sharp teeth
• Long, flexible neck

Limbs
• Two long, clawed fingers on hand (third smaller finger in *Archaeopteryx*)
• Leg has three sections of equal length — femur (thigh), tibia (shin), metatarsals (foot)
• Three main clawed toes on foot
• First toe (hallux) is shorter, higher on foot, and faces backward

Body and tail
• Compact, shortened body
• Body held parallel to ground
• Long tail with many bones (caudal vertebrae)

Breeding
• Laid eggs, from which babies hatched
• Chemical structure of eggshell is very similar

Same time

Think of *Compsognathus*. It is small, light, agile, and active. Surely such a dinosaur had very little evolution to do before it became a bird. Change the proportions of a few bones, add some feathers, make a few other adjustments, and the result flies away! Also, it is tempting to assume that *Archaeopteryx*, the first known bird, was the first bird ever to exist, and that all modern birds evolved from it.

But *Archaeopteryx* and *Compsognathus* lived at the same time,

155-150 million years ago. So one could not have evolved from the other. *Archaeopteryx* was already some way along the road of bird evolution, which probably took millions of years. As far as we know, *Compsognathus* did not exist at this earlier period.

Was *Archaeopteryx* a dead-end?

Also, some experts consider that early bird evolution went along several different paths. The one followed by *Archaeopteryx* may have begun with a small theropod but turned out to be a dead-end. No bird today has the *Archaeopteryx* features of teeth in the mouth or bones in the tail.

This suggests that other birds, as yet unknown from fossils, existed before *Archaeopteryx* and were on the main evolutionary line to modern birds. Recent discoveries concerning the evolution of the bird wing from the five-fingered vertebrate hand support this view.

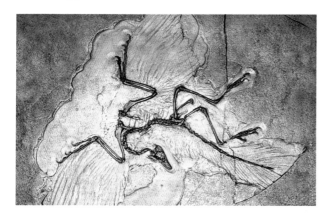

Computer analysis

Cladistics is a method of grouping items such as animals according to certain shared similarities that have been inherited from a common ancestor. This method follows strict rules, rather than relying on a general impression that one animal is similar to another and concluding that the two must be related. Cladistics shows closeness of relationship — but not necessarily who evolved from what.

Cladistic analysis of hundreds of features or traits of birds, theropods, and other dinosaurs lined them up as follows:

 Coelophysis
 Tyrannosaurs
 Ornithomimosaurs
 Coelurosaurs
 Dromaeosaurs
 Troodontids
 Birds

The computer analysis revealed that one of the closest theropod relatives of birds was the medium-sized, pack-hunting *Deinonychus* (see volume 8 in this series).

This does not imply that *Deinonychus* was the ancestor of birds. That would have been impossible, since *Deinonychus* lived in the Middle Cretaceous Period 115-110 million years ago, at a time when birds were already established. What the analysis shows is that *Deinonychus* and birds share more features, inherited from a common ancestor, than birds share with any other kinds of dinosaurs.

◄ *Archaeopteryx* fossil

Sprawled out in death, *Archaeopteryx* clearly displays its long, clawed limbs and bony tail.

▼ *Compsognathus* on the run

Compsognathus was similar in body shape to *Archaeopteryx*, and it would not be hard to imagine it winged and flying rather than running.

Dinosaurs with feathers

In recent years, many new kinds of dinosaurs, birds, and other animals have been described from fossils found in China (see page 102). Two examples are *Caudipteryx* and *Protoarchaeopteryx*, which are dated to between 120 and 150 million years ago. Their fossils have clear imprints of feathers. But the preserved bones show that they were much more dinosaurlike than *Archaeopteryx* and too heavy to fly.

These specimens throw more doubt on the theory that birds alone had feathers and that therefore any feathered animal must be a bird. *Caudipteryx* and *Protoarchaeopteryx* seem more clearly to be small ground-living theropods, which had a particular type of nonscaly body covering — in other words, they were feathered dinosaurs.

→ The early bird

Few prehistoric animals are as well known as *Archaeopteryx*, whose name means "ancient wing." Few fossils have been more studied, caused more controversy, or been sold for more money.

Despite its great fame and importance in evolutionary history, there are only seven known specimens of *Archaeopteryx*. Six consist of part or most of a skeleton, and one of just a feather. They were all found in one area in Bavaria, Germany, and date from the Late Jurassic Period about 156-150 million years ago. They formed in extremely fine-grained limestone rock known as "lithographic limestone." The tiny grains allowed the smallest details of the original bones and feathers to be preserved.

New identities

The first fossil specimen of *Archaeopteryx* was found in a limestone quarry at Solnhofen, Bavaria, in 1861. A second specimen came to light in 1877, this time with a skull, and a third, headless like the first, in 1956.

Two other specimens were already in museum collections when they were restudied and identified as *Archaeopteryx* in 1970 and 1973. The first had been thought to be a pterosaur, the second the dinosaur *Compsognathus*. It goes to show how similar these small skeletons can be, and how *Archaeopteryx* was initially mistaken for a dinosaur.

The features of *Archaeopteryx*

The skeleton of *Archaeopteryx* is shown on page 98. It had many features of a small theropod dinosaur, especially in the structure of its hands, clawed fingers, hips, legs, tail, skull, and teeth. The specimens range from about the size of a chicken to that of a small turkey.

The wings, feathers, and tail of *Archaeopteryx* and other prehistoric birds are discussed in detail on later pages. So are the mechanics of truly sustained, powered, controlled flight, as opposed to occasional gliding or clumsy flapping.

▶ A desert island

Fossils found in the same type of rock as those of *Archaeopteryx*, as well as the nature of the stone itself, show that this creature lived on what we might call a "desert island." In the Late Jurassic Period this area of Europe had warm, shallow, saltwater lagoons scattered with small islands that received little rainfall. Scientists have hardly any reason to think there were tall trees, so the idea that *Archaeopteryx* could flap its wings and glide from one tree to another as pictured here may be wishful thinking. Perhaps *Archaeopteryx* scavenged along the tide line on the beach or waded and fished in the shallow lagoons.

The flight of *Archaeopteryx*

Could *Archaeopteryx* fly? Not very well. It did not have a breastbone, or sternum, with a deep flange, the keel. This is where the powerful pectoral (breast or chest) muscles of a modern bird are anchored, which flap the wings downward for uplift during flight. Also, the wishbone, or furcula, of *Archaeopteryx* was relatively small. This V-shaped bone holds the sternum and chest area against the shoulders. It needs to be big to strengthen the

upper body for the mechanical stresses of flight.

Puzzling feathers

However, the feathers of *Archaeopteryx* closely resemble those of the modern pigeon. They had an asymmetric, airfoil shape that created lift as the wings flapped and passed through the air. And there were both primary and secondary feathers, which ensured both good lift and aerial control (see page 101). If the feathers had been simply for protection or appearance, or to keep in body warmth, would they need this airfoil shape?

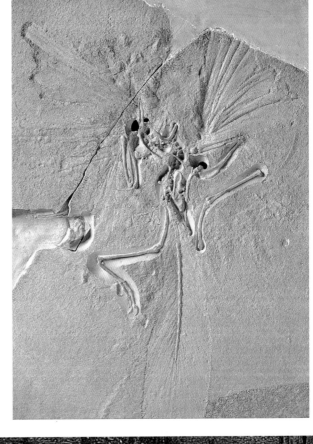

▶ Rare specimen

One of the few fossils of the "bird-reptile" so far discovered, this specimen of *Archaeopteryx lithographica* is about 150 million years old. The outlines and patterns of its wing feathers are preserved in amazing and beautiful detail. The long tail with its feathers dangles below, and the bent, distorted legs jut out left and right.

More about the "bird-reptile" ▶

⇒ More about the "bird-reptile"

Archaeopteryx is particularly interesting because of its mixture of bird and reptile features. Its place in evolution is unclear.

A dinosaur-bird mosaic

It wasn't so much that, in body and skeleton, *Archaeopteryx* was a halfway grade between dinosaur and bird. Instead, it was like a mosaic, with some features that were almost fully those of a bird and others that were almost fully those of a dinosaur.

The bird features included a relatively large brain, a furcula (or wishbone) in the upper chest, the pubis part of the hipbone parallel to the ischium part, and four clawed toes on each foot with the first toe shorter and facing backward for perching.

The dinosaur features were long narrow jaws lined with tiny teeth, reptilelike openings in the skull, ribs in the belly (gastralia) as well as the chest, a long, flexible backbone that extended into the tail, a flexible attachment between the backbone and the hips, and three long clawed fingers on each hand.

Archaeopteryx may have been somewhere on the evolutionary line between dinosaurs and birds. If so, current evidence suggests it was more closely related to the former. It could have been an early offshoot of this line but an evolutionary dead-end (see previous page). Other creatures, their fossils as yet unknown to us, were evolving from small theropod dinosaurs and were destined to be the ancestors of birds today.

Climbing and gliding

If *Archaeopteryx* did not fly, what did it do? It had a feature not found in birds today, three finger-claws that projected from about halfway along the front of each wing. Perhaps it used these and its clawed toes to clamber and haul itself up tall plants, trees, or rocks. Then it could launch itself on a short, flapping glide to the ground or to another tree.

Its place in evolution

What is the place of *Archaeopteryx* in the grand scheme of evolution? Was it the first bird, a feathered dinosaur, or an intermediate between the two — a "missing link" that isn't missing any more?

Take away the feathers, and *Archaeopteryx* becomes almost indistinguishable from other small theropod dinosaurs of the period. Its birdlike features are just like the birdlike features found in many other dinosaurs.

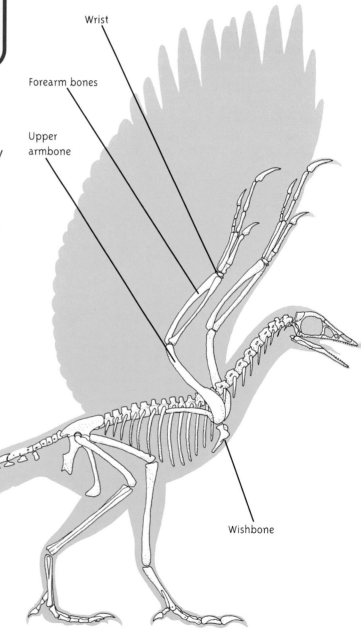

Wrist

Forearm bones

Upper armbone

Wishbone

▲ **Wings aloft**
Archaeopteryx may have stretched its wings high into the air during flapping flight, perhaps to glide from one tree to another.

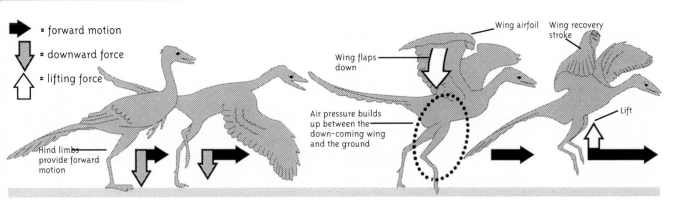

- = forward motion
- = downward force
- = lifting force

Wing airfoil
Wing recovery stroke

Wing flaps down

Hind limbs provide forward motion

Air pressure builds up between the down-coming wing and the ground

Lift

▲ The ground-up or cursorial origin of flight (see page 17)

The colorful bird?

No one knows the color of *Archaeopteryx*. The original colors do not remain in fossils – the objects change to rock and become the color of that rock. In the 1990s some advanced work began on the microstructure of fossil shells and fish scales, which have tiny ridges or pits that could indicate the colors of light reflected from their surfaces. The preserved feathers of *Archaeopteryx* give a good idea of their size, shape, and arrangement over the body. But you can make them any color you fancy – rainbow-bright like a bird of paradise to attract a mate, dull like a thrush for camouflage, black like a raven, white as a swan.

A curious bird

Only one bird today has wing-claws like those of *Archaeopteryx*. Even then, it has only one claw per wing and only while it is young. This is the hoatzin, a strange-looking inhabitant of South American forests. The hoatzin has a straggly crest and a head that seems too small for its body. It nests in trees above water. If the chick is threatened, it flops out of the nest and plops into the water below to escape. After the danger passes, it uses its wing-claws to climb the tree back to the nest. The adult bird lacks these claws.

DATA BASE

Name	*Archaeopteryx*
Pronounced	Ark-ee-OPP-terr-icks
Meaning	"ancient wing"

What it ate Insects, worms, lizards, mammals, and other small animals, possibly fish and crabs

Length (nose - tail-tip) 20 inches (51 centimeters)
Standing height 15 inches (38 centimeters)
Weight about 3 pounds (1.4 kilograms)

When it lived Late Jurassic Period 150 million years ago
Where it lived Europe (Germany)

Class Aves (Birds) or Reptilia (Reptiles)
Order Archaeornithiformes or Saurischia

The origins of flight

Why do birds fly? Why did the early birds take to the air in the first place? How did they evolve body features that allowed them to master sustained, controlled flight?

Besides birds, only two other animal groups today are truly at home in the air – insects long before the birds and bats long after. So we assume that flight has evolved at least three times.

Leaving aside the exact identity of the first birdlike fliers and the origins of feathers (see page 97), there are numerous theories about the pressures that led to the evolution of flying birds. Many fall into one of two main camps. These are the air-down and the ground-up ideas.

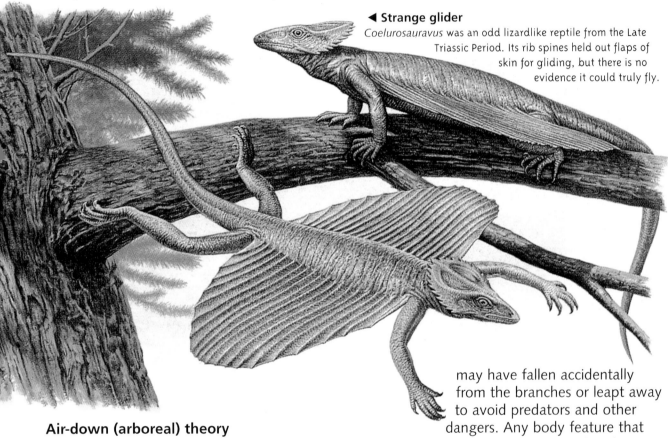

◀ Strange glider
Coelurosauravus was an odd lizardlike reptile from the Late Triassic Period. Its rib spines held out flaps of skin for gliding, but there is no evidence it could truly fly.

Air-down (arboreal) theory
The first "birds" arose from tree-climbing animals – maybe dinosaurs, maybe not. They may have fallen accidentally from the branches or leapt away to avoid predators and other dangers. Any body feature that helped them glide or parachute rather than plummet would be a great advantage. Gradually this feature would enlarge by natural selection and become modified for controlled flapping rather than passive parachuting. Gliding would evolve into true flight.

Several kinds of animals today show stages in the process. There are flying squirrels, flying lemurs (colugos), flying possums (gliders), flying frogs, flying lizards, flying fish, and even flying snakes. None of these are true powered fliers, but some are supreme gliders. They have membranes or flaps of skin or similar surfaces that help to break the fall. In birds these surfaces are formed by feathers.

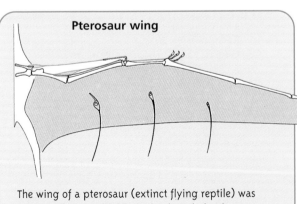

Pterosaur wing

The wing of a pterosaur (extinct flying reptile) was supported along the front edge largely by the very long bones of the fourth finger.

The third way

The secret of bird flight is in the wing's downstroke. The outer, hand part of the wing swivels to push air behind it, generating forward thrust. This propels the bird forward, making air flow over the main inner part of the wing. The airflow creates a lifting force because of the wing's airfoil shape, which is curved more on the upper surface than the lower one. Lift and thrust together keep the bird in the air.

To swivel and push, the hand part of the wing must flex sideways. This is a complex movement, but the same joint flexibility was already present for perhaps another reason in medium-sized theropods such as *Deinonychus* and *Velociraptor* (as well as in *Archaeopteryx*). It may have evolved in these dinosaurs as a way of snapping the hands forward suddenly, to catch prey in a twist-and-clap motion.

Ground-up (cursorial) theory

The first "birds" arose from fast-running, ground-dwelling animals, such as small theropod dinosaurs. They were already slim, agile, lightweight, active creatures. Dashing along on their back legs, body almost upright, they could have held their arms out for balance and control when turning, as they evaded predators and danger and also grabbed prey (see panel above).

The appearance of small, lightweight feathers on the arms allowed these dinosaurs to lengthen their stride. The forelimbs became small, winglike extensions (see page 99). Larger feathers allowed them to leap further and glide between strides. The arms would become stronger and begin to flap, allowing the creature to move faster through the air than on the ground. Gradually flying replaced gliding.

Preadaptation

The air-down idea would allow for gradual change in the bones, joints, and muscles to cope with the power needed for sustained flight and the stresses this puts on the body. Parts of the arms of small theropods, in particular, were already suited, or "preadapted," to becoming wings (see panel below).

Mechanical and aerodynamic factors make the ground-up theory less likely to be correct. An early version of wings could cause air resistance and produce a slowing-down force, or drag, making the animal run more slowly, not faster. If the wings gave lift, this would reduce the animal's grip on the ground and so lessen the powerful kicking motion that pushed it forward. The theory works best if we suppose that wings suddenly appeared that were already extremely aerodynamic, like those of modern geese and swans.

Folding forelimbs

In 1997 a new dinosaur discovery was announced from Patagonia and Argentina in South America. Named *Unenlagia*, it lived about 90 million years ago and is included in the dromaeosaur group of theropods along with *Deinonychus*. Indeed, its body structure is midway between *Deinonychus* and *Archaeopteryx* (although the latter lived 60 million years earlier). *Unenlagia* could lift its arms up and forward and then fold them by its sides in the way that modern birds fold (and flap) their wings. However, the arms of *Unenlagia* were not long enough for proper flight. It may have flapped them to gain lift as it ran or jumped, as described by the ground-up theory.

All about feathers ▶

→ All about feathers

Feathers make a bird – at least, in today's world. How did they originate and why? For insulation, protection, coloration, predation, or flight?

A bird's feathers form a lightweight, smooth, airproof, low-friction surface for moving through the air. The wing feathers in particular make a large, flexible, and maneuverable surface for powering flight and steering. Feathers also act as insulation to keep in body warmth and as protection against knocks and bumps. They are cleaned and oiled during preening so that they stay waterproof. And their colors and patterns may resemble the surroundings and help to camouflage a bird, or they may be bright and gaudy to stand out from the background and attract a mate during courtship.

Types of feathers

Feathers are made of the protein keratin. This is the same substance that forms our own outer layer of skin and our hair and nails. It also forms the claws, hooves, and horns of other mammals, the scales on a bird's legs – and the scales on a reptile's body. Presumably the scales on dinosaurs were made of keratin too.

Each feather grows from a pit in the skin called a follicle. Like our hair, feathers are dead, although each has a nerve and a muscle at its base.

▲ Creature of mystery
Fossils of a Late Triassic creature named *Protoavis* were studied in the late 1980s and early 1990s. Here it is reconstructed as an *Archaeopteryx*-like bird with the crocodilelike rauisuchian reptile *Postosuchus* passing beneath. However, the exact identity of *Protoavis* is hotly disputed. It is unlikely that it predates the earliest well-known bird, *Archaeopteryx* itself, by more than 600 million years.

They grow in regular patterns over the skin and are replaced once or twice every year at the molt.

The feathers that cover the body and wings are contour feathers. Under them are much softer, filamentous (threadlike) down feathers. They form an insulating layer that traps air and keeps in body warmth.

Which came first?

Although the earliest known bird, *Archaeopteryx*, already had well-evolved flight, or contour, feathers, we do not know how well it could fly (see page 96). Did feathers evolve in birds specifically for flight? Or did they evolve for some other purpose, perhaps in the ancestors of birds – probably small theropod dinosaurs – and become adapted for flight later? In this case, there are not only bird feathers but reptile feathers too.

An insulating blanket

It is generally agreed that feathers developed from reptile scales. Gradually, the scales evolved hairlike, frilly, or fluffy edges. The evolutionary advantage of this could have been insulation, because their owner was warm-blooded (see pages 68-69 for explanation of warm-bloodedness). Flight came later as a secondary function.

A recent fossil find from China could support this view. It is *Sinosauropteryx*, a coelurosaur-type dinosaur about 20 inches (51 cm) long, similar in size and shape to *Compsognathus*. It lived around 140-120 million years ago. The remains show that its shoulders, neck, back, and tail seem to be covered in threadlike structures, which could be downy feathers. However, the fibers of the "feathers" are parallel and unbranched, rather than branched as in flight feathers.

Design for a purpose

Another theory is that feathers began as traps or nets for flying insects. A small theropod dinosaur would jump into the air and envelop its victim in its long-feathered arms. Some bats and birds such as nightjars can use this technique. Perhaps this is why birds and theropod dinosaurs are able to swivel their hand joints (see page 101).

An alternative view is that contour feathers are so superbly designed for flight in every feature and detail that they must have evolved for this specific purpose, probably in tree-dwelling reptiles. Downy, insulating feathers came later, which means warm-bloodedness came later too. If we accept this theory, then dinosaurs were cold-blooded; they evolved into birds with flight feathers; then down feathers appeared with or because of warm-bloodedness.

Sun and rain

Birds such as ostriches, ducks, and falcons use their feathered wings to protect their eggs or chicks. They hold out the wings over the nest to shield the eggs or young from too much sun or rain. Did feathers begin in this way, as sunshades or umbrellas? Fossils of the

▲ Living together
In this Late Cretaceous scene birds perch around and on the head of *Deinosuchus*, a crocodilian reptile, lurking in the water, while kritosaurs pass by in the background, and a pterosaur (left) glides away.

▶ Later bird tracks
The birds that made these fossilized tracks lived well after the Age of the Dinosaurs, in the Eocene Epoch of the Tertiary Period about 50 million years ago.

theropod *Oviraptor* from Mongolia indicate that it died with its arms encircling or covering its eggs. However, there were no traces of feathers.

Parts of a feather
An individual bird feather has a base and a central tapering shaft. Paired barbs branch from either side of the shaft. The barbs, in turn, also branch into small barbs called barbules. They form tiny hooks, which zip together to give the whole feather its shape. As a bird preens, it rehooks any undone barbules and rearranges its feathers into neat layers, as well as cleaning them and spreading water-repelling oil from its body glands over them.

Birds evolve

Archaeopteryx is still one of the earliest and best-known birds from the fossil record. But as the Cretaceous Period continued other birds started to crop up and show increasing variety.

As explained previously (see page 93), bird bones are fragile and unlikely to be preserved. So the fossil record for birds is even more patchy and full of gaps than for dinosaurs and other animals. However, the fossils that have been discovered – especially recent finds from East Asia – show how birds evolved into various shapes and sizes through the Cretaceous Period. Well before the end of the period, representatives of at least four modern groups were present. They were shore birds, sea birds, loons (divers), and wildfowl (ducks, geese, and swans).

▼ Diving onto prey
The small, pointed teeth of *Ichthyornis* lend weight to the notion that it was a fish-eating sea bird, similar to modern terns. We can imagine it diving into the water from its flight, as terns and gannets do today.

▲ A bird of its time
The wings of *Archaeopteryx* were not quite the same as those of modern birds because they had three separate, clawed fingers. The snout looked like a bird's but was lined with small, sharply pointed teeth.

Trends for the air
The fossils show the general trend toward skeletal features that improved flight. These include:
- Generally smaller or fewer bones and also fusion of adjacent bones, which meant loss of joint flexibility, but also loss of joint parts and so saving of weight.
- This happened especially in the skull, jaws, wings, ribcage, spine, and hips.
- Increased size of the braincase of the skull to hold a larger brain, presumably with more complex behavior.
  - Thinner and more obviously hollow bones to save weight.
  - Loss of heavy teeth and the development of a horny, much lighter beak.
    - A flange or keel to the sternum (breastbone), for attachment of the powerful pectoral (chest) flight muscles.
    - Fusion and elongation (joining together and lengthening) of the bones in the hand, to make the wing stronger and longer.

The wishbone

In a modern bird the wishbone, or furcula, is a V-shaped bone in the upper chest. It holds the shoulder joints apart and braces them against the breastbone (sternum) for extra strength.

The wishbone works as an elastic spring. When the pectoral flight muscles make the wings flap down for their power stroke, the shoulders are pulled together and the V is squeezed narrower. The energy thus stored is then released as the bone springs back to help the wings flap back up again. They do this by means of a pulleylike arrangement of the muscles and tendons around the bones.

Originally the wishbone was probably not springy, just an anchor for arm muscles, as in *Archaeopteryx* (right).

The wishbone may be equivalent to the collarbones, or clavicles, found in mammals, including ourselves. Most dinosaurs do not seem to have had clavicles (or breastbones). However, it is now known that some theropods had them, as shown by their fossils — supporting the idea that birds evolved from these dinosaurs.

The evidence that dinosaurs had clavicles was dubious until 1997, when such bones were clearly identified in a *Velociraptor* fossil from Mongolia. They are thinner than in a bird's wishbone but otherwise very similar and in the same place.

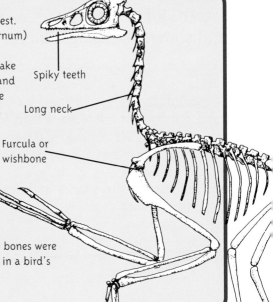

Spiky teeth

Long neck

Furcula or wishbone

- Fusion of the bones in the hip, at the expense of being able to run well. This shows how forelimbs took over from hindlimbs as the main method of moving.
- Shrunken and fused bones in the tail part of the backbone, forming the stubby pygostyle, or "parson's nose."
- Toes adapted for gripping and perching on twigs and branches, rather than standing on flat ground.

Flying for fish

Most of these trends are shown by *Ichthyornis*, which lived in the Mid-Cretaceous Period in North America. It stood about 6 inches (15 cm) tall, and reconstructions show a stout, ternlike sea bird with a large head, long and slim toothed jaws with a beak, pointed wings, and small feet. The jaws and teeth resemble those of a young mosasaur, a marine reptile of the lizard group (not a dinosaur). Other birds from Cretaceous times included *Hesperornis* from North America and *Mononykus* from Mongolia.

DATA BASE

Name	*Ichthyornis*
Pronounced	Ick-THEE-orn-is
Meaning	"fish bird"

What it ate
Fish, other surface sea creatures

Length	(nose - tail-tip) 8 inches (20 centimeters)
Standing height	6 inches (15 centimeters)
Weight	about 8 ounces (0.27 kilogram)

When it lived	Mid-Cretaceous Period 100 million years ago
Where it lived	U.S. (Kansas, Texas, Alabama)

Order	Ichthyornithiformes (toothed, ternlike birds)
Family	Ichthyornithidae

→ Taking to the water

Bird wings have been called "a fickle product of evolution." If they are not vital for flight in a particular type of bird, they have become adapted to many other functions – from sunshades to paddles.

In a typical bird the wings have little function other than flight. Most birds fly chiefly to find food or escape from danger. In some unthreatening habitats, these two survival pressures may be relaxed. Then wings lose their vital importance and can be shaped for another task – or they can shrink away.

Other uses

For example, large, long-legged birds can run fast and defend themselves against enemies. So their wings become available for other tasks. In the ostrich they have evolved to shade the eggs or chicks from the hot sun and also to display as the male courts the female.

On many oceanic islands there are – or were – few large predators. Flight is less vital, and so the wings shrink away, as in the kiwi of New Zealand.

▲ Like divers

Hesperornis (in the foreground) resembled modern birds called divers. Flying past in the background are *Nyctosaurus* pterosaurs.

Fly-and-swim

Sea birds live among their food, and swimming can become more important that diving. So some sea birds have evolved with wings that can both fly and aid swimming, as in razorbills and guillemots. The penguins have taken this trend further. They cannot fly, but they are supreme paddlers.

▶ **Coastal bird**

Because of its awkward walk, *Hesperornis* probably nested near the water's edge. It had a long, slim, pointed beak, and parts of the jaws were lined with little pointed teeth, like those of *Ichthyornis*. Coprolites (fossilized feces) presumed to come from this ancient bird contained fish remains. If this is so, then *Hesperornis* was certainly piscivorous (a fish-eater). This underwater view shows two *Hesperornis* swimming up toward a pliosaur. One has caught a baby plesiosaur.

Land to air to water

The evolution from flying to swimming was already evident in the Late Cretaceous bird *Hesperornis* from North America. But in this case it was the feet, not the wings, that provided propulsion. This bird stood about 5 feet (1.5 meters) tall and, like *Ichthyornis*, had small, sharp teeth in its beak for gripping slippery, fishy prey. Its breastbone, or sternum, had almost no keel, and there were only traces of its wings left – having been used so little, they had almost disappeared.

Waddling gait

Hesperornis swam by using its powerful back legs, set well back under its body in the best position for mechanical thrust, and its big, widely spread, webbed or lobed feet. In this respect it moved in the same way as a loon or grebe today, and not as a penguin, which "flies" through the water using its wings. By the same token, *Hesperornis* would walk on land with the waddling gait of today's auks, such as the guillemot or puffin.

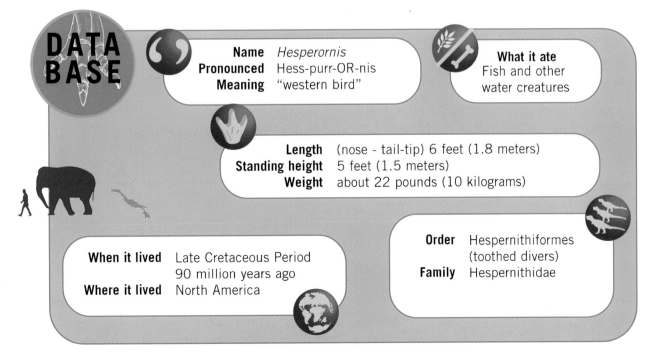

DATA BASE

Name	*Hesperornis*
Pronounced	Hess-purr-OR-nis
Meaning	"western bird"

What it ate
Fish and other water creatures

Length (nose - tail-tip) 6 feet (1.8 meters)
Standing height 5 feet (1.5 meters)
Weight about 22 pounds (10 kilograms)

When it lived Late Cretaceous Period 90 million years ago
Where it lived North America

Order Hespernithiformes (toothed divers)
Family Hespernithidae

⇒ Dinosaurs down under

Since 1980 exciting discoveries of dinosaurs and other fossils have been made in Australasia. They shed fresh light on the history of the earth and establish new ideas about dinosaur groups, diets, lifestyles, and survival abilities.

Through prehistory the world map has changed. Geologists have discovered that the earth's crust is made up of plates floating on semiliquid. The plates move around, bumping into and grinding past each other. This idea is called plate tectonics (tectonics means "building"). The continents sit on the plates, and they continue to move, a process called continental drift. New studies have revealed what was happening in the southern hemisphere during the Age of Dinosaurs. They are based especially on fossils recovered at Dinosaur Cove, an enormously rich area of Early Cretaceous remains in the coastal Otway Ranges near Melbourne, Australia.

Toward the South Pole

The general picture is that about 150 million years ago, as the Jurassic Period drew to a close, the landmasses of Australia and Antarctica separated from the rest of a supercontinent called Gondwana. During the following Cretaceous Period, Australia stayed connected to Antarctica. Both were near the South Pole, and Australia's southeastern corner was well within the Antarctic Circle.

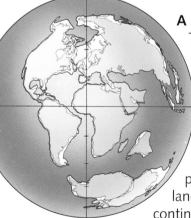

Late Jurassic

Late Cretaceous

A colder climate

The fossil remains of plants and rock minerals suggest that the climate of the time was cool, perhaps averaging 46-50°F (8-10°C). Because of the position of the landmass, there was continuous darkness between six and 12 weeks through the winter, while for about the same period in the summer it was continuously light. Nevertheless, there were plants such as ferns, ginkgoes, cycads, and podocarp, and also evergreen and deciduous trees.

The rich seams of fossils at the Australian sites represent many animal groups, including insects, fish, amphibians, birds, and reptiles such as lizards, turtles, flying pterosaurs, and freshwater plesiosaurs. And dinosaurs.

Migrate or hibernate?

The larger herbivorous dinosaurs probably migrated south in the summer and north in the winter, followed by their predators.

Smaller dinosaurs would be unable to keep up on such long journeys. Perhaps they

▶ **Australian iguanodontid.**
Muttaburrasaurus, named after the place in Queensland where it was found, was a large iguanodontid.

Dinosaur hunting in Australia

A road sign near Dinosaur Cove, Australia (left) was intended to warn drivers of the presence of kangaroos, but a volunteer worker at the dinosaur mine altered it to mean "Beware — dinosaurs!" In the center picture Tom Rich examines the skull and tail of a fossil hypsilophodont, a small dinosaur about the size of a pet dog that lived some 100 million years ago. The shape of the interior of the skull, which corresponds to the shape of the brain, reveals that the part or lobe of the brain dealing with sight was relatively large. This suggests the dinosaur could have adapted to a long winter period of darkness, as experienced today in the polar regions. In the laboratory (right) a researcher prepares a fossilized bone for study. It involves removing it from the rock or matrix in which it was embedded, using a fine-tipped drill.

survived winter by hibernating in caves or among rocks or buried beneath the soil. Many lizards and snakes do this today in cooler temperate regions. Alternatively, unlike reptiles today, they stayed active in the cold because they were warm-blooded.

A selection of Australasian dinosaurs

All of these dinosaur groups are covered in other volumes of the series, and their fossils have been found at or near Dinosaur Cove in Early or Mid-Cretaceous rocks, unless stated.

- Ostrich dinosaurs or ornithomimosaurs, similar to those found in South Africa, but earlier and more primitive in structure than the North American types such as *Struthiomimus* from the Late Cretaceous Period.
- Oviraptosaurs, a group of small theropods that includes *Oviraptor*.
- The single claw of a theropod estimated to be about 25 feet (7.6 meters) long, perhaps resembling the large "heavy claw" dinosaur *Baryonyx*.
- A miniversion only 8 feet (2.4 meters) tall of the great and fearsome theropod *Allosaurus*. It was living here in the south some 20 million years after *Allosaurus* itself died out in North America.

- Claws similar to those of the huge theropod *Megalosaurus*, an early relative of *Tyrannosaurus*.
- The only Australian member of the sauropods – the *Diplodocus* and *Brachiosaurus* group – found so far is *Rhoetosaurus*. It is older than the other specimens, having been found in Jurassic rocks in northeastern Australia.
- Some of the most abundant remains are of small dinosaurs known as hypsilophodonts. They were lightly built, chicken-sized, two-legged runners. Outwardly they resembled small theropods, but they were plant-eaters and belonged to the other main dinosaur group, the Ornithischia. There are fossils of perhaps five or more species, including *Leaellynasaura*, a parrot-beaked plant-eater.
- Fossils of an *iguanodon*-type dinosaur, *Muttaburrasaurus*. They were not found at Dinosaur Cove, but further north in Australia, in the state of Queensland.
- Armored dinosaurs or ankylosaurs, with fragmentary remains of an animal no bigger than a sheep.
- Horned dinosaurs or ceratopsians, in the same group as *Triceratops*, but only the size of today's sheep or pigs.

What were "dinosaur cousins?"

They included the flying pterosaurs, the swimming plesiosaurs and ichthyosaurs, and other great reptiles that shared the Mesozoic world with the dinosaurs.

The dinosaurs were undoubtedly the main group of large animals on earth during the Mesozoic Era from about 245 to 65 million years ago. Fossil evidence seems to show that they dominated the landscape. But many other animals existed at this time. Various insects scuttled on land and buzzed in the air. Fish swam in the seas, rivers, and lakes. Amphibians lurked in streams and swamps. Mammals and birds appeared then too.

The Age of Reptiles

The Mesozoic Era is commonly called the "Age of Dinosaurs." A better name might be the Age of Reptiles. In addition to the dinosaurs the reptile group included many other great creatures that thrived in the water and in the air. Many are described in this book. In the water they included:

- the placodonts, some resembling crocodiles and others more like turtles;
- the nothosaurs, with long necks and flipperlike limbs designed for swimming;
- the long-necked, flippered plesiosaurs (plesiosauroids) and the shorter-necked, flippered pliosaurs (pliosauroids), also in the oceans;
- the dolphin-shaped ichthyosaurs, another sea-dwelling group;
- the fearsome, sharp-fanged, whalelike mosasaurs, yet another marine group (closely related to today's lizards).

And during this time there were flying reptiles called pterosaurs with batlike wings.

Still around today

The dinosaurs and other reptile groups mentioned above had all died out or became extinct by the end of the Mesozoic Era 65 million years ago. However, three main groups of reptiles that lived then still survive today. They are:

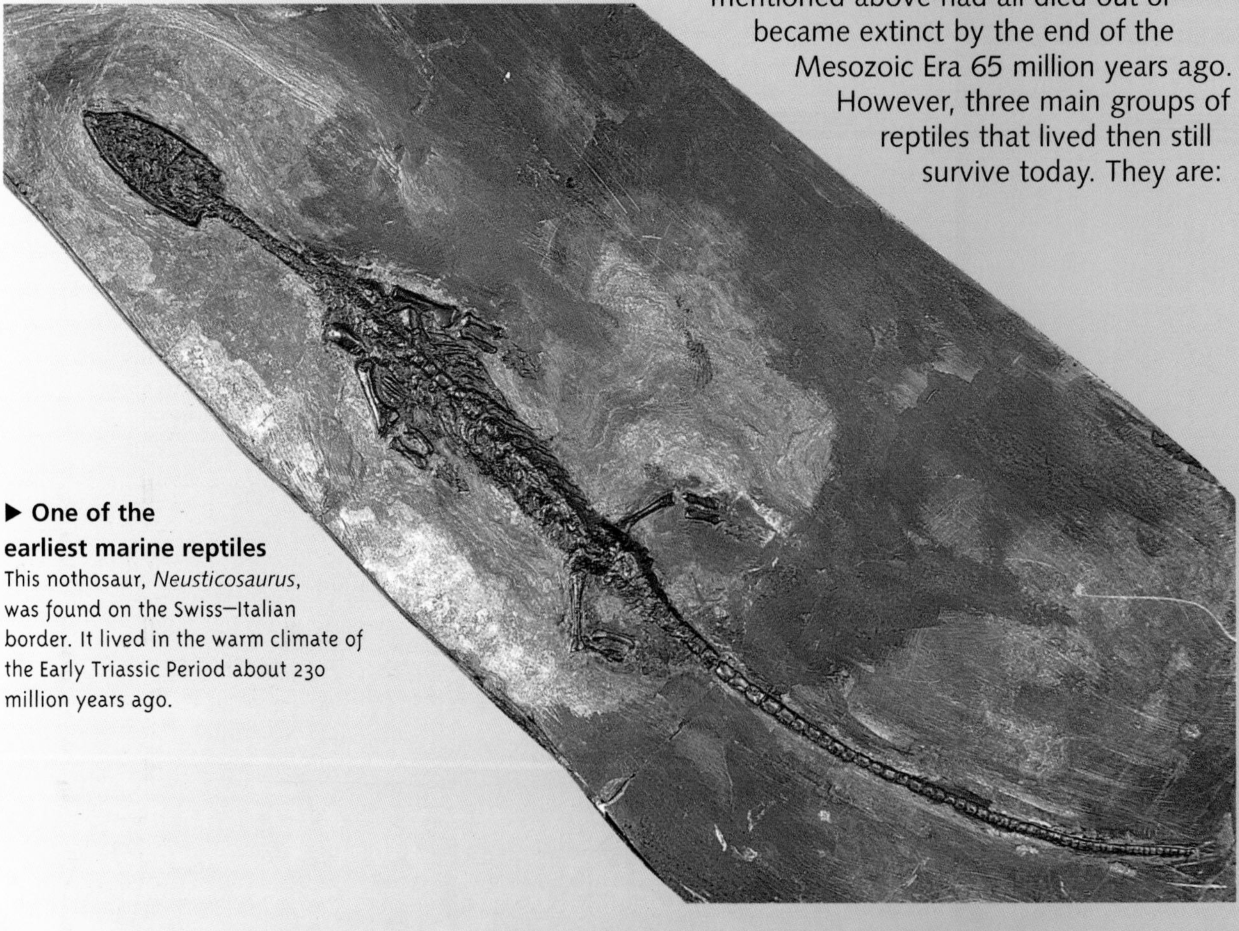

▶ One of the earliest marine reptiles
This nothosaur, *Neusticosaurus*, was found on the Swiss–Italian border. It lived in the warm climate of the Early Triassic Period about 230 million years ago.

- the crocodilians, including crocodiles, alligators, caimans, and gharials (or gavials);
- the chelonians, which are the turtles, tortoises, and terrapins;
- the lizards, which – along with the snakes – are in the reptile group known as squamates.

Why did the dinosaurs and many of their reptile

▲ Reptile representatives
The Nile crocodile (above) and the spotted bush snake (below) are modern survivors of the reptile group that first appeared in the Mesozoic Era.

cousins perish, while these three reptile groups survived into modern times? This puzzle is also discussed at the end of the book.

What is a reptile?

The dinosaurs, pterosaurs, ichthyosaurs, and other animals mentioned here are all reptiles. What exactly is a reptile?

- A reptile is a vertebrate animal, that is, it has an internal skeleton built around a vertebral column (or backbone).
- A typical reptile has four limbs, although some types, such as snakes, have lost them during evolution.
- A typical reptile has scaly skin, although a few types have lost scales and instead have a leathery body covering.
- A typical reptile lays tough-shelled eggs, although some types, such as certain snakes (and perhaps ichthyosaurs in the past), give birth to babies.

Flippers and wings

No dinosaur, as far as we know, could fly in the air. Nor were there any dinosaurs that spent their lives swimming in the sea. But several other groups of reptiles evolved these lifestyles.

Reptiles probably evolved from amphibians around 300 million years ago. This was during the Late Carboniferous (Pennsylvanian) Period, the next-to-last period of the Paleozoic Era that came before the Mesozoic Era.

These first reptiles, such as *Hylonomus*, had a great advantage over the amphibians. They could live their whole lives on land and breed there too. Reptiles have scaly, waterproof skin and lay tough-shelled eggs. In comparison, amphibians have moist skin and lay jellylike eggs or spawn. Amphibians have to stay near water or dampness to avoid drying out and also to allow their spawn to hatch into the young water-living forms called larvae or tadpoles. Baby reptiles, on the other hand, develop safely inside their leathery, waterproof eggshells until they are big enough to hatch. Reptiles survive even in the driest deserts.

Back into the sea

The dinosaurs became the main reptile group to take advantage of the land-dwelling adaptations. Other reptile groups followed different paths of evolution. Some went into "reverse," returned to the water, and developed features such as paddle- or oar-shaped limbs for swimming. They included placodonts, nothosaurs, plesiosaurs, and ichthyosaurs – sometimes called "sea dragons" and now all extinct. Turtles and crocodiles also became water-living, or aquatic, and still exist today.

Up into the sky

In two groups of reptiles the forelimbs or arms evolved into wings for flying. One group became the winged reptiles or pterosaurs. The other group started as small, meat-eating dinosaurs. Instead of becoming another type of reptile, they turned into the birds (see chapter 5 above).

Why leave the land?

Why did so many types of reptiles leave the dry land and return to the lakes, seas, and oceans? One reason may have been competition from the dinosaurs. As the dinosaur group spread and became more diverse, its members began to specialize in all kinds of land-based foods. They ranged from ferns, conifer trees, and other plants, to insects, worms, and many kinds of animals – especially other dinosaurs.

In the seas there were no dinosaurs. There were also rich food supplies of fish, shellfish, jellyfish, starfish, and many other creatures. These potential meals lived at all levels in the ocean from the surface waves all the way down to the seabed. So different types of reptiles evolved to feed at these different levels. Pterosaurs swooped on them from above. Crocodilians and longer-necked plesiosaurs hunted at or near the surface. Mosasaurs, ichthyosaurs, and shorter-necked plesiosaurs could dive to deeper water in search of prey.

◀ **Moist skin**
Frogs are amphibians. They have moist skin and live in or near water to keep from drying out.

Holes in skulls

The reptiles, living and extinct, are a vast and diverse group of animals. It is possible that in terms of evolution they are not a homogeneous group — that is, they did not evolve from a single type of ancestor. Different types of reptiles may have arisen at different times in different places from different ancestors — probably various types of amphibians. Because of this diversity it is very difficult to classify them. (See also pages 16-17 for more information on apses.)

One feature that has been used to classify reptiles is the number and position of temporal fossae. These are holes in each side, or temple region, of the skull (but not the eye sockets or the nostrils). Some reptiles have no temporal openings. Some have one lower pair. Others have one upper pair. Still others have two pairs, a lower one and an upper one.

- **Anapsids** They were the earliest reptiles, and had no temporal holes in the skull. Their living representatives are the turtles and tortoises. The anapsids probably gave rise to the other three groups.
- **Synapsids** This group had just one pair of lower temporal holes. They included the mammallike reptiles, which were very successful before the dinosaurs and were the ancestors of today's mammals.
- **Euryapsids** This group had one pair of upper temporal holes. They include most of the so-called "sea dragons" — placodonts, nothosaurs, and plesiosaurs. There are no living representatives.
- **Diapsids** They had both upper and lower temporal holes in each side of the skull. They include lizards and snakes and also the archosaurs — the "ruling reptile supergroup" that takes in dinosaurs, crocodiles, and pterosaurs, and perhaps also the descendants of dinosaurs — the birds. Recent research has shown that ichthyosaurs were probably diapsids too, rather than euryapsids (see pages 116-121).

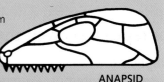

ANAPSID

SYNAPSID

DIAPSID

EURYAPSID

PERIOD	TRIASSIC	JURASSIC	CRETACEOUS	TERTIARY

Turtles

Birds

Dinosaurs

Pterosaurs

Crocodiles

Placodonts

Plesiosaurs

Nothosaurs

Ichthyosaurs

Mosasaurs

Lizards

Snakes

⇨ Problems of sea and air

Taking to the air or water is far more complicated than simply evolving flippers or wings. It affects many parts and systems of an animal's body.

The reptile body evolved to live on land. It has four limbs to walk and run, strong muscles to produce these movements, heavy bones to support the skeleton, and lungs to breathe air. A modern reptile is also "cold-blooded," with a relatively slow rate of body chemistry, or metabolism, and lays eggs with tough, waterproof shells.

Dinosaurs kept most of these features and adapted them in many different ways, with huge success. For the reptiles that took to the air or water there were many new problems to overcome, especially in breathing and movement, but also in body metabolism (see opposite) and egg-laying.

Breathing

Most water animals breathe by gills. These frilly body parts are designed to absorb vital oxygen that is dissolved in the water. Fish, sea slugs, octopuses, and tadpoles (young amphibians) all have gills.

Land animals have lungs. They do the same job as gills, that is, absorbing oxygen. But lungs absorb it from the air by the process we know as breathing.

The Mesozoic reptiles that returned to the water did not evolve gills in place of lungs. They stayed as air-breathers. So, when they had been swimming underwater they would have to return to the surface to take breaths of air. Sea reptiles of today, such as marine turtles and sea snakes, also do this, as do sea

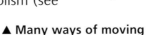

▲ Many ways of moving
Corythosaurus, a dinosaur of the Cretaceous Period, pauses on a hill. In front the ocean-dwelling *Cryptoclidus*, a Jurassic plesiosaur, swishes by and two *Ichthyosaurus* frolic in the water. Two *Pteranodon*, pterosaurs from the Cretaceous Period, swoop through the air.

mammals such as whales, seals, dolphins, and sea cows.

Some of these prehistoric reptiles developed special adaptations. Nostrils on top of the head, rather than at the front of the nose, meant that they could breathe on the move, without having to lift the whole head out of the water. Today's whales and dolphins have

▼ Streamlined speed
The dolphin moves smoothly through water by swishing its tail up and down, unlike fish and the extinct marine reptiles whose tails swished from side to side.

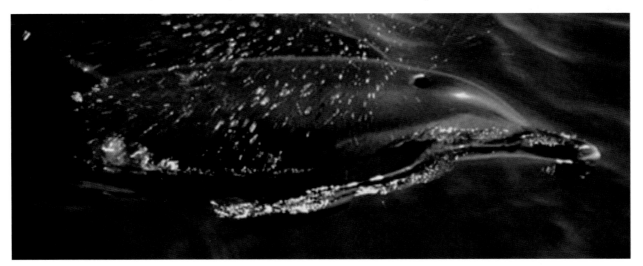

the same adaptation and hardly break the water's surface when they breathe. The nostrils are called the blowhole.

Perhaps the prehistoric marine reptiles had specialized lungs and body chemistry so that they could hold their breath for many minutes while submerged. However, since these features cannot be preserved as fossils, we do not know for sure.

Movement in water

Land animals move about mostly in two dimensions – forward-backward and side to side. Water and air have three dimensions. So swimming and flying animals need a form of propulsion to go forward or sideways, but they also need a form of lift to help them move up or down.

One solution is feet or whole limbs shaped like flippers, paddles, or oars, as found in plesiosaurs. The limb can provide lift or propulsion using a simple forward-back rowing motion. Or it can do the same with an up-down flapping motion, as used by birds for flying (see below).

Another solution is a long, deep tail that can be swished from side to side. Fish move by this method, and among reptiles, crocodiles do too. So did the early reptile *Mesosaurus*. This lizardlike creature had webbed feet and also a long, tall tail, flattened from side to side. It lived during the early Permian Period.

Water is a much more dense or "thicker" substance than air. It offers more resistance, which means that it is harder to push your way through it. But the smoother and more streamlined your shape, the less resistance the water has. So fast-moving water animals are shaped like submarines. The ichthyosaurs and mosasaurs were especially streamlined with almost fish-shaped bodies.

Movement in air

Four main groups of animals have truly conquered the air with powered, sustained flight. They are insects, birds, and bats today – and in Mesozoic times pterosaurs. All four types use flapping flight. Flapping the wings pushes the air down and back, propelling the body up and forward.

▶ **Arched wings**
The curve or arch of the African fish eagle's wings gives it lift. Pterosaur wings also had this airfoil section.

Also, the wing can be curved or arched from front to back. This curved shape is known as the airfoil shape or section. Airplane wings have an airfoil section more curved on the upper surface than the lower surface. It makes air flow faster over the upper surface of the wing than over the lower surface as the plane moves forward. The difference in air speed creates the upward lift. Pterosaur wings had airfoils.

Flapping and airfoils also work in water, acting as hydrofoils. The mechanics of flying and swimming are similar because both water and air are fluids – they can flow. The flippers of some plesiosaurs, ichthyosaurs and similar marine reptiles had a hydrofoil shape, as do the flippers of penguins today. Penguins are flightless in air, but they "fly" through water with great speed.

For flying animals lightness is vital. Pterosaurs evolved large arm muscles to flap their wings but small bodies and light bones, like birds of today. They also had small teeth or even none at all, as teeth are the heaviest body parts.

The fish-lizards

The reptiles that became most completely adapted to life in Mesozoic seas were the ichthyosaurs. On the outside they looked more like fish or dolphins than reptiles.

Evolution sometimes produces similar solutions to the problems of a certain lifestyle in very different kinds of animals. One example concerns flight and the wings of birds, bats, and pterosaurs (see page 122). Another is the body shape or outline that is most effective for fast swimming. Several very different animal groups have come up with similar answers. They include bony fish such as marlin and tuna, sharks such as the tiger and mako, mammals such as dolphins and porpoises, and in Mesozoic times the reptiles known as ichthyosaurs.

This "coming together" of different animals so that they look similar as a result of similar lifestyles is known as convergent evolution.

At home in the ocean

Ichthyosaurs were the most specialized of the Mesozoic sea reptiles. They could not have moved on land at all. Their streamlined body shape was very similar to that of fish such as mackerel, tuna, and marlin, which can reach speeds of more than 40 miles per hour (about 65 kilometers per hour).

The modern mammals called dolphins have a similar outline. The main difference here is that dolphins lack rear flippers, and their tail fins, or flukes, are horizontal, sticking out sideways, while the tails of ichthyosaurs were vertical as are of those of fish

Origins of the ichthyosaurs

The early evolution of the ichthyosaurs is not very clear. They may have been descended from land-based reptiles rather than from reptiles that had already taken to the water. They were thought to belong to the euryapsid group of reptiles (see page 113), along with other "sea dragons" such as nothosaurs and plesiosaurs. But recent research using computerized three-dimensional analysis of a fossil ichthyosaur skull found in Japan shows that they were possibly diapsid reptiles. This would mean that ichthyosaurs were more closely related to lizards and snakes, giving their name – which means "fish-lizards" – added significance.

◄ **Ichthyosaur swimmers**
A shoal of *Shonisaurus* have the sea to themselves – but sharks may be lurking close by. *Shonisaurus* was one of the largest ichthyosaurs and rivaled the later pliosauroids such as *Kronosaurus* in size.

Rise and demise

The ichthyosaur group, order Ichthyosauria, appeared in the Early Triassic Period. Early types such as *Cymbospondylus* were shaped more like eels and wriggled rather than swam. They were well established in their fishlike shape by the Middle Triassic Period. By the Late Triassic some had reached huge sizes, such as *Shonisaurus*, which was almost 50 feet (15.2 meters) long. At the other end of the size range the Middle Triassic *Mixosaurus* was only about 3 feet (1 meter) in length.

The ichthyosaurs reached their peak of success during the Jurassic Period. By Middle Cretaceous times, around 100 million years ago, they were fading away. This was perhaps due to competition from the sharks, which were undergoing another burst of evolution and becoming faster with keener senses.

▲ **Beached creatures**
Several *Shonisaurus* lie on a beach, helpless out of the water.

▼ **No rear flippers**
A dolphin leaps clear of the water, revealing its streamlined shape.

Living in the water

Like all water-dwellers, ichthyosaurs had many special adaptations to their bodies that allowed them to move, see, and hear underwater.

▲ Underwater meal
An *Ichthyosaurus grendelius* eats an ammonite, as youngsters look on with interest.

Flippers and flukes
A typical ichthyosaur had a very smooth, streamlined, torpedo-shaped body. The four legs had become two sets of flippers, the front pair usually longer than the rear pair. In some fossils a carbon film deposit around the skeleton reveals the shape of the soft tissues and body outline, including the shapes of the fin, paddles, and tail flukes. It shows a triangular dorsal (back) fin, like that of a shark or dolphin, and a tail with two lobes, or flukes. The rear end of the backbone, made up of caudal vertebrae, had a slight bend in it where it went into the lower of these flukes. Both the dorsal fin and tail flukes were probably made of stiff connective tissue, muscle, and perhaps cartilage (gristle), covered in skin.

How they swam
Ichthyosaurs did not use their flippers for propulsion as plesiosaurs did. The flippers worked as hydrofoils to provide lift as the reptile moved forward. They could also be tilted to steer, swerve, and brake. The front or pectoral fins of a shark do the same job. In some ichthyosaurs, the stenopterygiids, each flipper had five long toes or digits, with many extra bones in each digit. In other types of ichthyosaurs, ichthyosaurids, there were extra digits in each flipper too – up to nine.

The dorsal fin gave stability, like the keel of a boat. It stopped the ichthyosaur's body from tilting or rolling from side to side.

Its main propulsive power came from the tail. It swished from side to side, as in fish. The tail bones were joined by ball-and-socket joints so they could flex sideways. Long blocks of muscles down the sides of the body pulled the tail. The animal probably also wriggled its body to help propulsion.

Breathing
Ichthyosaurs, like all reptiles, were air-breathing creatures. The nostrils were set far back on the upper snout, just in front of the eyes. So the animal needed only to touch the surface with its upper head to take a breath of air and also look around above the waves.

Ichthyosaurus galore
Ichthyosaurus is one of the best-known of all prehistoric animals. Hundreds of beautifully preserved skeletons, with the bones still joined, or articulated, as in life, have been found. Many come from near Holzmaden in Germany. A shallow sea covered this area during the Jurassic Period.

A sensitive reptile
Ichthyosaurus had huge ear bones in its head. They carried sound vibrations from the air or water around it to the inner ear. So *Ichthyosaurus* must have had good hearing. It also had excellent eyesight, as its eyes were very large. Around each eyeball was a ring of spokelike bones called sclerotic ossicles. They prevented the eye from collapsing under the pressure of the water around it and helped with focusing.

In the Late Jurassic ichthyosaur *Ophthalmosaurus* the eye sockets were 4 inches (10 centimeters) across and took up almost all of the rear skull (see illustration on page 120).

▼ Sea mammals
The sea is home not only to fish, but also to mammals such as seals and sea lions. These animals come ashore to breed, unlike whales and ichthyosaurs.

▲ Different tails
The tail fin, or fluke, of a humpback whale is horizontal. Ichthyosaurs had vertical tail fins,.

Fish-lizards inside and out

Thanks to the large number of well-preserved ichthyosaur skeletons, we know quite a lot about how these animals ate, gave birth, lived, and died.

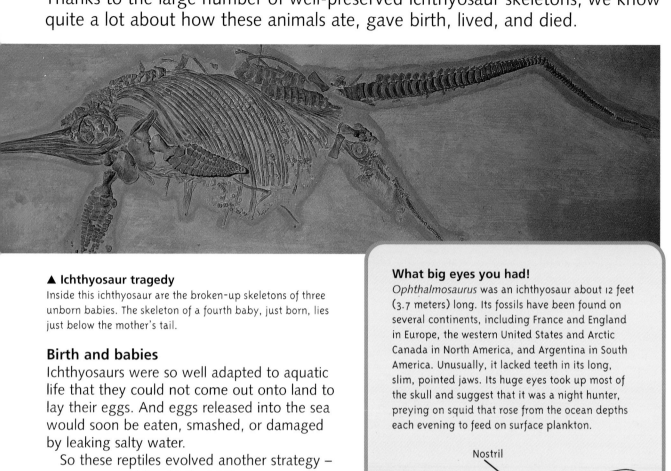

▲ Ichthyosaur tragedy
Inside this ichthyosaur are the broken-up skeletons of three unborn babies. The skeleton of a fourth baby, just born, lies just below the mother's tail.

Birth and babies
Ichthyosaurs were so well adapted to aquatic life that they could not come out onto land to lay their eggs. And eggs released into the sea would soon be eaten, smashed, or damaged by leaking salty water.

So these reptiles evolved another strategy – pregnancy and live birth. Ichthyosaur mothers carried their developing young inside their bodies until the babies were big enough to be born well formed and survive in the water. We know this because many fossils

What big eyes you had!
Ophthalmosaurus was an ichthyosaur about 12 feet (3.7 meters) long. Its fossils have been found on several continents, including France and England in Europe, the western United States and Arctic Canada in North America, and Argentina in South America. Unusually, it lacked teeth in its long, slim, pointed jaws. Its huge eyes took up most of the skull and suggest that it was a night hunter, preying on squid that rose from the ocean depths each evening to feed on surface plankton.

Nostril

Nostrils

Sclerotic ring

◀ Live young
Dolphins give birth to live young, as the ichthyosaurs did.

have been found of adult ichthyosaurs, such as *Ichthyosaurus* and *Stenopterygius*, with the perfectly formed developing skeletons of baby ichthyosaurs inside them. In one amazing fossil the mother has been preserved in the process of giving birth to her baby. It is emerging tail first – just as in a modern shark, dolphin, or whale.

▼ Ichthyosaur interior

As well as the usual preserved bones, carbon film fossils of the soft tissues show the shape of the whole ichthyosaur. They include the outlines of the dorsal fin, paddlelike limbs, and tail flukes, as drawn in pink. A ring of bony plates, sclerotic ossicles, surrounds the eyes. The front limbs have more than the usual five digits, and the rear limbs are smaller.

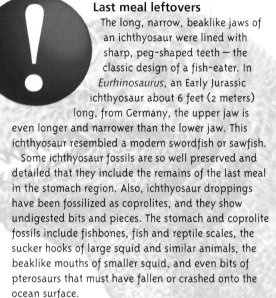

Last meal leftovers

The long, narrow, beaklike jaws of an ichthyosaur were lined with sharp, peg-shaped teeth — the classic design of a fish-eater. In *Eurhinosaurus*, an Early Jurassic ichthyosaur about 6 feet (2 meters) long, from Germany, the upper jaw is even longer and narrower than the lower jaw. This ichthyosaur resembled a modern swordfish or sawfish.

Some ichthyosaur fossils are so well preserved and detailed that they include the remains of the last meal in the stomach region. Also, ichthyosaur droppings have been fossilized as coprolites, and they show undigested bits and pieces. The stomach and coprolite fossils include fishbones, fish and reptile scales, the sucker hooks of large squid and similar animals, the beaklike mouths of smaller squid, and even bits of pterosaurs that must have fallen or crashed onto the ocean surface.

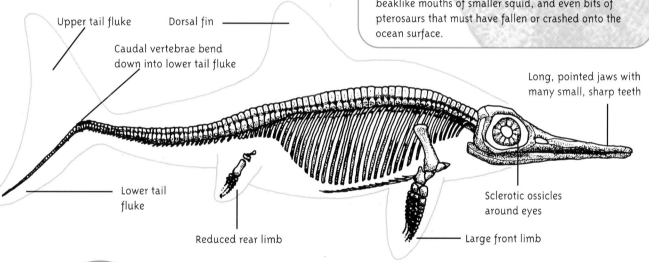

Upper tail fluke

Dorsal fin

Caudal vertebrae bend down into lower tail fluke

Lower tail fluke

Reduced rear limb

Long, pointed jaws with many small, sharp teeth

Sclerotic ossicles around eyes

Large front limb

DATA BASE

Name	*Ichthyosaurus*
Pronounced	IK-thee-owe-SORE-us
Meaning	"fish-lizard"

What it ate Smaller fish, squid, and similar sea creatures

Length (nose - tail-tip) 6 feet 6 inches (2 meters)
Weight about 200 pounds (90 kilograms)

When it lived Jurassic to Early Cretaceous Periods 180-140 million years ago
Where it lived North America (Alberta), Europe (England, Germany), Greenland

Order Ichthyosauria
Family Ichthyosauridae

Taking to the skies ▶

⇒ Taking to the skies

At the start of the Mesozoic Era the only truly flying animals were insects such as dragonflies. Soon they were joined by the only types of reptiles fully to conquer the air – the pterosaurs.

The pterosaurs, "winged lizards," were a huge and hugely successful group of animals. They spread and thrived throughout the Age of Dinosaurs and evolved into hundreds of different kinds. Their fossils have been found on every continent except Antarctica – so far. They used to be pictured as slow, lazy, clumsy creatures that could just about glide. But modern views suggest they were busy, active fliers, capable of twists, turns, and other aerobatic maneuvers (see page 115).

Pterosaurs are sometimes called "pterodactyls," meaning "wing fingers." However, this term is sometimes used to refer either to the short-tailed pterosaurs (see below) or to the pterodactyloid family Pterodactylidae to which *Pterodactylus* itself belongs. "Pterosaur" is a better general name for the whole group.

A class of their own?

Pterosaurs were so different from other reptiles, both living and extinct, that some experts suggest they should be placed in a major group of their own, the class Pterosaura. This would be separate from the class Reptilia that includes the dinosaurs, plesiosaurs, ichthyosaurs, lizards, snakes, crocodiles, and turtles. So pterosaurs would no longer be

◄ **Flying reptile**
This fossilized *Quetzalcoatlus northropi* dates from the Late Cretaceous Period 70 million years ago. It was found in Texas.

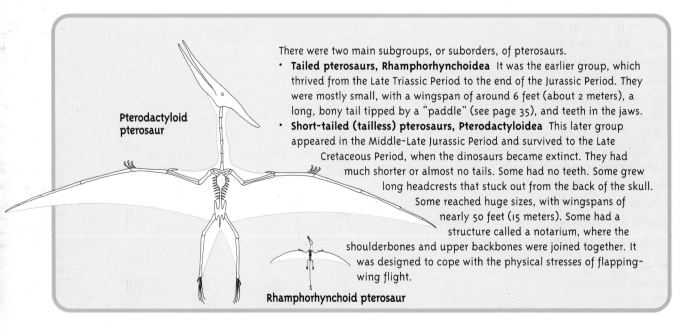

There were two main subgroups, or suborders, of pterosaurs.
- **Tailed pterosaurs, Rhamphorhynchoidea** It was the earlier group, which thrived from the Late Triassic Period to the end of the Jurassic Period. They were mostly small, with a wingspan of around 6 feet (about 2 meters), a long, bony tail tipped by a "paddle" (see page 35), and teeth in the jaws.
- **Short-tailed (tailless) pterosaurs, Pterodactyloidea** This later group appeared in the Middle-Late Jurassic Period and survived to the Late Cretaceous Period, when the dinosaurs became extinct. They had much shorter or almost no tails. Some had no teeth. Some grew long headcrests that stuck out from the back of the skull. Some reached huge sizes, with wingspans of nearly 50 feet (15 meters). Some had a structure called a notarium, where the shoulderbones and upper backbones were joined together. It was designed to cope with the physical stresses of flapping-wing flight.

Pterodactyloid pterosaur

Rhamphorhynchoid pterosaur

◄   Fish-lizards inside and out

classed as reptiles. However, for the time being, pterosaurs are included with the reptiles. Like dinosaurs and others, they have their own reptilian group or order, Pterosauria.

Fast chemistry

Pterosaurs had lightweight bodies and front limbs that could be used as wings. But it is not only their remarkable body structure that makes them so unusual among reptiles. Sustained flight is an extremely fast-action, high-energy process. The only modern large animals that fly are the birds and, among mammals, the bats (pictured above). They are both warm-blooded creatures. Their lungs are extremely efficient at breathing in oxygen, which is needed for the active flight muscles. And then their hearts can pump rapidly enough, and their body chemistry work fast enough, to supply large amounts of energy and oxygen in the blood to the muscles.

Warm blood and body

From what we know about the metabolism, or body chemistry, of living animals, it's probable that pterosaurs were warm-blooded too. The regular reptilian cold-blooded body simply could not process energy quickly enough for flight. And it couldn't move its muscles fast enough for long enough either.

Well-preserved pterosaur fossils support this idea because they show that these animals had a hairy or furry body covering, like mammals today. The furry coat is mainly for insulation to keep the heat inside a warm-blooded body.

▶ **High activity**
Flapping-wing flight uses up a great amount of this small bird's energy.

Pterosaur flight features
* Arms (forelimbs) modified as wings.
* Large but lightweight skull, with the bone reduced from plates to bars and girders.
* Large eye sockets with a protective ring of bones called sclerotic ossicles.
* Long, slender jaws, lacking teeth in later types to save weight.
* Strong neck, shoulder, and arm bones to cope with the anchorage and pull of the flight muscles.
* Wide, slablike sternum, or breastbone, with a keel to anchor the huge chest flight muscles (as in birds).
* A vastly elongated fourth finger to support most of the wing membrane at the front.
* A wing membrane, or patagium, made from tough skin strengthened with fibrous rods and muscle fibers.
* Three small, clawed fingers at the front of the wing.
* A small, slim, light body.
* Short, thin legs.
* Long, lightweight feet.

⇨ The largest-ever flier

Quetzalcoatlus was the largest flying creature ever – about the size of a small plane. It was also among the last of the pterosaurs.

In 1971 a fossilized upper-arm wing bone (humerus) from a pterosaur was found in rocks dating back 65 million years to the end of the Cretaceous Period. The discovery was made at Big Bend National Park, western Texas. The amazing fact about the find was that the bone was huge – 3 feet (1 meter) long.

Further searches brought to light other wing bones, including a finger bone over 4 feet (1.2 meters) long. Gradually, a picture emerged of this great new find, which was called *Quetzalcoatlus*. It was a huge pterosaur, closely related to the previously known *Pteranodon* but even more massive. It was one of the few pterosaurs whose fossils have been found in rocks that formed on land rather than beneath the sea.

A picture of the giant

Quetzalcoatlus had long, toothless, sharply edged jaws, probably covered in life with a horny beak. The crest on the back of the skull was short, low, and slender. Its neck was very long, but had little flexibility, especially from side to side.

The immense wings of *Quetzalcoatlus* were held out mainly by long finger bones, as in other pterosaurs. These finger bones supported a length of almost 10 feet (3 meters) in each wing. To give extra strength, three of the five finger bones were not hollow. They were like two struts joined along their length at right angles to form a girder with a T-shaped cross-section.

How did *Quetzalcoatlus* live?

From the rocks and fossils found at the Big Bend site it seems that *Quetzalcoatlus* flew over sandy floodplains and meandering rivers 250 miles (400 kilometers) away from the sea. It may have landed and used its long, straight, stiff neck to probe in the sand, mud, and pools for shellfish and other small animals in the way that herons probe their swamps for their meals. It has also been suggested that the creature fed on carrion (the carcasses of dead animals), like huge reptilian vultures.

How well could pterosaurs fly?

As a group, pterosaurs probably had a wide range of flying abilities much like modern birds.

- Most pterosaurs lived near the sea because their fossils are found in the types of rocks that form along the coast or on the seabed. These reptiles probably used winds blowing up cliffs, updrafts, thermal currents, and sea breezes to glide and soar, like modern albatrosses, petrels, and other seabirds.
- Some pterosaurs would use flight merely to escape predators or danger and get out of trouble, returning to the ground as soon as possible. Gamebirds such as pheasants and partridges also do this.
- Other pterosaurs would have been skilled aerial acrobats, able to fly fast and slow and to twist and turn in midair, like modern hawks. Perhaps some hunted other pterosaurs.

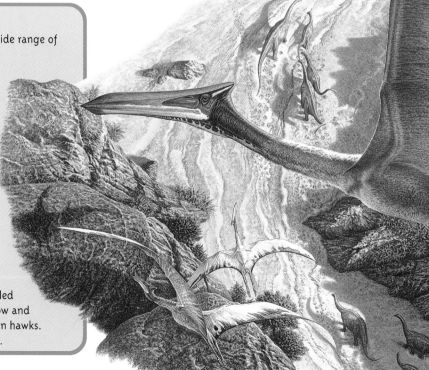

DATA BASE

Name *Quetzalcoatlus*
Pronounced KWET-sal-coe-AT-lus
Meaning "feathered-serpent god"

What it ate
Uncertain, possibly burrowing shellfish, crustaceans such as crabs, or carrion

Length (nose - tail-tip) 28 feet (8.5 meters)
Wingspan 36-39 feet (11-12 meters)
Weight 190 pounds (86 kilograms)

When it lived Late Cretaceous Period 70-65 million years ago
Where it lived North America (Texas, Alberta), Asia (Russia), Middle East (Jordan), Africa (Senegal)

Order Pterosauria
Suborder Pterodactyloidea
Family Azhdarchidae

Pterosaurs on the ground

Recently discovered fossils of pterosaur footprints in Europe and North America have helped show how pterosaurs got about on the ground. The prints were of both the three-clawed "hands" part of the way along the wings and of the five-toed feet. They were between 1 inch and 6 inches (2.5 and 15 centimeters) long and so probably belonged to pterosaurs with wingspans of between 2 and 10 feet (0.6 to 3 meters).

The prints or tracks were made on the muddy shores of lakes or seas. In general, they show that a pterosaur crawled and moved about on all fours, its hands sinking deeper into the mud than its feet. The distance between the left and right prints of both front and rear limbs was similar. This suggests that the pterosaur had its body tilted upward, so its head was quite high. When the limbs were stretched out sideways, the hands were actually further apart than the feet. So, when the hands were brought inward, the arms would either bend at the elbow or straighten up below the body. That would raise the head and front of the body.

Pterosaur gallery

In the birdless world of the early Jurassic Period pterosaurs would have been the only large flying animals. Even when birds appeared, about 150 million years ago, these winged reptiles probably continued to dominate the skies.

Gallodactylus

Dsungaripterus

Dsungaripterus

This short-tailed pterosaur from the Late Jurassic and Early Cretaceous Periods had a sharp, upturned beak with a few peglike teeth halfway along its length. Oddly, the upper snout had an upright keel along its length, which merged into the skull between the eyes. Its wingspan was almost 10 feet (3 meters).

Pterodaustro

The unique feature of this Early Cretaceous, goose-sized, short-tailed pterosaur was the brushlike fringe on its lower jaw. It worked as a sieve to filter tiny animals from water – like a miniature version of the baleen (whalebone) in the mouth of a great whale. The fringe had up to 500 bristles. *Pterodaustro* probably waded or skimmed,

trawling its lower jaw through the water until the bristles were loaded with tiny creatures, which it then licked off and swallowed.

Ctenochasma

A Late Jurassic, short-tailed type, *Ctenochasma* had comblike rows of bristles in both its upper and lower jaws. It probably swished its head through the water to filter small creatures such as shrimps into its brushlike mouth, as a flamingo does today. It had a 4-foot (1.2-meter) wingspan.

Preondactylus

One of the smallest pterosaurs, dating from the Late Triassic Period, *Preondactylus* had wings only 18 inches (45 centimeters) across. It belonged to the tailed pterosaur group, and its pointy

Pterodaustro

teeth suggest that it fed on small creatures such as insects.

Sordes

Gallodactylus

A Late Jurassic, pterodactyl-type pterosaur, *Gallodactylus* had the long, narrow wings of a soaring seabird, with a total span of 4 feet 6 inches (1.3 meters). There were several long, sharp, curved teeth – but only at the tips of its long, slender jaws – for catching fish. It could probably hang upside-down from its hooked feet, like a bat.

Ctenochasma

Sordes

Fossils of this Late Jurassic, crow-sized pterosaur were found in 1971 in Khazakhstan, Asia. They clearly show the dense covering of fur all over the body except for the tail.

Anhanguera

A large pterosaur with wings spanning 13 feet (4.3 meters), *Anhanguera* lived during the Middle Cretaceous Period. It had a central keel running along the top and bottom of the beak, and peglike teeth for grabbing fish and other slippery sea animals.

Anhanguera

Preondactylus

Introduction to the ornithopods ▶

⇒ Introduction to the ornithopods

Today's grasslands and forests support many kinds of plant-eating mammals, from small mice and voles, through medium-sized deer, wild pigs, and goats, to large zebras, antelopes, and gazelles. In the Age of Dinosaurs the ornithopods – the "bird-footed" dinosaurs – were reptilian versions of these grazers and browsers. They were among the most numerous and varied herbivores of the time.

The best-known animals of the African plains are perhaps the lions, leopards, and other big cats, and the huge plant-eaters such as elephants, rhinos, and giraffes. But by far the most numerous large animals are the antelopes, gazelles, zebras, gnus, and other herbivores.

There were many herbivores living in the Age of Dinosaurs too. They belonged mainly to the dinosaur group called ornithopods. They are called "bird-footed" because their feet and toes resembled those of today's birds. They were the "standard herbivores" of the time.

Groups of ornithopods

The ornithopods included:

- fabrosaurs such as *Lesothosaurus* or *Fabrosaurus*, although they can also be viewed as an earlier and separate group;
- heterodontosaurs, including *Heterodontosaurus*;
- hypsilophodonts such as *Hypsilophodon*;
- dryosaurs such as *Dryosaurus*;
- camptosaurs, including *Camptosaurus*;
- iguanodonts, especially one of the best-known of all dinosaurs, *Iguanodon*, and also

the sail-backed *Ouranosaurus*;
- hadrosaurs, or "duck-billed" dinosaurs, which are a large and fascinating subgroup in their own right, and are covered separately in Chapter 9 of this book.

This chapter describes these and other members of the Ornithopoda group. They lived at various times through almost the entire Age of Dinosaurs, from about 200 million years ago to the great extinction of all dinosaurs 65 million years ago.

Herbivores then and now

Herds of herbivores such as deer browse peacefully in our woodlands today. In dinosaur times, these mammals had not yet evolved. Instead there were ornithopod dinosaurs chewing leaves and wandering among the trees.

▲ White-tailed deer – a browser

Deer are among the most numerous of large herbivores found today. They are woodland browsers, like some of their reptilian equivalents in the Age of the Dinosaurs.

◄ Early dinosaur models

The types of ornithopods called iguanodonts, in the shape of *Iguanodon* itself, were some of the first dinosaurs to be studied and named by scientists. And these nineteenth-century lifesized versions constructed for the gardens of London's Crystal Palace were some of the first models to be made of any dinosaur. However, our ideas about dinosaurs have changed greatly since, and the models are now regarded as fascinating but inaccurate historical curiosities.

Main features of the ornithopods

- A birdlike hipbone, or pelvis. (This is the single most important feature by which all ornithischian dinosaurs can be identified.)

- An extra bone at the tip of the lower jaw, with a horny, beaklike covering.
- A trellislike arrangement of bony ligaments supporting the backbone.
- In most types a bone in the eye socket called the palpebral bone. Its function is still unclear.
- Early ornithopods were mostly small, only a few feet long, lightly built and agile.
- They were bipedal — they walked and ran on their two larger back legs, holding the two smaller front legs off the ground like "arms."
- Later ornithopods were much bigger and more heavily built, the size of a car or small truck, with larger front legs.
- However, they probably still mostly ran on two legs.

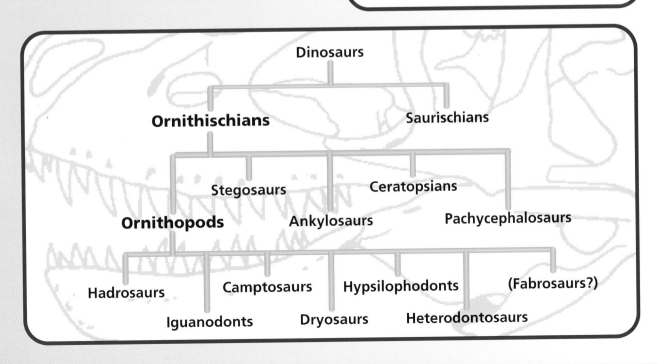

The finding of *Iguanodon* ▶

→ The finding of *Iguanodon*

Iguanodon was probably the second kind of dinosaur to be discovered and described in a scientific way – even before the word "dinosaur" itself had been made up!

Iguanodon is one of the best-known members, not only of the ornithopods, but of the whole dinosaur group. Fossils from hundreds of individuals have been discovered, along with trace fossils such as trackways and droppings (see page 143). From this evidence we can reconstruct *Iguanodon* and recreate its lifestyle in more detail and with more confidence than we can for almost any other dinosaur.

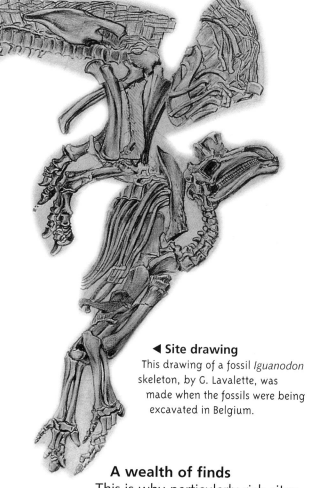

Doubtful beginnings

The first known *Iguanodon* fossils were probably a shinbone found in southern England in 1809 and some teeth in 1819. The animal was reconstructed in 1822 and in 1825 it was named by Gideon Mantell (1790-1852), a physician and fossil hunter.

When fossils from around 39 individuals were discovered in a mine at Bernissart in Belgium in 1878, more accurate reconstructions of this mysterious beast could be made. Experts of the day began to think of *Iguanodon* standing in a kangaroolike posture and having a spike on its thumb. He pictured it like a lizard, walking on all four limbs, which sprawled out sideways.

Exposing fossils

Iguanodon fossils are now known from dozens of sites in Europe and Asia, where rocks of the Early to Middle Cretaceous Period lie at or near the surface. Fossils usually come to light when rocks are exposed or worn away by the action of the rain, wind, and sun. This occurs especially in areas such as the Badlands of the U.S., the Australian outback, the African savanna, the Gobi Desert in Asia, and the pampas of South America.

In Europe such harsh conditions are rare. Fossils, including those of *Iguanodon*, are more likely to be exposed by the actions of people at building sites, quarries, and mines or perhaps by the action of the sea along rocky coasts.

◄ **Site drawing**
This drawing of a fossil *Iguanodon* skeleton, by G. Lavalette, was made when the fossils were being excavated in Belgium.

A wealth of finds

This is why particularly rich sites for *Iguanodon* fossils include the rocks and quarries of the Weald in southeast England, a quarry at Nehden in Germany, and the mine at Bernissart. From the numbers of remains it is thought that *Iguanodon* was a very common animal across the lowlands of Europe during the Early to Middle Cretaceous Period.

Fragmentary remains that may or may not be *Iguanodon*, along with fossilized footprints possibly made by this dinosaur, have been found in Africa, North and South America, and Australia.

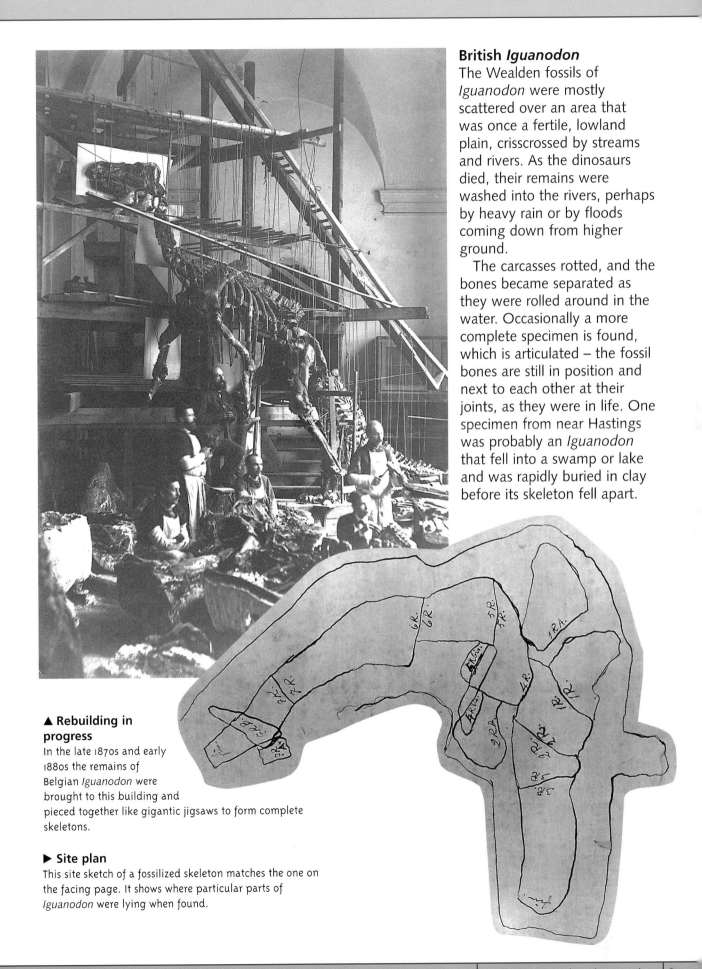

British *Iguanodon*

The Wealden fossils of *Iguanodon* were mostly scattered over an area that was once a fertile, lowland plain, crisscrossed by streams and rivers. As the dinosaurs died, their remains were washed into the rivers, perhaps by heavy rain or by floods coming down from higher ground.

The carcasses rotted, and the bones became separated as they were rolled around in the water. Occasionally a more complete specimen is found, which is articulated – the fossil bones are still in position and next to each other at their joints, as they were in life. One specimen from near Hastings was probably an *Iguanodon* that fell into a swamp or lake and was rapidly buried in clay before its skeleton fell apart.

▲ Rebuilding in progress

In the late 1870s and early 1880s the remains of Belgian *Iguanodon* were brought to this building and pieced together like gigantic jigsaws to form complete skeletons.

▶ Site plan

This site sketch of a fossilized skeleton matches the one on the facing page. It shows where particular parts of *Iguanodon* were lying when found.

Reconstructing *Iguanodon*

Putting *Iguanodon* together has been easy thanks to an abundance of bones found at several sites.

▲ Together at last
This *Iguanodon* skeleton was laid out in the position in which it was discovered.

Belgian *Iguanodon*

In 1878 a clay-filled crack or fissure was discovered running through a coal mine at Bernissart, about 1,000 feet (300 meters) below the surface. The clay was packed with fossilized whole skeletons of about 39 *Iguanodon*, as well as remains of many other animals and plants of the time.

The rocks bearing the skeletons were broken into manageable lumps and sent to the laboratory of the Natural History Museum in Brussels. Before the lumps were removed from the mine, the position of each skeleton was carefully recorded. So were the nature and condition of the surrounding rock. Every piece had its own reference number. The skeletons could therefore be assembled much more easily. Sadly, the First World War made further excavation impossible. The Bernissart mine was abandoned in 1921 and soon flooded.

Hand and finger bones

The bones of *Iguanodon*'s fingers have many details that allow accurate reconstruction. The joints between the thumb bones show that this first digit was probably almost rigid. The three middle fingers could bend backward to take weight. The joints of the fifth or little finger were extremely flexible. The dinosaur could probably bend it across the palm to grasp objects — rather like our own thumb, but on the other side of the hand (digit five rather than digit one).

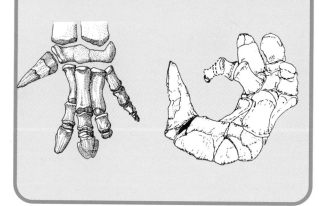

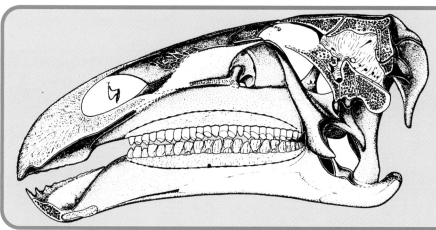

Skull
Iguanodon had long, horselike jaws, and the end of the mouth formed a toothless beak. This was probably covered with sharp-edged horn. The 100 or so cheek teeth grew in parallel rows, forming a continuous platform for grinding food.

German *Iguanodon*

Scattered bone fragments found in clay at the abandoned Nehden quarry stimulated a major excavation of the site in 1980-82. The site was divided up into a grid and a map made. Then the remains were removed layer by layer. This method produced an excellent three-dimensional picture of the remains. At first glance, if you looked at the usual overhead view, the bones seemed to be scattered at random. But the full three-dimensional record showed that the skeletons, including that of a youngster, were lying vertically in the clay.

Reconstructing *Iguanodon*

The great number and variety of *Iguanodon* fossils make the task of reconstruction relatively straightforward.

The skeleton itself is known from many well-preserved and articulated specimens. Muscle scars, roughened patches where muscles were anchored to the bones, can be clearly seen. In turn, this information shows the size and arrangement of the muscles and how they worked in the hips, back legs, shoulders, arms, and jaws. In building up the picture of the way the muscles joined on to bones, comparative anatomy is important. Comparisons are made with the muscle systems of other, related animals, especially living reptiles. Other evidence for the leg musculature comes from fossilized footprints or trackways, which reveal how *Iguanodon* walked and ran (see page 134).

DATA BASE

Name	*Iguanodon*
Pronounced	Ig-WAH-no-don
Meaning	"iguana tooth"

What it ate Plant-eater, feeding on rich swamp vegetation such as horsetails, ferns, cycads, bennettileans, and small conifers

Length	(nose - tail-tip) 30 feet (9.1 meters)
Standing height	14 feet (4.3 meters)
Weight	5 tons (5.1 tonnes)

When it lived	Early to Middle Cretaceous Period 135-110 million years ago
Where it lived	Europe (England, Belgium, Germany, Spain), Africa (Tunisia), Asia (Mongolia), North America (South Dakota, U.S.)

Order	Ornithischia (bird-hipped dinosaurs)
Suborder	Ornithopoda
Family	Iguanodontidae

Lifestyle of *Iguanodon*

Iguanodon was large and powerful but probably lived peacefully unless attacked.

Posture

Modern reconstructions of *Iguanodon* picture the dinosaur standing on its two back legs, main body horizontal, to counterbalance the weight of the head and upper body in front with the large tail behind. The neck is bent in a shallow S shape to raise the head, and the tail is held out rigidly behind.

A feature of the ornithopods is a vertebral column, or backbone, in which large projections of bone from the upper vertebrae are bound tightly together by lengthways bony tendons. This stiffened the backbone and made it look like a length of grid fencing (see opposite). Perhaps

Iguanodon could tilt its body up at its hips, lowering its tail for balance, to browse on higher vegetation. Or it could lean forward and take the weight of the upper body on its front legs when walking on all fours or browsing on low vegetation. But it was unable to bend the main part of its backbone much or to prop itself on its tail like a kangaroo.

Movement

Iguanodon had a small, irregular-shaped bone in its chest, which few other dinosaurs had. It may have evolved to cope with the physical stresses imposed on the chest when moving on all fours.

The relative lengths of the upper and lower leg bones, when compared with those of living animals, give clues about dinosaur posture and movement. Modern fast runners such as gazelles

▲ A formidable herbivore
Iguanodon was no small and timid plant-eater. A predator would have had trouble overcoming it. The thumb with its spike was almost 12 inches (30.5 cm) long. However, we have very few fossils of large predators in Europe dating from the Early to Middle Cretaceous Period. Was this lack of carnivores one reason why *Iguanodon* were so plentiful?

▲ Herbivore herd-dwellers
Zebras are peaceful herbivores, which live in herds as *Iguanodon* probably did .

Male and female?
Specimens of *Iguanodon* that have attained full adult size, as shown by the body proportions and bone development, seem to fall into two groups. There are large, heavy ones and there are smaller, more lightly built individuals.

They could have been two distinct species, but it is unlikely. The study of ecology today shows that two such similar species, living at the same time and in the same place, would be competing directly for food and other resources.

Another explanation is that these two groups represent two sexes, male and female. In modern mammals, the males are usually larger. But in modern reptiles, such as crocodiles and snakes, the females are sometimes bigger. The evidence from *Iguanodon* fossils does not tell us for certain which is which.

and cheetahs have bones in the shin and foot, that are proportionally longer than the bones in the upper leg. The bulky muscles that move the bones are concentrated in the hip and upper thigh, while the lower leg contains only lightweight bones and long, slim tendons. This is the condition found in the ornithopod *Dryosaurus.*

Iguanodon, on the other hand, had fairly long thighs compared with the shins and feet. This implies it was not a rapid sprinter but would pound along at perhaps 8-10 miles per hour (13-16 km/h).

Lifestyle
The place that an animal occupies in its environment – where and how it lives – is called its ecological niche. For example, sharks and tigers are top predators today. In the Age of Dinosaurs *Allosaurus* and *Tyrannosaurus* probably played that part.

Iguanodon may well have filled a niche equivalent to modern wild horses and zebras or large antelopes. They lived in large herds (see pages 142-143), peacefully wandering through the tropical forests and scrublands. They could reach up perhaps 15 feet (4.6 meters) for high vegetation or flop down onto all fours to graze on low-growing ferns and horsetails.

Trellis backbone
These are ossified, or bony, tendons. They are bands of fibrous tissue attaching muscles to bones. A trellis or grid pattern of such tendons along the upper flangelike projections of the backbones is a typical feature of ornithopod dinosaurs.

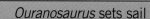

Ouranosaurus sets sail

"Sail-backed" animals have come and gone many times during evolution. Among them were various reptiles, including a few types of dinosaurs, such as the *Iguanodon*-type ornithopod *Ouranosaurus*.

Ouranosaurus is one of the best-known of the "sail-backed" dinosaurs. They had fin- or saillike structures on their backs. The sail was probably a thin sheet of muscle and connective tissue sandwiched between skin. It was held up by tall, stiff, straplike bones called neural spines, each projecting from one of the vertebrae (backbones). In *Ouranosaurus* the longest of these projections were about 3 feet (1 meter) long.

Several other kinds of dinosaurs had such huge, saillike structures on their backs. They included the carnosaur *Spinosaurus* (see opposite) and the sauropod *Rebbachisaurus*. Shoulders and flanks were protected by long, sharp spines pointing forward and sideways.

Similar to *Iguanodon*
The fossils of *Ouranosaurus*, which was about 23 feet (7 meters) long in life, come from Early Cretaceous Period rocks in Niger, Africa. An almost complete skeleton was found in 1966 and described for science in 1976. In general, it was an animal very like *Iguanodon*, with shorter arms than legs, hooves on its fingers and toes, and a spiked thumb. However, it showed variations too. The front of the snout was flattened and beaklike, almost as in a hadrosaur, and there was a bony bulge just in front of each eye.

Why the sail?
The sail may have served as a heat-exchanger. The skin of the sail had a rich blood supply, and its large surface area worked like a radiator. As the dinosaur stood sideways-on to the sun, the sail could soak up the sun's warmth. Blood flowing from the sail then spread the heat around the body. In the early morning this process would make *Ouranosaurus* warmer and active before other sailless reptiles. So it could move fast, get to the food before the other animals, and also escape from attackers.

If *Ouranosaurus* became too hot, it could stand in the shade with the sail sideways-on to a cool breeze. Blood would carry heat from the body into the sail, and from there the heat would be blown away. Today African elephants flap their huge ears to lose

▲ **Stiff back, flexi-neck**
The arms and hands of *Ouranosaurus* were smaller than those of *Iguanodon*, with hooves on the second and third fingers only. The typical stiff, weight-bearing wrist joint and thumb-spike were present. The fin structure would make the backbone and tail of *Ouranosaurus* fairly rigid. However, to compensate, the cervical (neck) vertebrae and their joints show that the neck was short but ultraflexible.

Skull structure

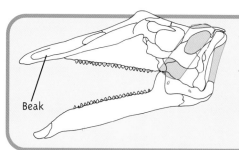

Ouranosaurus had a long, low skull with a wide snout and flat, toothless "beak," more like the bill of a duck than the snipping edge of a tortoise. The large jaws were worked by powerful muscles, which were attached to the prong at the back of the lower jaw for extra leverage. The many grinding cheek teeth resembled those of *Iguanodon*. A pair of bony bumps above the nostrils was again like the duckbilled dinosaurs rather than the iguanodontids.

Beak

excess body heat.

Same sail

The same reasoning would apply to another sail-backed dinosaur, *Spinosaurus*. This theropod or carnivorous dinosaur lived in the same place and at the same time as *Ouranosaurus*. It was larger but it also had a back sail with spines that were even longer than those of *Ouranosaurus*, up to 6 feet (almost 2 meters). Perhaps predator and prey evolved the same answer to the same

If not temperature control, then why?

Temperature regulation is one of the most convincing explanations for the sail on the back of *Ouranosaurus*. But there are other possibilities:

- The spinal extensions may have supported a fleshy hump like that of an American bison or some kinds of antelopes. The hump may have been for sexual display at courting time.
- A similar hump could be a food store of body fat, as in the camel.
- A thin sail made mainly of skin could have been brightly colored for sexual display or recognition, as in the modern lizard *Hydrosaurus* from Southeast Asia.

◄ **Prehistoric inhabitants of the Sahara**
Ouranosaurus and a gigantic crocodile, *Sarcosuchus*, lived in what was then a lush environment of rivers and forests.

DATA BASE

Name	*Ouranosaurus*
Pronounced	OO-ran-oh-SORE-us
Meaning	"brave monitor lizard"

What it ate Plant-eater, browsing on tall ferns, cycads, and early flowering plants

Length	(nose - tail-tip) 23 feet (7 meters)
Standing height	12 feet (3.7 meters)
Weight	1-2 tons (1-2 tonnes)

When it lived	Middle Cretaceous Period 115 million years ago
Where it lived	Africa (Niger)

Order	Ornithischia (bird-hipped dinosaurs)
Suborder	Ornithopoda
Family	Iguanodontidae

Teeth with high ridges

One of the most widespread and numerous dinosaurs of its time, *Hypsilophodon* is known from many well-preserved skeletons.

Hypsilophodon is named from its teeth, which are tall and ridged. It was one of the smallest ornithopods. The hypsilophodonts are named after it. This family, whose characteristic feature is the high-ridged teeth, includes *Othnielia* and *Tenontosaurus* (see page 140), *Orodromeus* (see page 144), and possibly *Dryosaurus* and *Nanosaurus* (see page 140).

Up in the trees

Fossils of *Hypsilophodon* come mainly from the Isle of Wight, in southern England. They were first discovered in about 1849, and further specimens came to light in the 1850s-60s. At first they were thought to be remains of young *Iguanodon*. But in 1869-70 the eminent zoologist Thomas Henry Huxley (1825-95) realized they were from a different animal, and he renamed them *Hypsilophodon*. (Huxley also studied the links between dinosaurs and birds and many other aspects of prehistory. He strongly supported the theory of evolution by natural selection, as proposed by Charles Darwin in his 1859 book *On the Origin of Species*.)

Down from the trees

Hypsilophodon was small for an ornithopod – only waist-high to a human. Its size and other aspects revealed by those early studies

Small and swift
From the Isle of Wight fossils we can picture a small group of *Hypsilophodon* nibbling ferns, horsetails, and other low vegetation in the swamps. The size, lightness, and proportions of this dinosaur suggest it was a swift, agile runner. Its main form of defense was to dodge the attacker and dart away, using its stiffened tail for balance and steering.

suggested its similarity to the tree kangaroo of today. Many reconstructions in the first half of the 20th century showed these dinosaurs perched in trees, grasping the branches with birdlike perching feet. In the 1970s new studies found no evidence for this tree-dwelling way of life. *Hypsilophodon* came down to earth as a fast, agile, bipedal (walking on two legs) ground-dweller.

▲ On the prowl

Hypsilophodon was not much larger than a pet dog. With its relatively large eyes and capacious snout, it would peer about the landscape and sniff the air, relying on its keen senses to gain

Died together

About 23 well-preserved *Hypsilophodon* skeletons, some almost complete, have been found in

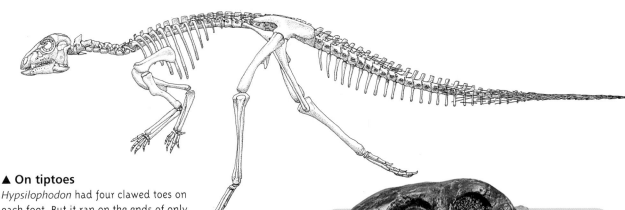

▲ On tiptoes

Hypsilophodon had four clawed toes on each foot. But it ran on the ends of only the second, third, and fourth. The first toe was shorter. Early students of these fossils thought that the first toe faced backward and acted against the other three to form a grasping structure, as in some perching birds. This was one strand of evidence for the "tree-dinosaur" reconstruction. *Hypsilophodon* also had five stubby fingers with claws.

a small area of cliff rocks on the south-west coast of the Isle of Wight. The rocks are of Early Cretaceous age and contain hardly any other fossils. One explanation is that a small herd of *Hypsilophodon* was trapped by the rising tide, perhaps in the quicksands at the edge of the shallow sea that covered much of northern Europe during this time. Further evidence for herd dwelling is discussed on pages 142-143.

Narrow nose

The snout of *Hypsilophodon* was relatively tall but narrow from side to side (as shown in the view from above of the skull, see page 141). It would allow the dinosaur to poke among vegetation for the choicest soft shoots, buds, and young leaves. Selective feeding like this may take more effort than grabbing large mouthfuls of food. On the other hand, chewing and digesting large quantities of food, of which most is unsuitable and only a little is nutritious, could use up even more energy and bodily raw material. So, *Hypsilophodon* had probably found the most efficient method of feeding.

DATA BASE

Name *Hypsilophodon*
Pronounced hip-sill-OH-foh-don
Meaning "high-ridge tooth"

What it ate
Plant-eater, probably browsing low-growing swampy vegetation such as ferns and horsetails

Length (nose - tail-tip) 7 feet 6 inches (2.3 meters)
Standing height 3 feet 3 inches (1 meter)
Weight 50 pounds (22.7 kilograms)

When it lived Early Cretaceous Period 120 million years ago
Where it lived Europe (England, Spain), possibly U.S. (South Dakota)

Order Ornithischia (bird-hipped dinosaurs)
Suborder Ornithopoda
Family Hypsilophodontidae

A conservative family

Hypsilophodontids were small to medium-sized ornithopods that first appeared in the Late Jurassic Period, spread across most of the world, and survived until the end of the Cretaceous Period.

The hypsilophodontids, including *Hypsilophodon* itself (see pages 138-139), probably evolved from the types of ornithopods called fabrosaurs. The hypsilophodonts evolved generally larger body size, more efficient jaws and teeth for chewing food, and big eyes for good vision. They became especially diverse during Cretaceous times in Australia.

However, the hypsilophodontids did not change very much over tens of millions of years. One of the first kinds, *Othnielia* from the Late Jurassic Period, was very similar to one of the last, *Thescelosaurus* from the Late Cretaceous Period – almost 90 million years later. Those of the species that differed most from the typical body design were the semiarmored types with two rows of bony plates, or scutes, along the back, and the largest well-known member of the group, *Tenontosaurus.*

Tenontosaurus

This very large hypsilophodontid, "sinew lizard," is known from fossils dating to the Early to Nid-Cretaceous Period at various sites in North America, including Arizona, Montana, Oklahoma, and Texas. It was up to 25 feet (7.6 meters) long and weighed around 1 ton (1 tonne). Because of its size, it is sometimes included in the iguanodontid group, but its teeth are mostly hypsilophodontid.

The arms of *Tenontosaurus* were relatively long and sturdy, so it may have spent more time walking on all fours than other hypsilophodontids. Half of its total length was the heavy, thick tail, which was stiffened by bony tendons at its end.

One famed specimen of *Tenontosaurus* was found associated with five specimens of the dinosaur *Deinonychus*. This predator, a theropod related to *Velociraptor*, had a huge claw on each foot for ripping prey. The original remains may have been washed together by chance, such as by a river in flood, before fossilizing. However, maybe something more exciting happened, such as a pack of *Deinonychus* attacking and slashing at *Tenontosaurus* (see also chapter 8 in this book).

Othnielia

This hypsilophodont lived in Late Jurassic times. Its fossils have been found in Utah and Wyoming. In 1877 a celebrated American fossil hunter and professor at Yale University, Othniel Charles Marsh (1831-99), named them *Nanosaurus* but they were renamed in his honor in 1977. Some specimens are less than 5 feet (1.5 meters) long.

Othnielia had the typical hypsilophodont build: slim body, long tail, long, slender rear limbs, and short, armlike front limbs with five-fingered hands. Its teeth were unusual because they were entirely covered in enamel, a very hard substance. Usually only the chewing

◄ **Wary feeder**
Tenontosaurus watches a flock of pterosaurs as it feeds, aware that the flying reptiles may have been disturbed by a major predator.

▶ **Early Cretaceous landscape**
A hypsilophodontid, its tail held stiffly horizontal, travels through Montana some 130 million years ago.

Other hypsilophodonts
• *Valdosaurus*, "Wealden lizard," from the Early Cretaceous Period in Europe and perhaps Africa.
• *Zephyrosaurus*, "west wind lizard," from the Early Cretaceous Period in North America.
• *Fulgurotherium*, "Lightning Ridge beast," from the Early to Middle Cretaceous Period in Australia.
• *Loncosaurus*, "Lonco lizard," from the Late Cretaceous Period in South America. However, it could be a carnivore from the very different theropod group of dinosaurs!

surfaces have such a covering. This may show that the plants it ate were very tough.

Parksosaurus
One of the last hypsilophodontids, *Parksosaurus* ("Parks's lizard") survived in Late Cretaceous times in Alberta, Canada. It was only around 8 feet (2.4 meters) long and may have perished in the great mass extinction that finished off all other dinosaurs. Like other later hypsilophodontids it had very large eyes, perhaps for searching for prey in the gloomy undergrowth.

Thescelosaurus
A widespread dinosaur of Late Cretaceous times in western North America, *Thescelosaurus*, or "wonderful lizard," was almost 12 feet (3.7 meters) long. It was a mixture of hypsilophodontid and iguanodontid features, quite bulky, with teeth at the front of its upper jaw, thighs and shins of equal length, and five toes on each foot. It was probably much slower than a typical hypsilophodont, and had rows of bony lumps or studs along its back, which gave it a type of armorplated protection.

Leaellynasaura
This hypsilophodontid is described more fully in volume 5 of this series, along with the other Early Cretaceous "polar dinosaurs" of Australia. It was a typical bipedal, parrot-beaked, plant-eating hypsilophodontid, standing only waist-high to a human. Its eyes were not just large, as in other members of the

family, but huge. So were the optic lobes, the parts of the brain that receive visual information as nerve signals from the eyes. This feature may have helped *Leaellynosaura* to survive in the seasonal cool darkness of its semipolar landscape. It also has a connection with the question whether it was cold-blooded or warm-blooded (see pages 68-69).

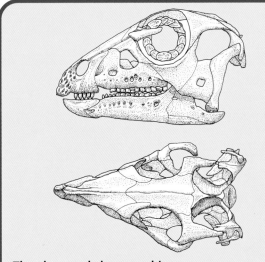

The chop-and-chew machine
At the front of its mouth *Hypsilophodon* had incisor-type teeth in the middle bone of the upper jaw. They probably bit down onto a horny beak that covered the bone of the lower jaw. This part of the mouth chopped vegetation. The cheek teeth were tall and sharp-ridged, almost like chisels. During chewing, the lower jaw moved up within the upper jaw, making the upper bones tilt outward and the lower ones tilt inward. The cheek teeth ground past each other, slicing and chewing food, while the cheek pouches kept it in the mouth. As the teeth wore out, they were replaced regularly.

Herd of dinosaurs? ▶

⇒ Herd of dinosaurs?

Did dinosaurs live in groups, even interacting socially with each other? If so, why? Hardly any reptiles today are herd-dwellers...

It is one of the basic laws of nature that herbivores fall prey to carnivores. So herbivores need protection from carnivores. It comes in various forms, such as large body size and strength, sharp weapons like tusks or hooves or horns or antlers, sharp senses and extreme speed for quick escape, or tough plates or shields of armorplating on the body.

Another aspect of defense is "safety in numbers." There are various advantages to group living for herbivores, as follows.

1 Always on guard

Most animals in a group are feeding or resting at any one time. But the chances are that there are a few members who are alert and on guard, looking and listening and sniffing for potential danger. If it is detected, they can warn the others, by sights and sounds, and trigger a mass escape.

2 Confusion in the ranks

In a fleeing herd of zebra, a flock of birds, or a shoal of fish it is difficult to pick out an individual. The patterns and sounds they make change constantly as the members dodge, turn, and wheel at speed, like one huge "superorganism." So it is hard for a predator to track and attack a single member.

3 Finding food

Locating food is another advantage. This is especially noticeable as a flock of birds pecks its way across a meadow. The birds not only look for food but also watch each other. When one finds a rich source, it stops and eats. The others notice and gather around to see if there is enough to share. Likewise, in city centers pigeons or gulls soon gather around the tourist who has brought the bread or a bag of seeds.

4 Swamping the predator

Another advantage of group-dwelling comes during the breeding season. If all herd members produce babies at about the same time, there is suddenly a huge number of offspring. Animals are very vulnerable during this early period of life. But a limited number of predators can take only a limited number of young. The large number of possible victims swamps the hunters.

5 Collective defense

A predator might find it quite easy to overcome a single animal. But overcoming several of them — especially parents protecting their offspring — is a much more daunting prospect. So predators therefore generally do not attack herds of animals. They watch and wait around the edges until a young, old, or sick member gets separated from the herd or left behind.

▲ **Purposeful flight**
For birds such as these black-headed gulls the main advantage of flocking together is finding food and nesting sites.

▲ **Safety in numbers**
Perhaps the herbivore dinosaurs lived together in herds for protection like these blue wildebeest in Africa.

▲ **Many feet**
Collections of fossilized footprints, like this *Iguanodon* specimen, are evidence that the animals lived together in herds.

Evidence for ornithopod group living

There is evidence that some dinosaurs, including certain ornithopods, may have formed groups. Of course, some animals of the same kind gather together today for a reason — a rich source of food or a safe place to shelter or hibernate. But there is little social interaction, and when the reason for coming together has gone, they soon go their separate ways. Did some ornithopods form herds in which the members interacted socially and traveled, fed, and bred together?

• (Lack of) body defenses

Most of the ornithopods, especially the earlier types, were relatively small and defenseless creatures. *Hypsilophodon* was speedy and agile, but if cornered, it was hardly big and strong enough to put up much of a fight. Even *Iguanodon* had a medium bulk and two thumb-spikes, but not much more. A large, well-equipped predator could easily overcome one individual. The lack of body defenses may suggest that living in groups would protect the animals from danger.

• Footprints

Fossilized footprints of dinosaurs have been found all over the world. In 1997 sections of tracks were discovered in Australia that could link into a trail some 50 miles (80 kilometers) long. From a print's size and shape it is usually possible to say which main kind of dinosaur made them.

Trackways from southern England show that many *Iguanodon*-type dinosaurs passed the same way. The prints seem to be from a variety of individuals, and all face in much the same direction. It is more likely that a herd on the move made them, rather than one or a few individuals repeating the same journey over days, weeks, or months. This is partly because the environmental conditions that are needed for footprints to be preserved are very specialized and don't usually last much time. A typical *Iguanodon* footprint is about 2 feet (60 cm) across, with the three large digits showing clearly, and the foot is "pigeon-toed," that is, it points slightly inward.

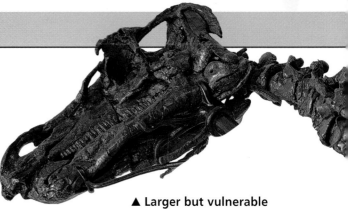

▲ **Larger but vulnerable**
Iguanodon was not very well protected. Living in groups may have made up for its lack of body defenses.

• Fossil accumulations

At some sites many dinosaur skeletons are discovered together. It is rarely possible to say if they actually died together. The bones could have been piled up over a long period, for example, by floodwaters at a bend in a river. It is this kind of chance that makes the legendary "elephants' graveyards" of modern times.

More than 30 *Iguanodon* specimens were found in a Belgian mine (see page 132). Perhaps they slid or fell into a ravine. Or they may have fallen in a mad stampede or suffered a landslide. On the other hand, floods may have washed the carcasses or bones into the gorge, even over several years.

The 20-plus *Hypsilophodon* specimens from the Isle of Wight (see pages 132-133) are in the same state of preservation, which suggests that the animals were rapidly buried in mud. Even their body postures are similar. So it looks as though they did both live and die together. Possibly they were all overcome by the same flood, fell into the same quicksand, or were cut off by the same rising tide.

▲ **A circle of protection**
Fully grown African elephants are awesome creatures, but their young need the protection offered by family and herd living.

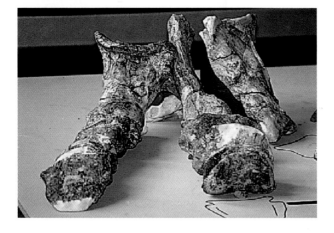

◄ **Printmakers**
Iguanodontid footbones made footprints that can be easily recognized. In many places they have been found in great numbers making up long trackways.

Nests, eggs, and babies

In the 1980s amazing discoveries in Montana caused a revolution in our ideas about the way dinosaurs produced their young.

In 1978 a chance find in a rock-and-fossil store in Bynum, Montana, led to the discovery of the preserved bones of dinosaur babies. Further digging at rocky hills near the town produced the fossilized remains of hundreds of dinosaur eggs, the nests they were laid in, the babies that had hatched from them, and in some cases eggs containing babies that had not yet hatched. The hills were investigated from 1979, and one has become known as "Egg Mountain."

The eggs, nests, and babies included two kinds of ornithopods that lived and bred at the same time and in the same region. One was the hadrosaur *Maiasaura* (see chapter 9). The other was a hypsilophodont, *Orodromeus*.

Neat nests

Orodromeus was very similar to *Hypsilophodon*, though slightly smaller. Dozens of *Orodromeus* nests were discovered, regularly spaced about 6 feet (2 meters) apart. This was a dinosaur breeding colony, probably on an island in what was once a shallow Late Cretaceous lake. "Egg Mountain" could have been "Egg Island."

Each nest was a shallow bowl-shaped area of scraped sand containing a number of eggs. In one of the best-preserved examples there are 19 eggs. They are laid in a neat pattern, spiraling out from the nest's center. The eggs were probably covered with vegetation and more sand to keep them hidden and warm.

Hatched and gone

The empty eggshells in the nests of the much larger hadrosaur *Maiasaura* were broken and fragmented. Probably they were trampled on by the youngsters that stayed in the nest after hatching.

The empty shells of *Orodromeus* were in better condition. In some the lower half of the shell lay almost undisturbed in the fossilized sand. It seems that the youngsters broke their way out through the upper half and left the nest right away.

Inside the eggs

There are many jumbled bones of *Orodromeus* hatchlings at the site. There are also some whole eggs. A CAT scanner (used in medical clinics to look at human tissue) made images of the interiors. The bones of the embryos, or unhatched babies, were visible on the scans. So the fossil eggs were cut open,

Herd of dinosaurs?

and the fossil embryos within carefully studied – the first time this had been done for any dinosaur.

Caring crocodile
Traditionally, reptiles have not been considered caring parents. But in the 1970s observations of crocodiles showed that the mother stays near the area of riverbank where she buried her eggs. When the babies are ready to hatch, she hears them squeaking and helps them emerge. She then carries them to the water in the safety of her mouth and even guards them for a time. We are still finding exciting new information, not only about dinosaurs but also about living reptiles. There is still a lot to learn.

◀ Rapid exit
This model of the nest, eggs, and babies of *Orodromeus* shows the hatchlings breaking out of the eggs. Scientists think that the babies left the nest immediately to fend for themselves, so they did not need parental care.

▶ Caring parents
Emperor penguins are caring parents. The father looks after the egg until the baby hatches.

Parental care
The legbones and joints of the unhatched babies were well developed. They would have been strong enough to allow the youngsters to leave the nest right after hatching. That would account for the untrampled eggshells.

In contrast, the legbones and joints of unhatched *Maiasaura* babies were not well developed. This meant the youngsters would have had to stay in the nest, hence the trampled shells. Researchers have gone on to propose that the *Maiasaura* babies must have been fed by caring dinosaur parents!

Fossilized eggs and other evidence of a small predatory dinosaur, *Troodon*, complete the picture. It was probably a meat-eater that followed the herbivore herds, bred on the fringes of their colonies, and snatched their eggs and babies to feed itself and perhaps its own offspring.

DATA BASE

Name	*Orodromeus*
Pronounced	OR-roe-droe-MEE-us
Meaning	"mountain runner"

What it ate
Plant-eater, probably browsing on low-growing vegetation

Length	(nose - tail-tip) 6 feet 6 inches (2 meters)
Standing height	3 feet (1 meter)
Weight	40 pounds (18 kilograms)

When it lived	Late Cretaceous Period 70 million years ago
Where it lived	U.S. (Montana)

Order	Ornithischia (bird-hipped dinosaurs)
Suborder	Ornithopoda
Family	Hypsilophodontidae

Dinosaur pack-hunters

The small and medium-sized meat-eaters, or theropods, lived mainly toward the end of the Age of the Dinosaurs.

Were dinosaurs "clever" or "intelligent"? If any were, they would have been found among the small and medium-sized meat-eaters of the theropod dinosaur group. They lived mainly during the Middle and Late Cretaceous Period, from about 100 to 65 million years ago. Some were as small as our pet cats, others were slightly taller than ourselves. Most could stand upright and walk and run on their two back legs.

The pack-hunting theropod dinosaurs were not nearly as big as the giant hunting dinosaurs such as *Allosaurus* and *Tyrannosaurus*. But they had large brains (for their body size) and prowled in ravenous packs. They were some of the most exciting yet sinister and scary of all dinosaurs.

Sharp creatures

These small and medium-sized theropods were fast and agile creatures. They had sharp senses, sharp claws, and sharp teeth. Some hunted in groups, mercilessly attacking larger victims. They included the early, lightweight dinosaurs known as coelurosaurs, the long-legged and swift "ostrich dinosaurs," or ornithomimosaurs, and the dreaded pack-hunting dromaeosaurs, or deinonychosaurs – "raptors" such as *Deinonychus* and *Velociraptor*.

Some of the smallest theropods from the coelurosaur group, such as *Coelurus*, *Ornitholestes*, and *Compsognathus*, are described mainly in chapter 5 of this book, which looks at the evolution of birds from dinosaurs.

Today's small-medium carnivores

Think of a carnivorous, or flesh-eating, animal of today. Larger types are lions,

◀ **Battle to the death**
In the semideserts of Mongolia some 80 million years ago a *Velociraptor* tries to steal dinosaur eggs or babies from their nest. But the parent, an early ceratopsian (horned dinosaur) called *Protoceratops*, fights back with a vengeance. It bites the raptor's arm with its strong, sharp, beaklike mouth. The story continues on page 26.

tigers, bears, and wolves. During the Age of Dinosaurs their equivalents would have been the huge carnosaur theropods such as *Allosaurus*, *Ceratosaurus*, *Carnotaurus*, *Tarbosaurus*, and *Tyrannosaurus*.

Today there are also a whole host of smaller hunters that are just as fierce and deadly. They include smaller cats like lynx, bobcat, caracal, and ocelot, the pack-hunting African wild dogs, various kinds of foxes, mustelids such as minks, otters, weasels, stoats, and martens, many kinds of mongooses, and the catlike civets and genets. They all show the bodily features needed by a creature that preys on other animals — agile and fast movements, strength with stealth, pointed teeth and claws, and keen senses both to detect victims and to remain unnoticed by them until the last moment.

The dinosaur family

Dinosauria

Saurischia   Ornithischia

Theropods   Sauropods

Carnosaurs   Dromaeosaurs   **Oviraptosaurs**
     Coelurosaurs   Ornithomimosaurs

What were the small and medium-sized theropods?

The Theropoda, or "beast-foot," group of dinosaurs was made up of two main subgroups. One included the smallish theropods described in this book. The other included much larger meat-eaters such as *Allosaurus*, *Ceratosaurus*, *Spinosaurus*, and *Tyrannosaurus*. These huge hunters are known as the carnosaurs and are described in chapter 3.

In turn, the Theropoda, or theropods, were one subgroup of the Saurischia, or "lizard-hips."

Features of a "raptor"

The dromaeosaurs included Deinonychus, Dromaeosaurus, and Velociraptor. They are often known as "raptors" — which can mean "predator" or "thief" or "plunderer." This term is also used to describe birds of prey such as eagles, hawks, and falcons.

- Small to medium size (for dinosaurs), mostly less than 13 feet (4 meters) long.
- Large head with powerful jaws and long, sharp, curved teeth.
- Large brain for the body size.
- Keen senses, especially eyesight.
- Strong front legs or arms and grasping hands with fiercely clawed fingers.
- Long, muscular back legs for fast running.
- A huge, sickle-shaped claw on the second toe of each foot, which could be used like a switchblade to slash at enemies or prey.

These smaller hunters also had their equivalents in dinosaur times. They were the small and medium-sized theropods that are described in this volume. Prowling, stalking, and hunting, they survived for millions of years.

▶ Predators for prey

Lions and tigers are deadly large predators for large prey. So are medium-sized and smaller cats like the caracal for smaller prey. The caracal is exceptionally lithe, yet muscular and agile. It is capable of great leaps 10 feet (3 meters) straight up into the air – perhaps like the raptor dinosaurs from millions of years ago.

Main groups of theropods

The predatory dinosaurs, or theropods, were among the first groups of dinosaurs to appear on earth, more than 200 million years ago.

There were several subgroups of theropod dinosaurs. They were mostly active animals, and some may have been warm-blooded. Many had birdlike features such as hollow bones for lightness, large eyes, and relatively big brains. As described in chapter 5, birds probably arose from theropod dinosaurs. Indeed, some scientists view birds as "feathered reptiles."

▲ Over fallen leaves
The ostrich dinosaur *Struthiomimus* walks under a tree and over its fallen leaves during the Late Cretaceous Period. The dinosaur's zebralike stripes are guesswork. Fossils do not allow us to know the colors and patterns of dinosaurs or other prehistoric animals. But the leaves were real. Fossils show that broadleaved trees evolved in the Cretaceous.

▶ A mud bath
A group of the early and well-known theropods *Coelophysis* cool off in the mud of a part-dried waterhole in a forest clearing. In the foreground is the dark shape of a very early type of crocodile, known as a sphenosuchid. Crocs began as small land predators that grew in size and took to the water.

Well-known yet mysterious
Some of the theropods are well known because many of their fossils have been found, often preserved in excellent condition. But other types are more mysterious, known from only a few fossil fragments. This is because many theropods were small, lightly built animals. Their fragile bones had less chance of preservation than the thick, solid bones of more heavily built dinosaurs. Also, being meat-eaters, these smaller theropods were less common than the plant-eaters further back along the food chains. So they are less likely to crop up in the fossil record.

Unclear evolution
For these and other reasons the origins of the small and medium-sized theropods are partly guesswork. Scientists often group them by size or general body shape, rather than by true evolutionary links.

There following are broad groupings. More details are given in the descriptions of the individual dinosaurs throughout the book. (The largest theropods, the carnosaurs, are described in chapter 3.)

Coelurosaurs
In general, the earliest well-known theropods were the coelurosaurs ("hollow-tailed lizards"). They included *Coelophysis*, *Syntarsus*, *Coelurus*, *Ornitholestes*, and one of the tiniest of all dinosaurs, *Compsognathus*. The coelurosaurs lived mainly during the Triassic and Jurassic periods and were small, slim, light creatures. Most of their bones were hollow to

save weight, hence their name. *Coelophysis* is described in this chapter, while chapter 5 includes most of the other coelurosaurs.

Segisaurus was a very small theropod dinosaur from the Early Jurassic Period. Its fossil remains are not complete enough to give it an accurate description or grouping. It may have been a coelurosaur in a group of its own or a different type of dinosaur.

Dromaeosaurs

These theropods were small or medium in size and very strongly built. Often called raptors, they include *Deinonychus*, *Dromaeosaurus*, and *Velociraptor*. There is good fossil evidence that some types hunted in packs. With their large brains, sicklelike foot claws, and sharp teeth, they were extremely well-equipped predators. The dromaeosaurs survived through most of the Cretaceous Period.

Ornithomimosaurs

The "bird-mimic lizards" are also known as ostrich dinosaurs. This is because of their similarity in size, shape, and bodily proportions to the ostrich we know today. This group flourished at the end of the Age of Dinosaurs during the Late Cretaceous Period and included *Ornithomimus*, *Struthiomimus*, *Dromiceiomimus*, and *Gallimimus*.

Oviraptosaurs

Oviraptor was another small, birdlike dinosaur with a beaked mouth. *Ingenia* was also possibly a member of the oviraptosaur group. These dinosaurs existed during the Late Cretaceous Period. They differed from the ostrich dinosaurs mainly in the structure of their hands.

Origins of theropods

The ancestors of the small and medium-sized theropods were among the first dinosaurs to evolve, during the Middle Triassic Period some 230-220 million years ago.

Dinosaurs belong to the larger group called archosaurs, or "ruling reptiles." It also includes the flying reptiles known as pterosaurs, which are extinct, and the crocodiles, which survive today. Among the early archosaurs were thecodont reptiles such as *Ornithosuchus* from Scotland. They lived during the Triassic Period and could walk upright on their two hind legs. Ornithosuchian thecodonts may have been the ancestors of the whole theropod group, from *Coelophysis* to *Tyrannosaurus*.

As evolution continued, the dinosaurs themselves appeared, probably in the shape of the earliest theropods. They included *Eoraptor* and *Herrerasaurus*, both from Argentina in South America and both dated at about 230-225 million years ago.

These first theropods were little different from their thecodont ancestors. They were small, light, speedy, sharp-toothed predators that ran on their hind legs and may have hunted in packs. They and their ancestors are described in chapters 1 and 2 of this book.

⇨ Dinosaurs at Ghost Ranch

Coelophysis is probably the best-known of the early theropods – and of any early dinosaur. Many hundreds, even thousands, of fossilized skeletons have been found at Ghost Ranch, New Mexico.

Coelophysis is one of the earliest dinosaurs known from plentiful fossilized remains. It was a coelurosaur about 10 feet (3 meters) long from nose to tail-tip. It stood almost as tall as a human being on its larger back legs. Its shorter front legs were held out like arms.

   Coelophysis was slim and lightly built and had lots of small, sharp teeth. It lived during the Late Triassic Period about 225 million years ago in what is now New Mexico and Arizona.

The finding of Coelophysis

The fossils of several *Coelophysis* dinosaurs, possibly a family group, were found and named in the 1880s near Abiquiu in New Mexico. Then in the 1940s large numbers of well-preserved but jumbled bones, representing at least several hundred skeletons, were found together by an expedition revisiting the same site, now named Ghost Ranch. These individuals were of different sizes, from very young hatchlings to small and large adults – possibly females and males.

   Why did so many dinosaurs perish at the same site? They may have lived together in a pack. Or they could have been overcome by a large disaster, such as when a flash flood filled a dry desert river and washed the drowned, widely scattered bodies into one site. Fossils of dinosaurs very similar to *Coelophysis* have been found in other parts of the world, including South America, Europe, Asia, and Africa. One example is *Syntarsus* from Zimbabwe, which is almost identical to *Coelophysis*. More than two dozen *Syntarsus* individuals were preserved together. This evidence supports the idea that these creatures lived in groups.

◀ Grabbing a meal
Coelophysis had a long, flexible neck that could be curled into an S shape and darted out rapidly like a snake. The long, narrow jaws were lined with sharp, serrated teeth. They were ideal for grabbing prey such as a scampering lizard, one of the newly evolved small mammals, a little dinosaur — or even the young of its own kind (see panel opposite).

▲ The scent of death

Hundreds of *Coelophysis* scamper through a Late Triassic fern and conifer forest in search of food. Their keen sense of smell will lead them to a nearby river, where the drying pools have left easy meals in the shape of fish gasping in the shallows.

Birdlike features

Like other coelurosaurs and other smaller theropods, *Coelophysis* had many birdlike characteristics. They included hollow bones (hence its name, meaning "hollow form"), certain fused bones in the ankles and the hips, and four-toed feet like most modern birds. Each foot had three long, thin toes on the ground and the fourth (actually the first or big toe) held off the ground. Each toe had a sharp claw. Like the feet, each hand had four digits or fingers, but only three were long enough to be useful.

Dinosaur cannibals!

The Ghost Ranch site has yielded many fascinating fossils. In particular, two of the adult *Coelophysis* skeletons contained the bones of *Coelophysis* babies in their body cavities (see picture on next page).

One possibility is that these adults were pregnant. But this is very rare among dinosaurs, which — like most other reptiles — bred by laying eggs rather than giving birth to young..

Further studies showed that the hipbones of the adult *Coelophysis* were too narrow for babies to pass through. So they could not have given birth.

A more gruesome explanation is that *Coelophysis* was a cannibal. It ate its own kind. In a large group, when other food became short, someone else's offspring would make a meal that could mean the difference between survival or starvation. Whether *Coelophysis* actively killed its victims or scavenged on dead bodies is not clear. Cannibalism happens today in some kinds of animals, ranging from crocodiles to sparrows, lions, and tigers.

⇨ Lifestyle of *Coelophysis*

Coelophysis probably lived with other members of its own kind. It was even possible it ate some of them!

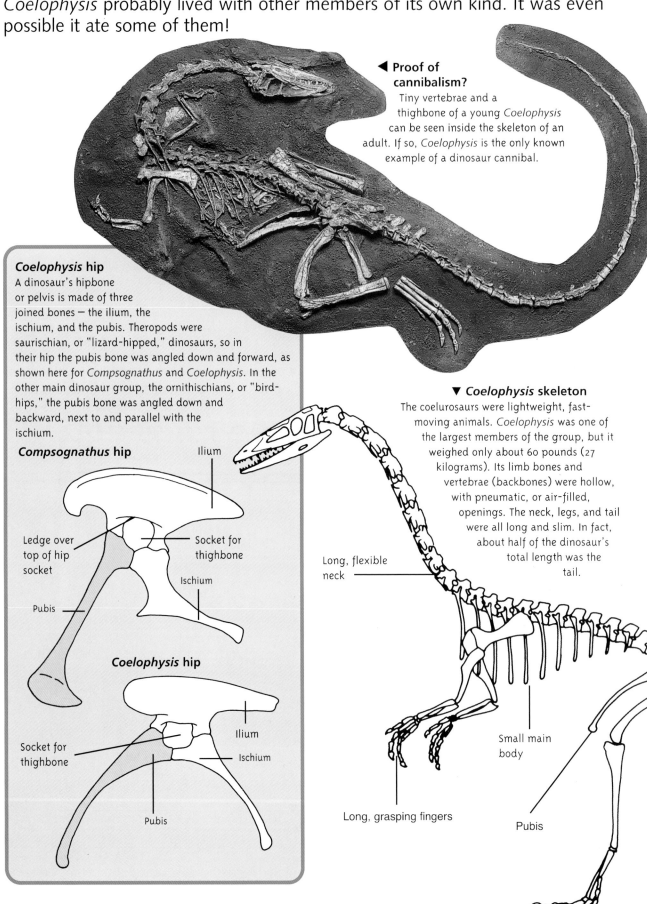

◄ Proof of cannibalism?
Tiny vertebrae and a thighbone of a young *Coelophysis* can be seen inside the skeleton of an adult. If so, *Coelophysis* is the only known example of a dinosaur cannibal.

Coelophysis hip
A dinosaur's hipbone or pelvis is made of three joined bones — the ilium, the ischium, and the pubis. Theropods were saurischian, or "lizard-hipped," dinosaurs, so in their hip the pubis bone was angled down and forward, as shown here for *Compsognathus* and *Coelophysis*. In the other main dinosaur group, the ornithischians, or "bird-hips," the pubis bone was angled down and backward, next to and parallel with the ischium.

Compsognathus hip

Ilium

Ledge over top of hip socket

Socket for thighbone

Ischium

Pubis

Coelophysis hip

Socket for thighbone

Ilium

Ischium

Pubis

▼ Coelophysis skeleton
The coelurosaurs were lightweight, fast-moving animals. *Coelophysis* was one of the largest members of the group, but it weighed only about 60 pounds (27 kilograms). Its limb bones and vertebrae (backbones) were hollow, with pneumatic, or air-filled, openings. The neck, legs, and tail were all long and slim. In fact, about half of the dinosaur's total length was the tail.

Long, flexible neck

Small main body

Long, grasping fingers

Pubis

DATA BASE

Name	*Coelophysis*
Pronounced	SEA-low-FYE-sis
Meaning	"hollow form"

What it ate Meat, including small animals such as lizards and possibly early shrewlike mammals

Length	(to tail-tip) 8-10 feet (2.4-3 meters)
Standing height	4 feet (1.2 meters)
Weight	50-60 pounds (23-27 kilograms)

When it lived	Late Triassic Period 225 million years ago
Where it lived	North America (Arizona, New Mexico)

Order	Saurischia (lizard-hipped dinosaurs)
Suborder	Theropoda
Family	Coelophysidae

Roaming the desert

The large numbers of *Coelophysis* fossils at one site suggest that these dinosaurs gathered in groups. If they did, and if the groups numbered dozens or hundreds, it's likely that *Coelophysis* fed on small, easy-to-catch food items rather than hunting large prey. One big victim caught by pack-hunting methods would feed only a small group, like the wolf pack today hunting a caribou or moose.

Fossilized footprints made by hundreds of small theropods have been found in what was originally soft mud in Connecticut. It therefore looks as though these types of dinosaurs went around in troops. As well as the footprints, one of the animals that made them has also been preserved at the site - a coelurosaur very similar to *Coelophysis*.

A social dinosaur?

Coelophysis could have roamed in troops in the open, sandy, semidesert terrain of the time. Its prey would have included the small shrewlike mammals that had newly appeared, little lizards, and the newly evolving, plant-eating dinosaurs such as *Revueltosaurus* and *Technosaurus.* Or perhaps groups of *Coelophysis* may have gathered near waterholes or seasonal rivers to feast on fish and other aquatic creatures.

Although *Coelophysis* may have gathered in groups, it was not necessarily a social animal. It may have been but it may not. Many individuals may have come together merely because there was a plentiful food source. They fed together but did not really interact with each other. They ignored one another. Another possibility is that individuals gathered together for breeding, so that the larger males and smaller females could pair off to reproduce.

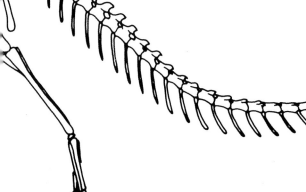

The "terrible claw"

One of the most exciting finds in the history of fossil-hunting, *Deinonychus* has taught us so much that the books on dinosaurs have had to be rewritten.

Fossils of *Deinonychus*, "terrible claw," were first discovered in Montana in 1964. They represented some of the most thrilling finds in modern paleontology. They helped establish firmly the dromaeosaur group, and place in this group two dinosaurs known from much earlier finds, *Dromaeosaurus* and *Velociraptor* (pages 158-159).

The study of *Deinonychus* remains revealed a theropod as tall as a human. It was strong, fast, agile, and well armed with sharp teeth in powerful jaws, gripping finger claws, and a massive, vicious foot claw (which gave the dinosaur its name). In addition, its large brain in relation to its body size suggested that it could have been "clever," that is, able to adapt and vary its behavior according to circumstances and to learn from experience. This has opened up whole new ways of thinking about dinosaurs and their lifestyles.

▲ Teeth of the killer
The hugely gaping mouth of *Deinonychus* extended almost to the back of the head. It was filled with sharp teeth like those of a shark. The large eyes were set on top of the head for good vision, and the nostrils sniffed the air for the smell of meat. The large-clawed hands add to the impression of a fierce and efficient killer.

Deinonychus skull, jaws, and teeth

Deinonychus had the lightweight, long-limbed body of its probable ancestors, the coelurosaurs. But the head was much larger in proportion to the body than a coelurosaur's. Also, the skull, although large, was light because of the holes in it that housed the large eyes and strong jaw muscles.

As in *Dromeosaurus*, the hinge joint between the upper and lower jaws was at the very rear of the skull. This meant that it could open its mouth in an extremely wide gape. The jaws themselves were lined with teeth like small steak knives, each about the size of a human fingertip, but thin and bladelike, with serrated, or wavy, edges.

The teeth were "recurved" – that is, curved back toward the neck. Once bitten, there was only one direction that a mouthful of food could go, and that was down the throat of *Deinonychus*.

A stiff tail

Deinonychus probably ran with its main body horizontal, parallel to the ground. The head and S-shaped neck would be balanced over the rear legs by the long tail behind. The tail backbones (caudal vertebrae) had long, rodlike parts that overlapped the backbones in front. There were also skilike chevrons beneath the tail bones, which had similar long, bony, overlapping rods. This turned the tail into a stiff, interlocking structure that could be flexed properly only at the base. Perhaps the rigid tail was used for steering as the dinosaur sprinted along.

Handy weapons

The hands of *Deinonychus* were almost half the length of the arm. The wrists were unusually flexible for a dinosaur. In fact, the hands could be turned toward each other (as we do when we clap), probably to grasp a small prey between them or to dig into a larger victim. The hands and wrists could also be folded against the body – like the wings of

▲ Dappled dinosaur
The skin color and pattern of this *Deinonychus* reconstruction would give excellent camouflage below trees in the dappled shade of a woodland. The big eyes would also be able to pick out victims and perhaps other pack members in the gloom.

a bird. This has led to suggestions that birds evolved from early raptor-type theropod dinosaurs.

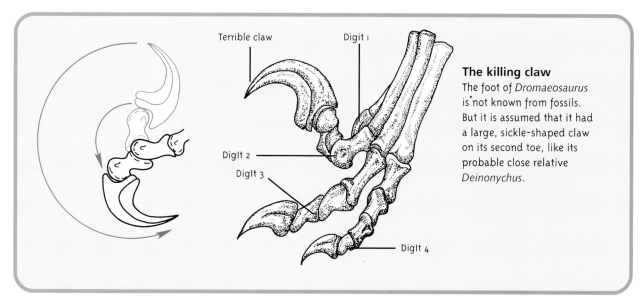

Terrible claw

Digit 1

Digit 2

Digit 3

Digit 4

The killing claw
The foot of *Dromaeosaurus* is not known from fossils. But it is assumed that it had a large, sickle-shaped claw on its second toe, like its probable close relative *Deinonychus*.

Deinonychus skeleton

Deinonychus was about the same height and weight as a man, but had a whole battery of defenses over its body from head to foot.

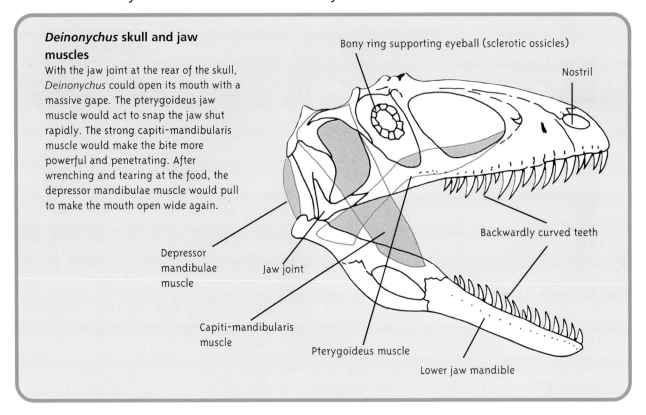

Deinonychus skull and jaw muscles

With the jaw joint at the rear of the skull, *Deinonychus* could open its mouth with a massive gape. The pterygoideus jaw muscle would act to snap the jaw shut rapidly. The strong capiti-mandibularis muscle would make the bite more powerful and penetrating. After wrenching and tearing at the food, the depressor mandibulae muscle would pull to make the mouth open wide again.

Bony ring supporting eyeball (sclerotic ossicles)

Nostril

Backwardly curved teeth

Depressor mandibulae muscle

Jaw joint

Capiti-mandibularis muscle

Pterygoideus muscle

Lower jaw mandible

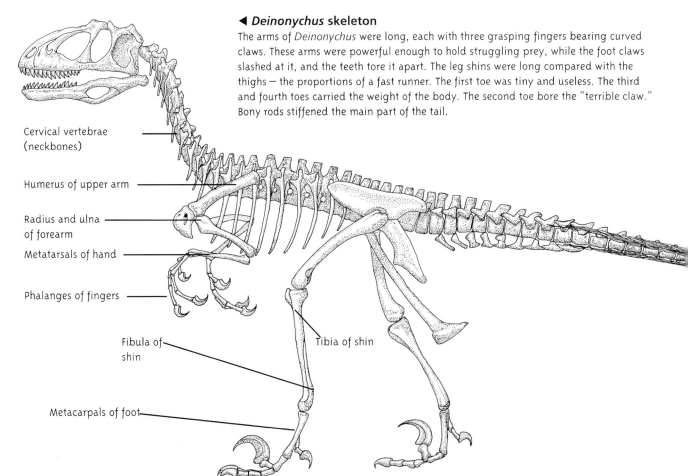

◄ *Deinonychus* skeleton

The arms of *Deinonychus* were long, each with three grasping fingers bearing curved claws. These arms were powerful enough to hold struggling prey, while the foot claws slashed at it, and the teeth tore it apart. The leg shins were long compared with the thighs — the proportions of a fast runner. The first toe was tiny and useless. The third and fourth toes carried the weight of the body. The second toe bore the "terrible claw." Bony rods stiffened the main part of the tail.

Cervical vertebrae (neckbones)

Humerus of upper arm

Radius and ulna of forearm

Metatarsals of hand

Phalanges of fingers

Fibula of shin

Tibia of shin

Metacarpals of foot

DATA BASE

Name	*Deinonychus*
Pronounced	DAY-non-EE-kus
Meaning	"terrible claw"

What it ate Meat-eater, hunting smaller victims alone or banding together as a pack to tackle larger prey such as big herbivorous dinosaurs

Length	10-13 feet (3-4 meters)
Standing height	6 feet (1.8 meters)
Weight	about 150 pounds (68 kilograms)

When it lived	Early-Middle Cretaceous Period 115-110 million years ago
Where it lived	North America (Montana, Wyoming)

Order	Saurischia (lizard-hipped dinosaurs)
Suborder	Theropoda
Family	Dromaeosauridae

The kick-slash

The leg bones and muscles of *Deinonychus* were designed for kicking out and making the claw curve in a slashing arc (see page 155). The ischio-trochantericus muscle would pull the leg back ready to kick. The ilio-femoralis muscle would raise the thigh. The femoro-tibialis muscle would straighten the knee and raise the shin to make the foot kick forward. The gastrocnemius muscle pulled on the foot to straighten the ankle as well. The flexor digitorum longus muscle, connected to the toes by long ropelike tendons, bent the second toe, and so the claw slashed in its arc.

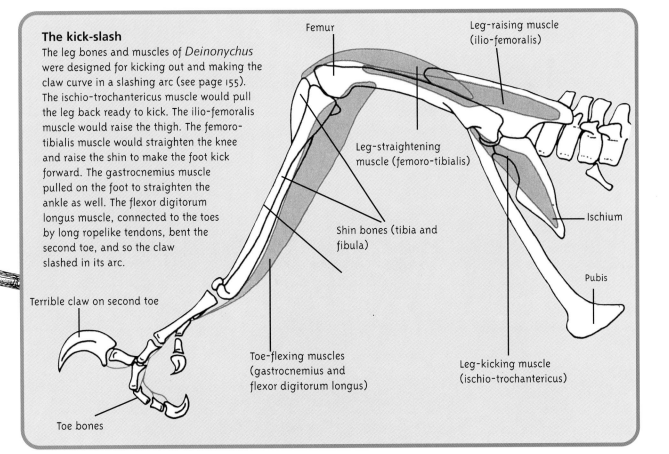

Femur

Leg-raising muscle (ilio-femoralis)

Leg-straightening muscle (femoro-tibialis)

Ischium

Shin bones (tibia and fibula)

Pubis

Terrible claw on second toe

Toe-flexing muscles (gastrocnemius and flexor digitorum longus)

Leg-kicking muscle (ischio-trochantericus)

Toe bones

Velociraptor

The "speedy predator" has become one of the best-known of all dinosaurs, partly thanks to the starring role of its close relatives in blockbuster movies!

The remains of *Velociraptor* were first found in Mongolia during large fossil-hunting expeditions there in the 1920s. Like those of *Dromaeosaurus*, they were identified as a theropod – either a large coelurosaur or a small carnosaur. Then the discovery of *Deinonychus* remains established the dromaeosaur group more firmly, and *Velociraptor* took its place in that group.

Obviously a predator, it was about the size of a very large dog and would have stood chest-high to a human. It was armed with sharp teeth, finger claws, and the especially large second toe claws of its relatives. *Velociraptor* had fewer teeth than *Dromaeosaurus,* and its long, low head and snout made it look something like a crocodile.

Fight to the death

In 1971 two extraordinary fossilized animals were uncovered in the Gobi Desert of Mongolia. They were a *Velociraptor* and a *Protoceratops* apparently locked in combat. *Protoceratops* was a pig-sized, plant-eating, horned dinosaur with a protective neck frill. It was an early relative of *Triceratops* and is described in chapter 11 of this book.

◀ **Distant relatives**
Like *Deinonychus*, *Velociraptor* had a huge claw on the second toe of each foot. In general build the two animals were quite similar, apart from the low head shape and the smaller size of *Velociraptor*. However, during the Age of Dinosaurs they were separated by thousands of miles of distance (from Mongolia in Asia to Montana in North America) and also by about 30 million years of time. Possibly the descendants of *Deinonychus* found their way to Asia across the Beringia land bridge (now the Bering Strait between northeastern Russia and Alaska).

Velociraptor seemed to have its hands around the head shield of *Protoceratops* and the large claw on one foot kicking into its neck. But it also seemed that *Protoceratops* had fought back. It had crushed *Velociraptor's* ribcage with its powerful jaws and then bitten and locked its beaklike mouth into the arm of *Velociraptor* (see page 146).

Not an after-death encounter
The fossil skeletons of *Velociraptor* and *Protoceratops* are very well preserved, with many bones still joined together as they would have been in life. So it is very unlikely that the two animals died separately and came together afterward as the chance washing together of two isolated skeletons. (Compare the finding of *Deinonychus* and *Tenontosaurus*, see page 154.)

The best explanation is that these two creatures really did get into a fight to the death. Where they fell, locked together, the desert sands swept over their bodies and buried them. And there they stayed, preserved in the sand, for more than 70 million years.

Why the fatal battle?
Why – if our assumption is correct – did *Velociraptor* and *Protoceratops* engage in this deadly battle?

▲ **Meal at last**
Velociraptor finally settles down to eat its multislashed, blood-spattered victim, a small sauropod dinosaur, in this colorful reconstruction. The tigerlike stripes add to the image of this raptor as a fierce yet cunning predator.

- Perhaps the smallish predator (*Velociraptor*) was caught in the act of stealing eggs or young from the nest of the herbivore (plant-eater, *Protoceratops*). (Many fossilized nesting sites, eggs, and young of *Protoceratops* have been found in the region.)
- Possibly *Velociraptor* attempted to attack the plant-eater, but found it too strong and powerful to overcome. *Protoceratops* was less than 3 feet (1 meter) high, but it was a bulky animal weighing up to 400 pounds (180 kilograms) – four times as heavy as *Velociraptor*.
- Maybe a pack of *Velociraptor* had attacked the *Protoceratops*, and in the battle one of their number had also got killed. Then perhaps the other raptors were frightened or fought off before they could rip up and eat their prey.

◄ **Buried in the sand**
The fossil bones of *Velociraptor* and *Protoceratops* see the light of day more than 70 million years after their fatal encounter. The paleontologist puts small fragments of tooth and bone onto the board for closer study.

Star predator

About the same size as a human, *Velociraptor* was physically well equipped and would have been more than a match for one of us.

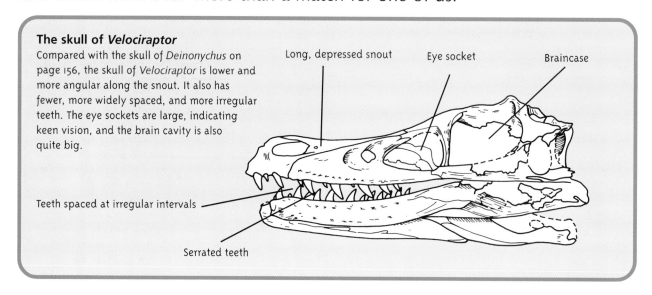

The skull of *Velociraptor*

Compared with the skull of *Deinonychus* on page 156, the skull of *Velociraptor* is lower and more angular along the snout. It also has fewer, more widely spaced, and more irregular teeth. The eye sockets are large, indicating keen vision, and the brain cavity is also quite big.

Long, depressed snout

Eye socket

Braincase

Teeth spaced at irregular intervals

Serrated teeth

▼ Camera, lights, action

Sinister red eyes add to the impression of clever cunning in the "Utah raptor," on which the *Jurassic Park* stars were modeled. The large size of the head in proportion to the body is evident in this hip-high view, about 2-3 feet (nearly 1 meter) from the ground.

Raptor hands

The talonlike finger claws of dromaeosaurs were effective weapons for holding, hooking, slashing, and tearing. Most theropods had three fingers. As they evolved, the meat-eating dinosaurs gradually tended to have fewer fingers. The early *Coelophysis* had four per hand (see page 150). The great *Tyrannosaurus*, at the very end of the Age of Dinosaurs, had only two on each hand.

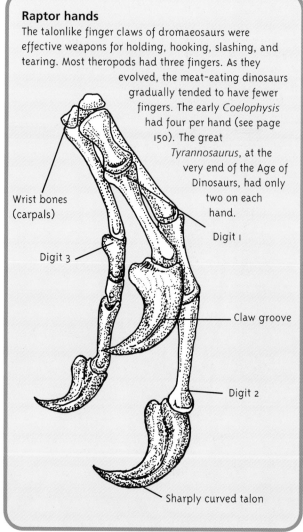

Wrist bones (carpals)

Digit 3

Digit 1

Claw groove

Digit 2

Sharply curved talon

Dinosaurs in the movies

Dinosaurs and other "prehistoric monsters" have long been big attractions in the movies. The much-mutated Godzilla, monster protector of Japan, was an early example. During the 1960s films such as *One Million Years BC* and *The Land That Time Forgot* cashed in on prehistory. They were stories of early cave-people (some of them very beautiful and dressed in fur bikinis) battling against dinosaurs, pterosaurs, and other great reptiles.

From this period too came *The Lost World* — the original version (not the second *Jurassic Park* movie) from the story by Arthur Conan Doyle, creator of the great detective Sherlock Holmes. It also starred several dinosaur-type animals, some easily recognized as modern reptiles such as lizards with extra make-up and cardboard frills glued to their bodies!

A basic problem with these dinosaur movies is that, according to scientific evidence, the last dinosaurs and the first humans were separated by a gap of more than 60 million years. *The Lost World* got around this by placing its "monsters" on a vast, cliff-edged plateau in the depths of a steamy tropical forest. Here, cut off from the rest of the world, evolution had almost stood still and dinosaurs still survived. Dinosaur movies moved into a new era of computer animation in the 1990s with *Jurassic Park*, directed by Stephen Spielberg, from the novel by Michael Crichton. The problem of the time gap between dinosaurs and humans was removed by recreating dinosaurs in today's world. This was done (in the story!) using genetic material found in dinosaur blood, which had been sucked by mosquitoes of the Mesozoic Period. The mosquitoes in turn had become trapped in amber and fossilized.

Various dinosaurs were featured, including the traditional *Tyrannosaurus*, also *Brachiosaurus*, ostrich dinosaurs, *Triceratops,* and the duckbilled hadrosaurs. However, the undoubted stars of *Jurassic Park* were the raptors. Modeled on *Deinonychus* and a larger version of *Velociraptor,* they were fast, agile, lethal — and also clever, cunning, organized, and a match for humans.

DATA BASE

Name	*Velociraptor*	
Pronounced	VEL-oss-ee-RAP-tor	
Meaning	"speedy predator"	

What it ate Meat-eater, possibly hunting smaller victims or cooperating in packs to kill large prey

Length (to tail-tip) 6 feet (1.8 meters)
Standing height 4.5 feet (1.4 meters)
Weight 100 pounds (45 kilograms) (Larger specimens of a similar dinosaur up to 11 feet (3.4 meters) long and 6 feet (1.8 meters) tall have also been discovered)

When it lived Late Cretaceous Period 80-70 million years ago
Where it lived Asia (Mongolia)

Order Saurischia (lizard-hipped dinosaurs)
Suborder Theropoda
Family Dromaeosauridae

The ostrich dinosaurs ▶

The ostrich dinosaurs

The tall, slim, beak-mouthed "ostrich dinosaurs" were a specialized group of theropods that included some of the fastest-running of all dinosaurs.

The last major group of small-medium theropods to appear during the Age of Dinosaurs was the ornithomimosaurs. The name means "bird-mimic lizards," but these dinosaurs do not resemble just any birds. They are commonly called the ostrich dinosaurs because they have the body build and proportions of today's ostriches and indeed of emus and similar large, flightless, fast-running birds. Ostrich dinosaurs did not have wings for front limbs, as ostriches do. They had small but strong arms with grasping, sharp-clawed fingers.

Another ostrichlike feature of the ostrich dinosaurs was the toothless, horny, beak-type mouth. They were the only theropod dinosaurs, apart from the oviraptosaurs, that lacked teeth.

Running across the plains
In North America and Asia during the Middle to Late Cretaceous Period, the ostrich dinosaurs roamed dry, scrubby terrain and lived lifestyles similar to the flightless birds of today. On their long back legs they jogged and sprinted across open plains in groups with their young. The horny beak probably snapped up small

▲ Racing along
The ostrich is one of the fastest runners in the whole animal kingdom and certainly the quickest on two legs. Its similarity to the ostrich dinosaurs is remarkable, especially in the concentration of muscles around the hip region, leaving the long legs very lightweight.

◄ Walking along
Great running speed was a new feature that ostrich dinosaurs like *Ornithomimus* brought to the Age of Dinosaurs. Huge predators such as *Tyrannosaurus* may have been able to run almost as fast, but their speed relative to body size was much lower than in the ostrich dinosaurs.

Pecking at shoots and fruit
Ostrich dinosaurs had an advantage over the ostrich of today. They could use their arms and hands to hold and pull, whereas the ostrich's wings cannot do this. Perhaps the dinosaurs were browsers. They drew twigs and branches down toward the mouth to nip off soft buds, juicy shoots, and fresh fruit. Or they could snatch small animals from the twigs and branches.

invertebrate animals like insects and worms, also small vertebrates such as frogs and other amphibians, little reptiles, birds and their eggs, and small mammals. The ostrich dinosaurs may have also eaten seeds, nuts, berries and other fruit, and shoots and other plant food. In fact, like the ostrich today, the ostrich dinosaurs were probably omnivores, snapping up and gulping down almost anything edible.

Early bird-mimics
Fossils of ornithomimosaurs have been found mainly in eastern Asia and western North America. One of the most primitive or ancient types was *Harpymimus*, known from a partial skeleton and skull fragment unearthed in Mongolia. It still had teeth – although very small and not much use – in the front of its lower jaw. They were presumably an evolutionary leftover from its ancestors, the coelurosaurs. *Harpymimus* also had primitive features in its hands and feet. It lived in the Early Cretaceous Period.

More early ostrich dinosaurs
Fossils of another very early ornithomimosaur have been found in Victoria, Australia. This area would have been below the Antarctic Circle in the Early Cretaceous Period, with an average yearly temperature of only about

50F (10°C). This and other fossil discoveries at the "Dinosaur Cove" region near Melbourne are described more fully in chapter 5 of this book.

Early Cretaceous fossils of ostrich dinosaurs have also been found in southern and eastern Africa. And in 1994 remains of the ostrich dinosaur *Pelicanimimus* were discovered in Spain and dated at 115 million years old. The *Pelicanimimus* group of ostrich dinosaurs is already known from Asia and North America, but the fossils there are less that 100 million years old. The Spanish version had 200 tiny teeth, each only the size of a grain of rice, in its very long, narrow jaws. Later members of the *Pelicanimimus* group had no teeth at all.

At the find in Spain the fine-grained limestone rock had also preserved the outline of a loose, balloonlike bag of skin below the lower jaw. This was presumably the dinosaur's throat pouch, much like the stretchy chin pouch of today's pelican – hence the name *Pelicanimimus*.

Late arrivals
The later ostrich dinosaurs, described over the following pages, lived mainly in North America. Their ancestors had probably come from Asia across the Beringia land bridge (now the Bering Strait between Alaska and Siberia).

⇒ Introduction to the hadrosaurs

During the Age of Dinosaurs the ornithopods or "bird-footed" dinosaurs were large and common plant-eaters. They must have dominated the landscape then, just as antelopes, gazelles, zebras, and other large herbivores throng the African plains today.

One of the biggest subgroups of ornithopods was the hadrosaurs. They are also known as the "duckbilled dinosaurs." They were among the most recent, most varied, most numerous, and most exciting of all dinosaurs.

The Age of Dinosaurs lasted more than 150 million years – from about 220 to 65 million years ago. Some groups of dinosaurs survived through much of this time. They gradually evolved, changing to cope with the varying climate, the comings and goings of other dinosaurs, and other kinds of animals and plants.

Not the hadrosaurs. They appeared fairly near the end of the Age of Dinosaurs, less than 100 million years ago. But they evolved, spread, multiplied, and diversified with astonishing speed. They have been described as the most successful of all dinosaur groups.

Revolutionary ideas

Hadrosaurs are fascinating for several reasons. Not only did they live in herds, but they had complex social lives. It is possible that they competed for dominance of the group and carried out courtship displays for mates. They set up breeding sites and made nests there. And they cared for their offspring.

The ornithopods

The hadrosaurs were members of the much larger dinosaur group, the Ornithopoda ("bird-feet"), so named because their feet and toes look like the feet and toes of today's birds. They were the "standard herbivores" of the time. Other groups of ornithopods included:

* fabrosaurs such as *Lesothosaurus* or *Fabrosaurus*, although they can also be viewed as an earlier and separate group;
* heterodontosaurs, including *Heterodontosaurus*;
* hypsilophodonts such as *Hypsilophodon*;
* dryosaurs such as *Dryosaurus*;
* camptosaurs including *Camptosaurus*;
* iguanodonts, especially one of the best-known of all dinosaurs, *Iguanodon*, and also the sail-backed *Ouranosaurus*.
  These other members of the Ornithopoda group lived at various times through almost the entire
Age of Dinosaurs. As cousins of the hadrosaurs they are described in Chapter 7.

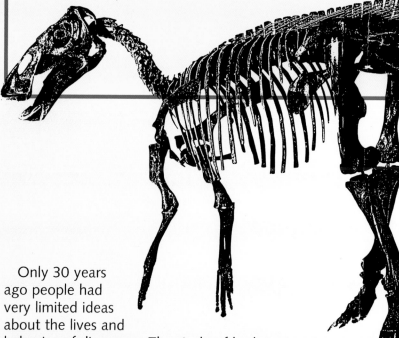

◄ Duckbilled dinosaur
Remains of many specimens of *Edmontosaurus* have been uncovered in western North America.

Only 30 years ago people had very limited ideas about the lives and behavior of dinosaurs. The study of hadrosaurs has changed our way of thinking about the Age of Dinosaurs and the prehistoric world. It has also led to exciting discoveries and new proposals about other dinosaur groups.

Were the duckbills water-dwellers?

Hadrosaurs were once thought to be excellent swimmers and live partly in the water – that is, they were amphibious. In the case of Hadrosaurus this was suggested more than a century ago (see page 170).There were several reasons for this, including:
* their ducklike beaks;
* head crests that could work as tubes or snorkels for breathing underwater;
* a deep, paddlelike tail, similar to a crocodile's, for swishing and swimming;
* apparently webbed fingers.
  However, the mainly water-dwelling lifestyle

is now doubted because:
* the duckbill is thought to be more like the tough, sharp-edged, continuously growing mouth of a turtle, suitable for snipping and clipping vegetation rather than dabbling;
* the breathing passages inside the head crests would not work underwater, since they would become flooded or clogged;
* for swimming the rear body, hips, and tail have to be able to swish from side to side, but the bone and joint structure in that region may have been too stiff for that;
* the finger webs were probably walking pads, like cushions, to absorb the weight of the front body.
  In addition, the remains of other plants and animals found with fossils of hadrosaurs indicate a life based on land (terrestrial), not water. However, they may have taken to the water to avoid predators .

About the "duckbills"

The hadrosaurs, or "duckbills," are named from the shape of their mouths. But although outwardly the mouth looks like a duck's beak or bill, there is an enormous difference within.

The front of a typical hadrosaur's mouth was like a duck's beak. It was made of tough horn, wide and outward-turning, flattened from top to bottom, and lacking teeth.

However, the similarity is only partial. A duck has no teeth at all. A hadrosaur, on the other hand, had in its cheeks hundreds of rasping, self-sharpening teeth that could cope with the tough vegetation of the Late Cretaceous Period.

Size and shape

Hadrosaurs were generally around 30-40 feet (9-12 meters) long from nose-tip to tail-end. They weighed between 2 and 5 tons (2-5.1 tonnes), about as heavy as today's African elephants.

In body shape and structure the hadrosaurs were similar to the very well-studied ornithopod *Iguanodon*. They probably ran on their two longer, stronger rear legs, but could stoop to walk on all fours.

Hadrosaurs were the last main group of ornithopods ("bird-footed" dinosaurs) to evolve. Indeed, they were among the last of all main dinosaur groups to appear, except for the meat-eating tyrannosaurs, including terrible *Tyrannosaurus* itself.

Hadrosaur family 1: Hadrosauridae

These hadrosaurs, known as the hadrosaurids, are sometimes called "flatheaded duckbills." Some did indeed have flat heads, that is, they did not have protrusions, extensions, or crests of bone on top of the head. Others had protrusions or crests, but of solid (not hollow) bone. They were among the first and last of the hadrosaurs and similar in many respects to the iguanodontids from which the hadrosaurs probably evolved.

Hadrosaur family 2: Lambeosauridae

The lambeosaurids were "hollow-crested duckbills." They had bony head crests or adornments that were hollow or tubular. The animals were common especially during the Middle-Late Cretaceous Period but began to fade out near the very end of the Cretaceous. There are further differences in the hipbones and backbones of the two families.

Main features of a hadrosaur
This reconstruction of the hadrosaur *Maiasaura* shows the main features of the group. This particular kind is a hadrosaurid. Most of the features are explained and discussed on later pages.

Heavy, deep tail to balance head and body over legs

Strong hind legs for bipedal (two-footed) walking

Evolution and spread

The first hadrosaurs evolved about 100 million years ago. The group rapidly developed a huge variety of species and spread across all northern continents. However, they were mostly absent from the Southern Hemisphere. This was probably because of continental drift and the different positions of the earth's landmasses.

In some classification schemes the hadrosaurs are split into two "families," the hadrosaurids and the lambeosaurids, as described above. In other schemes, the lambeosaurids are classed as a subfamily of the hadrosaurids.

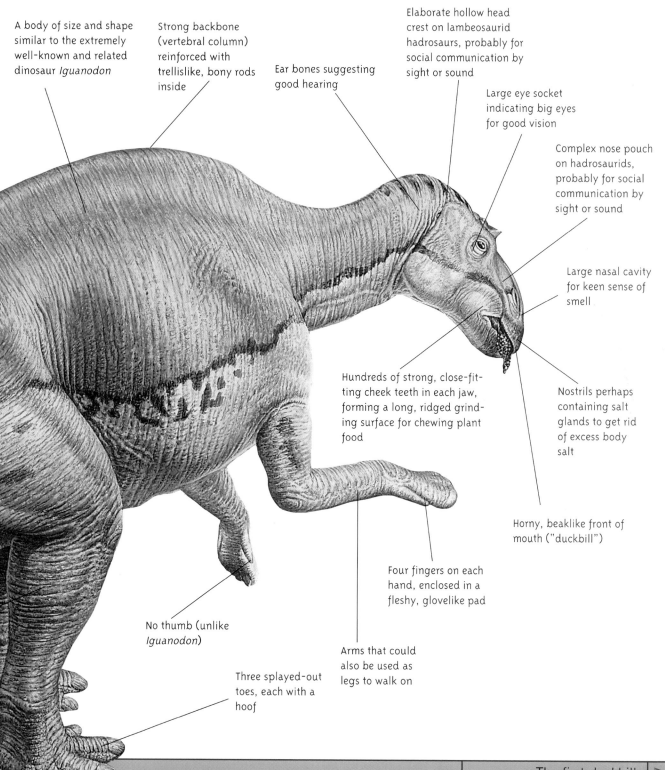

A body of size and shape similar to the extremely well-known and related dinosaur *Iguanodon*

Strong backbone (vertebral column) reinforced with trellislike, bony rods inside

Ear bones suggesting good hearing

Elaborate hollow head crest on lambeosaurid hadrosaurs, probably for social communication by sight or sound

Large eye socket indicating big eyes for good vision

Complex nose pouch on hadrosaurids, probably for social communication by sight or sound

Large nasal cavity for keen sense of smell

Hundreds of strong, close-fitting cheek teeth in each jaw, forming a long, ridged grinding surface for chewing plant food

Nostrils perhaps containing salt glands to get rid of excess body salt

Horny, beaklike front of mouth ("duckbill")

No thumb (unlike *Iguanodon*)

Four fingers on each hand, enclosed in a fleshy, glovelike pad

Arms that could also be used as legs to walk on

Three splayed-out toes, each with a hoof

The first duckbills

The hadrosaurs' key to success may have been their ability to eat the new kinds of plants that were spreading like wildfire across the globe. This was the type of vegetation that dominates our world today – the flowering plants.

The Age of Dinosaurs spanned most of the Mesozoic ("middle life") Era, which included the Triassic, Jurassic, and Cretaceous Periods.

During the Cretaceous Period in particular there were enormous changes in the natural world. The supercontinents of Laurasia and Gondwana began to split into the continents that we know today.

Also, the fossil record shows that a vast new group of plants was appearing. They were the flowering plants, or angiosperms. Today they are the dominant plant life. They include our familiar flowers, blossoms, herbs, grasses, bushes, and nonconifer trees.

A new landscape

During the Middle-Late Cretaceous Period flowering plants spread fast and took over many regions from the previously widespread nonflowering plants, such as conifers, cycads, horsetails, and ferns. Early types of flowering plants included magnolias and waterlilies. We can imagine that their bright petals brought fresh colors to a landscape that had before been mainly shades of green and brown.

Coping with the new foods

As the flowering plants evolved, they developed all kinds of defensive strategies against being eaten by herbivorous animals. They included tough, woody stems coated with hard bark and fibrous, stringy leaves and fruits. A herbivore eating them had to chew thoroughly to break them down into a soupy pulp that it could digest more easily. The hadrosaurs evolved to do just this.

Bodily features

Bactrosaurus was one of the earliest known hadrosaurs. It still had many features of its iguanodontid ancestors, especially in its general body shape. It was relatively small, some specimens being perhaps only 13 feet (4 meters) long. There are no good fossils of its hands, so it is not known if this dinosaur had lost the thumb-spike that is a trademark of the iguanodontid group.

Massed ranks of teeth

Iguanodontid dinosaurs such as *Iguanodon* had lots of cheek teeth with which they could chew. But this design was improved still further in *Bactrosaurus*, which had more teeth arranged in rows. *Bactrosaurus* was one of the first creatures to have these typically hadrosaur "teeth batteries."

◀ **A new sight**
Early hadrosaurs such as *Bactrosaurus* were an exciting addition to the Middle Cretaceous landscape some 100 million years ago.

▲ **Duckbills' cousin**
A reconstruction of *Iguanodon*, which was one of the cousins of the hadrosaurs.

Part of the reason why this was an improvement was the way that the teeth and jawbones moved. As powerful muscles pulled the lower jaw up, the cheek region just above on it on each side of the skull opened or tilted outward thanks to a hinge on the side of the face. This allowed the lower jaw to rise almost within the skull. The surfaces of the lower teeth, which faced outward, rubbed past the surfaces of the upper teeth, which faced inward.

Ground to a pulp

The teeth had ridges running from front to back – that is, at right angles to the up-down movement of the teeth. So the plant material crushed between the upper and lower teeth was ground and scraped as if between two filing tools. The marks on the jaw and skull, where the chewing muscles were anchored, show that these muscles were extremely powerful. Fleshy cheek pouches kept the food in the mouth as it was being crushed.

A new type of dinosaur

Bactrosaurus had a low, flat head, with no lumpy protrusion or crest. This is a feature of the hadrosaurid family of hadrosaurs. However, in general build and other details, *Bactrosaurus* was more similar to the lambeosaurid family of hadrosaurs, such as *Corythosaurus* and *Parasaurolophus*.

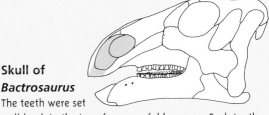

Skull of
Bactrosaurus
The teeth were set well back in the jaws for powerful leverage. Each tooth was made of layers of enamel and dentine. As it wore down with chewing, the tough enamel was lost more slowly, and so it stuck up from the teeth in ridges. This was what created the rough surface for chewing. When the teeth became too worn, they were replaced by a new battery of teeth grown from toothbuds in the bone.

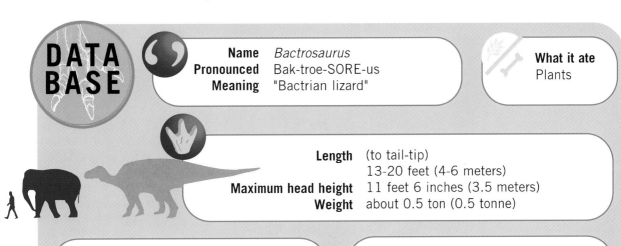

DATA BASE

Name *Bactrosaurus*
Pronounced Bak-troe-SORE-us
Meaning "Bactrian lizard"

What it ate
Plants

Length (to tail-tip)
13-20 feet (4-6 meters)
Maximum head height 11 feet 6 inches (3.5 meters)
Weight about 0.5 ton (0.5 tonne)

When it lived Middle Cretaceous Period
100 million years ago
Where it lived Asia (China)

Order Ornithischia (bird-hipped dinosaurs)
Suborder Ornithopoda
Family Lambeosauridae

⇒ The flatheaded hadrosaur

Hadrosaurus, "big lizard," was the first dinosaur to be described and named from fossils found in North America. Its remains were discovered in the 1850s in Haddonfield, New Jersey.

In 1858 fossil expert and University of Pennsylvania professor of anatomy Joseph Leidy examined the preserved bones of a giant lizardlike beast. They had been dug from a disused New Jersey marl pit by William Foulke. Leidy recognized that the teeth were similar to those of *Iguanodon*, a dinosaur known from Europe. So he proposed that the new find was another type of dinosaur.

   This was early in the history of dinosaurs as a distinct group of reptiles. The name Dinosauria had been coined only 17 years before, in 1841, by Richard Owen in London, England. Owen recognized that these great prehistoric animals were different from other reptiles, such as lizards and crocodiles. So he suggested that they should classified as a group on their own.

▲ A jumble of bones
These fossil bones from a flatheaded hadrosaur are laid out on the floor as they were excavated from the ground.

A new pose
Leidy studied the remains of several bones, including the vertebrae (backbones), hips, and limbs. He concluded that *Hadrosaurus* was partly bipedal, moving on its two rear legs, and partly quadrupedal. He drew a picture as he imagined it: running on its hind legs, with its body horizontal, balanced by its tail, and its front legs hanging loosely like arms by its sides.

   At the time this was a new idea. *Iguanodon* was still thought to be a reptilian version of a rhinoceros, with a stocky build and four legs of much the same length.

Wading in the shallows?
Like many others since, Leidy thought that *Hadrosaurus* was amphibious, spending time on land and in the water. This was mainly because of its posture (as researchers imagined it) and its deep, paddlelike tail, resembling a crocodile's. In the 1870s-80s Edward Drinker Cope went further with the amphibious theme. He suggested that *Hadrosaurus* was a great reptilian wader, with a ducklike beak for scooping up soft, aquatic vegetation.

However, these views are no longer popular

Always new teeth

Like its close relative *Kritosaurus*, *Hadrosaurus* had a bump on its nose but nothing that could be called a proper crest. It had the typical hadrosaur toothless beak and, further back in its jaws, hundreds of closely packed cheek teeth for chewing. As in most other dinosaurs, they were continually replaced, so there was always a sharp rasping surface to grind up plant food.

Family differences

The two families of hadrosaurs, the hadrosaurids and lambeosaurids, had obvious differences in their skulls (see page 166). There

Top of skull

Wide beak or bill Eye socket

Narrow snout

The broad beak

The view from above of the skull of *Edmontosaurus* shows how the front of the mouth was flattened and splayed outward to form the wide "duckbill." The snout narrows behind it, then widens into the main part of the head with the eyes, brain, and massive batteries of cheek teeth.

Jaws and teeth

The diagram below shows a vertical cross-section, or "slice," through a hadrosaur head from one side to the other. The grinding surfaces of the lower teeth (right) face up and out and meet the surfaces of the upper teeth, which face down and in.

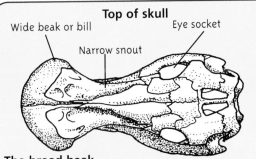

Cross-section through jaw

- Nostril
- Upper jaw
- Upper teeth
- Lower teeth
- Lower jaw

Lower jaw and teeth

Rasplike grinding surface

Tooth battery

Coronoid process

Jaw joint

Predentary bone

were also differences in the hipbones and backbones of the two families.

- In most lambeosaurids the ischium (the lower, rear-facing part of the hipbone or pelvis) ended in a structure that was like a foot or a hook; in hadrosaurids it was more like a rod.
- In lambeosaurids the pubis (front part of the hipbone) swelled out at the end into a platelike structure; in hadrosaurids it did not.
- The vertebral spines, which are the upward extensions of the backbones (vertebrae), were generally taller in lambeosaurids than in hadrosaurids.

DATA BASE

Name	*Hadrosaurus*
Pronounced	HAD-row-SORE-us
Meaning	"big lizard"

What it ate

Plants of various kinds

Length	30 feet (9.1 meters)
Maximum head height	13-14 feet (around 4 meters)
Weight	about 3 tons (3 tonnes)

When it lived	Late Cretaceous Period 80 million years ago
Where it lived	U.S. (New Jersey)

Order	Ornithischia (bird-hipped dinosaurs)
Suborder	Ornithopoda
Family	Hadrosauridae

⇨ Hadrosaur family life

Some of the most exciting of all dinosaur discoveries involve the hadrosaur *Maiasaura*. The existence of preserved nesting sites, eggs, and babies suggests that dinosaurs cared for their young.

In 1978 the locality of Bynum, Montana, in the foothills to the east of the Rocky Mountains, became the focus of world dinosaur study. Digging in the hills nearby uncovered one of the most amazing dinosaur sites ever found. From it have come the fossilized remains of thousands of dinosaurs, along with their nests, eggs, and offspring, from about 75 million years ago.

The main hadrosaur represented at the site is *Maiasaura*, the "good mother lizard." Another type of dinosaur found there is, like the hadrosaurs, a member of the ornithopod group. This is the hypsilophodont named *Orodromeus* (see chapter 7 above). A third type is the small predatory dinosaur *Troodon*.

◀ **Hi, mom!**
An adult *Maiasaura* peers over the edge of the scooped-out nest containing its newly hatched youngsters.

Adults, nests, eggs, and babies

An early find at the *Maiasaura* site was the fossilized skeleton of an adult, together with mound-shaped nests, fossil whole eggs, egg fragments – and 15 young dinosaurs only some 3 feet (1 meter) long.

The youngsters were probably not newly hatched. They had well-worn teeth, so they must have eaten food since emerging from their eggs. Their size, too, suggested they had been out of their shells for some time. Yet their remains were in and around the nest.

Staying at home

The conclusion was that the youngsters had hatched from their eggs and then remained in the nest. Since they needed food, it must have been brought to the nest. From similar nesting situations today in related animals we can assume that an adult brought the food, that it was an adult of their own species, that it was one of their parents, and that the parent was probably the mother.

Revolutionary ideas

These conclusions shook the late-1970s world of dinosaur study. Could some dinosaurs really have protected their eggs and been caring parents? Around the same time other pieces of

◀ **Nest among the leaves**
A *Maiasaura* hatchling breaks out of its eggshell, which has broken into many fragments. Another nestling is beginning to hatch out.

evidence were suggesting yet more revolutionary ideas. Some dinosaurs could have been warm-blooded, active, and intelligent. The traditional view of dinosaurs as slow, simple, cold-blooded creatures was being challenged to the core.

Other animal parents

In hindsight, perhaps the notion that dinosaurs cared for their offspring was not so strange. Many types of crocodiles, alligators, and caimans do this today. These animals are some of the closest living relatives of the dinosaurs. Again, we have only to think of the thousands of species of birds that are among the most active and devoted parents in the whole animal kingdom. And birds are also close relatives of dinosaurs, probably having evolved from certain smallish, meat-eating types such as the raptors (see chapters 5 and 8).

Nest construction

Since those early *Maiasaura* finds in the late 1970s thousands more fossilized specimens of this hadrosaur have been discovered. They include adults, more nests, and hatchlings (just-hatched young) only about 20 inches (50 centimeters) long.

The remains of the nests indicate that they were made in dry upland areas. Each was bowl-shaped and dug into the fine soil. Scooped-up earth formed a craterlike, raised nest platform and retaining wall, rather like a wide-mouthed, flattened volcano.

Each nest was about 10 feet (3 meters) in diameter, including the wall, and some 5 feet (1.5 meters) high. The craterlike depression in the middle was 6-7 feet (1.8-2 meters) across and 30 inches (75 centimeters) deep.

The breeding colony

There were signs that the nest had been redug year after year. This implies that individuals returned and scooped out their old nests to use for the current breeding season. So the nest site was visited, perhaps once each year –

▶ **Many new lives**
A reconstruction of a *Maiasaura* nest modeled on the site discovered in Montana, where layer upon layer of nests have been found.

just as some seabirds and birds of prey return to their regular nesting sites.

The nests were spaced quite regularly, about 25 feet (7 meters) apart. This is approximately the length of an adult *Maiasaura*. The image this gives us is of a nesting colony of these dinosaurs where each parent (or parents) tended its own eggs on a nest that was just out of reach of the immediate neighbors. That way the animals would avoid close contact and perhaps conflict.

Eggs in the nest

A female *Maiasaura* laid about 20 long, oval eggs, arranged in a circle, in layers one above the other. Probably the nest was lined with plants first, then each layer of eggs was covered with earth or sand and perhaps rotting vegetation too, for protection and warmth. As the vegetation decomposed, it would give off heat (like a rotting garden compost heap) that would help the eggs incubate or develop.

It is tempting to imagine that the parent checked and controlled the temperature of the eggs, as some birds do today, such as the mallee fowl and the emu of Australia. The parent *Maiasaura* could shade the nest from noon sunshine to prevent the eggs from becoming overheated. During a cool spell it might replace or add to the rotting plant matter to provide more warmth.

⇒ Hadrosaur growth

Maiasaura seem to have been efficient breeders and fast growers.

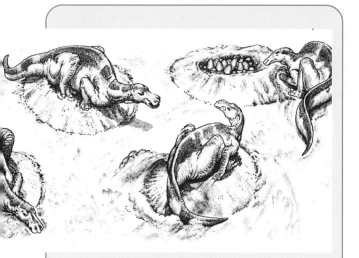

On the nests

In this combined scene four *Maiasaura* adults — presumably females — carry out different nesting activities at their colonial site. The individual lower right is digging out her nest, renovating last year's crumbling structure for the new season. The adult upper right has laid her eggs and is about to cover them with earth and vegetation. The female upper left takes up a defensive posture, neck craned and head ready to bite, to keep the others from her nest and its small patch of territory. The individual lower left rests after her trip away from the nest to feed.

▲ Juvenile *Maiasaura* skeleton

Like the young of many other animals, the juvenile *Maiasaura* had different bodily proportions from the adult. The head was larger, with a higher forehead and larger eyes, but a shorter snout and flatter mouth — the typical "baby face." The limbs were more slender too.

Timed breeding

Possibly the *Maiasaura* would time their breeding so that it happened during the warmest part of the year, when plants would flourish. (The climate was subtropical during the Cretaceous Period in central North America.) The parents gathered plenty of food for their young, who then grew very rapidly. Today's reptiles do the same in response to environmental conditions and the amount of food available. If food is scarce, they grow more slowly, or even stop growing. In times of plenty they develop much faster.

Running with the herd

So, in good conditions baby *Maiasaura* would develop rapidly. Support for this idea comes from their fossil bones. They do not show clear evidence of growth rings. Such rings occur when development happens in phases, perhaps seasonally or yearly (much like the annual growth rings seen in cut tree trunks). The young hadrosaurs could have done their early growing in one spurt, perhaps in one breeding season. They would soon be big and strong enough to journey with the herd.

Fast growth = warm blood?

What else does the fast growth of *Maiasaura* babies tell us? Some experts suggest that such

▼ **Smothered to death**

A *Maiasaura* herd is smothered by a fall of ash from a nearby volcanic eruption.

Adult *Maiasaura*

The adult *Maiasaura* was a fairly standard hadrosaurid reaching almost 30 feet (over 9 meters) in total length. It had a head rather like a horse's, a broad duckbill, powerful jaws, and batteries of rasping teeth. There was a solid, bony, hornlike crest above the eyes, which males may have used when contesting for females. The forelimbs were not especially strong or sturdy.

rapid growth would be faster than the rate found in almost any reptile today. It would have been more similar to the growth rates of birds and mammals – animals that have a higher rate of metabolism (body chemistry) because they are warm-blooded. This gives scientists reason to think that some dinosaurs may have been warm-blooded. This fascinating idea is explored in other books in this series (see chapters 5 and 9).

Fossilized eggs and other evidence of the small predatory dinosaur *Troodon* complete the picture. It was probably an opportunistic meat-eater, which followed the herbivore herds, bred on the fringes of their colonies, and snatched their eggs and babies to feed itself and perhaps its own offspring.

DATA BASE

Name	*Maiasaura*
Pronounced	MY-ah-SORE-ah
Meaning	"good mother lizard"

What it ate
Plants – ferns, palms, cycads

Length	26-29 feet (8-9 meters)
Maximum head height	14 feet (4.2 meters)
Weight	2-3 tons (2-3 tonnes)

When it lived	Late Cretaceous Period
	80-75 million years ago
Where it lived	U.S. (Montana)

Order	Ornithischia (bird-hipped dinosaurs)
Suborder	Ornithopoda
Family	Hadrosauridae

→ The crested hadrosaurs

The second main group or family of hadrosaurs was the lambeosaurids. Some of these dinosaurs had amazingly elaborate, hollow crests and other shapes on their heads. Why?

The two main families of hadrosaurs were the "flatheaded duckbills," or hadrosaurids, as described on previous pages, and the "hollow-crested duckbills," or lambeosaurids, which are shown on the following pages. Some of the major differences between the families are described on pages 166 and 171.

The lambeosaurids are named after one of their main family members, *Lambeosaurus*. The bony shapes on their heads contained air passages linked to the nostrils. These airways were primarily for breathing, but in the lambeosaurids they may well have had other uses – especially making loud noises as a way of communicating.

Origins of the "hollow crests"

These two families of dinosaurs are both commonly referred to as hadrosaurs. But were they closely related? In particular, did they have the same ancestors?

Perhaps. The two families appeared at about the same time, around 100 million years ago. *Probactrosaurus* may resemble a link between the ancestral iguanodontids and the early hadrosaurids. Then the lambeosaurids may have arisen from the early hadrosaurids.

Alternatively, the lambeosaurids could have evolved separately from the hadrosaurids. Their ancestors may have been another group of iguanodontids, which included the "sail-backed" *Ouranosaurus* (see chapter 7).

A mixed beast?

Tanius, sometimes called *Tsintaosaurus*, is one of the most unusual and controversial hadrosaurs. Indeed, it may not even have existed at all.

Tanius/Tsintaosaurus was a primitive hadrosaur, similar in some ways to *Saurolophus*. However, its skull appears, at first sight, to be fairly typical of the hadrosaurids such as *Edmontosaurus*. *Tanius/Tsintaosaurus* also had an extremely distinctive and unmissable feature: the tall, hollow, bony, tubelike "horn" atop its head - like that of the mythical unicorn.

Typically hadrosaur?

Tanius/Tsintaosaurus had the usual hadrosaur features of strong back legs, smaller front legs, bipedal stance, and heavy tail. It also had the typical slender, toothless, ducklike bill at the front of its jaws and rows of grinding cheek teeth at the back. However, the strange, tubelike horn on the head was anything but typical — but then, as explained opposite, we cannot be sure that it was a head horn at all!

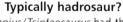

Reasons for the head horn

What was the horn for? Its thin bone was far too fragile to be a defensive weapon, as in today's rhinoceros or antelopes. There are many suggestions:

- The horn may have been covered in brightly colored skin and served as a visual signal, rather like a flagpole without the flag.
- The horn, with its strangely expanded, notched tip, may have supported a "flag" – a flap or pouch of skin. It could have stretched from horn-tip to snout-tip, like the sail of a yacht.
- Since the base of the horn was linked to the air passages in the nostril, the skin pouch may have been inflated like a balloon and used as a colorful visual signal or for making bellowing noises, or both.

But we know very little about *Tanius/Tsintaosaurus*, for example:

- It is possible that the jumbled fossil bones, skull, and horn of *Tanius/Tsintaosaurus* have been reassembled incorrectly. In all other hollow-crested hadrosaurs, such as *Parasaurolophus*, the crest points or slopes backward. Perhaps the hornlike crest of *Tanius/Tsintaosaurus* did so too.
- It is possible that the horn did belong to *Tanius/Tsintaosaurus*, but that it came from a different part of its body, not its head.

- The horn was found associated with fossils of *Tanius/Tsintaosaurus*, but it could be that this was merely a coincidence, and that the horn in fact came from a completely different animal!

If we take these doubts into account, there's no longer much point in trying to work out what the so-called "head horn" of *Tanius/Tsintaosaurus* was for!

▼ **The unicorn dinosaur**
The strange head tube was made of thin bone, fragile and easily broken in its exposed position on the head.

DATA BASE

Name	*Tanius/Tsintaosaurus*
Pronounced	TAN-i-us/Tsin-TAY-oh-SORE-us
Meaning	"of the Tan"/"Tsintao lizard"

 What it ate
Plants

Length	23-33 feet (7-10 meters)
Maximum head height	13-14 feet (4-4.3 meters)
Weight	about 1 ton (1 tonne)

When it lived	Late Cretaceous Period 70 million years ago
Where it lived	Asia (China)

Order	Ornithischia (bird-hipped dinosaurs)
Suborder	Ornithopoda
Family	Lambeosauridae? Hadrosauridae?

Life in the hadrosaur herd

Western North America near the end of the Cretaceous Period could have been a colorful and noisy place, as huge herds of brightly crested hadrosaurs bellowed, trumpeted, and honked their way across the landscape.

Fossil finds of skeletons and other body parts and extensive trackways of preserved footprints indicate that many kinds of hadrosaurs lived in herds. They may have numbered thousands of individuals. The head crests and other body parts provide some clues to the ways in which these dinosaurs carried out their social lives.

Who's who in the herd

The evidence of herd-dwelling mammals and flock-living birds today shows that group life can involve complex social interactions. They include:

- recognizing animals of the same species;
- perhaps recognizing individuals such as close relatives or mates;
- communicating warnings in case of danger, such as approaching predators;
- calling straying youngsters back to the safety of the group;
- awareness of the position or importance of individuals in the group, that is, knowing "who's boss" – who gives orders, who receives orders, who gets to eat first, who leads the way; and so on;
- awareness of the maturity, sex, and health of individuals that might come into consideration as mates, so that courtship and breeding efforts are not wasted.

▲ Facing the hazards together

A herd of *Maiasaura* travel through a rolling cloud of ash from a volcano.

Sights

The head crests of the hadrosaurs – especially the lambeosaurids – could have been useful for herd-dwelling in several ways.

- The size, shape, and color of the crest could serve as a marker for a particular species, allowing hadrosaurs to identify members of their own or other species in a mixed herd.
- The crest's size, shape, and color could also work as a personal marker, much like a fingerprint or flag. It would allow others to pick out an individual from the group.
- The appearance of the crest could signify a male, female, or juvenile. It would help at breeding time and also if the dinosaurs lived in family groups.
- All of these bright colors and patterns

would be little use unless the animals had good eyesight. The fossil skulls of hadrosaurs have large eye sockets or orbits, presumably for large eyes, indicating good vision.

Sounds

- The size and shape of the crest and especially the size and design of the air chambers and tubes inside would permit each species of hadrosaur to make its own type of sounds.
- In addition, if each individual in a species had a crest that was slightly different from any other individual's, it would be able to make its own unique sounds. Just as we can pick out and identify the voices of individual people, hadrosaurs could identify individual herd members from their unique loud, resonating calls.
- The males and the females would probably make slightly different sounds, so the males could make mating calls to females at courting time.
- Even in hadrosaurs that had no crests, they could probably use their inflatable nasal sacs or facial skin pouches to make sounds that could be produced only by a member of that species or even by a single individual.
- Snorts, bellows, trumpetings, and other noises would be little use unless the animals had good hearing. Apparently hadrosaurs did, since several fossils have been found with the ear bones present.

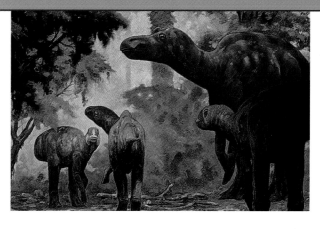

▲ Common senses
Maiasaura adults and juveniles probably communicated with each other by sights, sounds, and smell.

Smells

- The very large nasal passages could have given hadrosaurs an extremely keen sense of smell. This would mean they could use scent as well as sight and sound to recognize other animals.
- The hollowed-out areas at the nostrils in the front of the skull could have been salt glands. They would rid the body of excess salts and other minerals. Or it is possible that they were scent glands producing odors by which other animals could recognize the species, the animal's breeding condition, or even an individual itself.

▼◄ Eyes and ears
Creatures as different as elephants and ostriches live in groups, where many pairs of eyes and ears can help detect predators. In wooded areas where sight is less useful, sound signals become more important.

The largest crest of all ►

The largest crest of all

Parasaurolophus had the most striking crest of all the hadrosaurs. In some specimens it was almost 6 feet (nearly 2 meters) long.

The startling hollow crest of *Parasaurolophus* curved gracefully back from the top of the skull. It looked like, and indeed was once thought to be, a streamlined snorkel (underwater breathing tube). This was when scientists believed in the "amphibious hadrosaurs" theory explained on page 165. The snag in the amphibious theory is the lack of an opening at the upper end of the crest that would allow air to pass up and down it. In fact, the crest contains paired nasal passageways that run from the nostrils at the front of the snout, up the crest, then fold back on themselves and pass down again to the back of the throat.

The dinosaur trombone

As a sound-making feature, the crest in *Parasaurolophus* has been likened to a trombone. The long, thin-walled chambers would shake, or resonate, as air blew through them at a certain speed. In this way the dinosaur could call or signal to others in its family or herd (see page 178).

Another suggestion is that *Parasaurolophus* had a flap or frill of skin supported by the crest, which could have been attached to the neck and top of the back. When the dinosaur tipped its head down, the skin would be stretched and reveal its full coloration.

Protection against branches

Another possible explanation for hadrosaur crests is that they were "foliage deflectors." To run through thick vegetation, the dinosaur simply stretched its neck out, lowered its head, and charged. The crest would take the shock of impact against branches, leaves, and twigs.

◄ **Chewing needles**
Parasaurolophus could stretch upright and munch its way through conifer needles and other tough plant food. The striking tubular crest projected some 4–5 feet (120–150 cm) from the back of the head. The tall neural spines, or flanges, along this dinosaur's upper backbone supported a ridge along the top of the neck, back, and tail.

***Parasaurolophus* skeleton**
The size of the head crest of *Parasaurolophus* can be gauged from the length of this whole reconstructed skeleton, which is more than 33 feet (10 meters) long. The fairly stout front limbs would support the head and upper body as the dinosaur sniffed for low-growing food or stooped to drink at a pool. The trellislike bony rods along the sides of the vertebral spines in the backbone are clearly visible. So is the foot-shaped ending to the rear-pointing ischium bone in the hip.

DATABASE

Name *Parasaurolophus*
Pronounced Para-SORE-oh-LOAF-us
Meaning "beside-ridged lizard"

What it ate Plants

Length (To tail-tip) 33 feet (10.1 meters)
Head height 23 feet (7 meters)
Weight about 3 tons (3 tonnes)

When it lived Late Cretaceous Period 80 million years ago
Where it lived North America (Alberta, New Mexico, Utah, Alaska)

Order Ornithischia (bird-hipped dinosaurs)
Suborder Ornithopoda
Family Lambeosauridae

The horny casque- or helmetlike lump on the top of the head of a living bird, the cassowary, works in the same way. This flightless bird dwells in the dense rainforests of northeastern Australia and Papua New Guinea.

Crest variation

As in other lambeosaurid dinosaurs, there are specimens of *Parasaurolophus* with different-sized crests from the same time and place – dug from the same rock formations. They are now thought to represent males, females, and juveniles of the same species, rather than different species. The females seemed to have shorter and more curved or hooked crests.

A narrow bill

Parasaurolophus had a shorter snout than many other hadrosaurs and a narrow beak that seems suited more to nipping than grabbing. It could be an adaptation for

Female *Parasaurolophus* skull

The head crest of a (presumably) female *Parasaurolophus* is much shorter than the male's. It is also more curved or hooklike. The resonating qualities of this crest produce a higher or shriller note than a male's crest does. This difference between the crests in males and females is a secondary sexual characteristic (see page 18), also called sexual dimorphism (this means that the sexes differ in ways that are not directly connected with reproduction).

harvesting a particular kind of plant food. But its cheek teeth and jaw muscles were just as efficient as in other hadrosaurs.

▶ Nesting time

Like the other hadrosaurs, *Parasaurolophus* scooped out earth to make a bowl-shaped nest for 10-20 eggs. Juveniles may have been present at the breeding site. Compared with the reconstruction on the left, this animal has a bigger flap of skin along the bottom edge of the crest, curving around to the lower rear of the head.

Other hadrosaurs

In addition to the better-known hadrosaurs, various other "duckbilled dinosaurs" are known from less complete fossil evidence. They too roamed the Late Cretaceous world.

Many fossils of other animals, as well as preserved plants, have been found associated with the remains of various hadrosaurs. In Late Cretaceous times there were probably hollow-crested hadrosaurs (lambeosaurids) living on the lowlands close to the sea, where it was warm and damp. The crestless hadrosaurs (hadrosaurids) would have kept mainly to higher ground, where it was cooler and drier.

This difference in environmental conditions could be another reason for the evolution of the complex, hollow crests of the lambeosaurids. A series of long nasal passages, separated from the outside air by a thin layer of bone only, could work as a heat-exchange device. It would help pass heat gathered in from the surroundings into the body core of the animal and especially keep the head and all-important brain cool. The tall neural spines of the backbone may also have helped in cooling, as they did in the "sail-backed" dinosaurs such as *Ouranosaurus*.

Gilmoreosaurus

"Gilmore's lizard" was named after Charles Whitney Gilmore, a fossil expert who studied many dinosaur remains during the first part of the 20th century, and who first described this one. The remains came from Mongolia and are only fragmentary, but they suggest a Late Cretaceous small, primitive hadrosaur.

Brachylophosaurus

The "short-ridged lizard" was a hadrosaurid from the Late Cretaceous Period in North America. It was generally similar to *Maiasaura*, and its fossils have been discovered at several sites in North America, including Montana and Alberta.

Prosaurolophus

"Before-ridged lizard" was a flatheaded duckbill with a low, bony crest running forward from a knoblike protrusion on the top of the head to the tip of the broad snout. Its Late Cretaceous remains were found in Alberta and Montana, and suggest a hadrosaurid 26 feet (8 meters) long.

▼ **A small snack**
Parasaurolophus walkeri browsed on plants at head height.

▲ Full house

This may be how a *Parasurolophus* nest looked when the babies were hatching. They rested in the soil or vegetation, waiting for a parent to return with food.

▶Standing tall

In this *Prosaurolophus* skeleton the hipbone can be seen clearly between the backbone and the tops of the legs. It is standing over the broken remains of a fossilized tree stump.

Shantungosaurus

"Shantung lizard" is named after the region of China where fossils of an almost complete specimen were discovered. It was a Late Cretaceous type and similar to *Edmontosaurus* but very large – almost 50 feet (around 15 meters) long and weighing 5 tons (5 tonnes). Half of its length was the massive tail.

Hypacrosaurus

The "high-spined lizard" was a hollow-crested dinosaur from Late Cretaceous times in North America. It was about 30 feet (9 meters) long and had a half-circle head crest, lower but wider than that of *Corythosaurus*. Some of its fossils include youngsters only about 2 feet (60 centimeters) long.

⇨ Armored dinosaurs

The heavy, tanklike ankylosaurs and the plate-backed stegosaurs toughed it out during the Age of Dinosaurs.

Plant-eating animals tend to be prey for meat-eaters. The plant-eaters have various means of defense against their hunters. Some, like zebras and hares, are swift runners and speed to an escape. Others, like antelopes and rhinoceroses, have sharp horns for jabbing the enemy.

Another type of defense is armor. It may be over almost all the body as a strong shell, as in tortoises and turtles, and also in smaller creatures like beetles and snails. Or it can be more flexible because it is made of separate plates. Some animals, such as armadillos and pangolins, have armor like this covering most of their body.

▲ Safety in numbers
A group of stegosaurs enter a clearing on the way to a waterhole in the conifer forests of North America.

Slow and heavy
Millions of years ago there were armored and plated dinosaurs. They included nodosaurs, ankylosaurs, and stegosaurs. They evolved this means of defense against the predatory dinosaurs of their time, mainly the theropods like *Allosaurus* and later *Tyrannosaurus*.

These armored and plated dinosaurs were not fast or agile. They could not run and dodge. They were mostly medium-sized and too slow, lumbering, and heavy to run away. But they were well protected by hard, bony plates and shields, and numerous lumps and knobs in their skin. Some also had spikes, spines, and features like clubs. They had strength, power, and body weight on their side. They were indeed the tanks and armored vehicles of the Age of Dinosaurs.

The thyreophorans
The nodosaurs, ankylosaurs, stegosaurs, and

similar creatures belonged to the main dinosaur group (suborder) called Thyreophora, which means "shield-bearers." The various subgroups (families) of thyreophorans are described on the following page. They included such well-known types as *Stegosaurus*, *Ankylosaurus*, *Nodosaurus*, and *Scelidosaurus*.

The thyreophorans were all herbivores, or plant-eaters. They had small, beaklike mouths, little teeth and weak jaws. They could not reach very high and so fed on plants that grew low down or on the ground. Their armored plates, spikes, and clubs must have been very important to them.

A successful strategy

Fossil evidence suggests that the thyreophoran dinosaurs did not live in vast numbers or form great herds, as certain other dinosaurs did. Perhaps they were solitary, peaceful animals. But in terms of evolution their armor-plated strategy was very successful. The group first appeared during the Early Jurassic Period some 200 million years ago. They adapted, spread around the world, and thrived, especially during the Late Jurassic and Early Cretaceous Periods around 160-100 million years ago. A few types even survived until the end of the Age of Dinosaurs 65 million years ago.

Luckily for us, the armored and plated dinosaurs left thousands of fossilized remains – particularly the thick bony shields, lumps, and plates that covered their bodies. These remains provide fascinating glimpses into the lifestyles of these great beasts.

What were the plated and armored dinosaurs?

The stegosaurs, ankylosaurs, and similar armored or plated dinosaurs made up the group (suborder) of dinosaurs called the thyreophorans.

In turn, the thyreophorans were a subgroup of one of the two great groups of dinosaurs, the Ornithischia, or "bird-hips." Other members of the Ornithischia, which were all plant-eaters, included:

- the ornithopods, or "bird-footed" dinosaurs, itself a large group including the well-known *Iguanodon*, also (possibly) the fabrosaurs, heterodontosaurs, hypsilophodonts, dryosaurs, camptosaurs, and the hadrosaurs, or "duckbilled" dinosaurs;
- the horned dinosaurs or ceratopsians, with long horns on their heads and bony frills over their necks;
- the bone-headed dinosaurs or pachycephalosaurs, with thick crests or helmets of bone on their heads.

The nodular dinosaur

Nodosaurus, the animal that gave its name to its group, was a large, quadrupedal, armored, herbivorous ankylosaur from North America. Fossils of *Nodosaurus* were mentioned by the great fossil hunter Othniel Charles Marsh in 1889. However, they were not described until 1921. *Nodosaurus* had the typical pillarlike legs and broad, hoofed, weight-spreading feet of its group. The legs, shoulders, and hips had powerful muscles for weight-carrying, since the body armor would have been very heavy. Lack of fossil evidence means that little is known about the lifestyle of *Nodosaurus* and related armored dinosaurs.

An ankylosaur brought to life

Saichania was an ankylosaur whose remains are known from Central Asia. Like other reconstructions, this one — displayed in the Dinosaur Valley of the Silesian Zoo in Chorzów, Poland — is based on intelligent guesswork.

The first armored dinosaurs

The most ancient group of thyreophorans (armored and plated dinosaurs) was the scelidosaurids. Compared with their later cousins, they were small and only lightly protected.

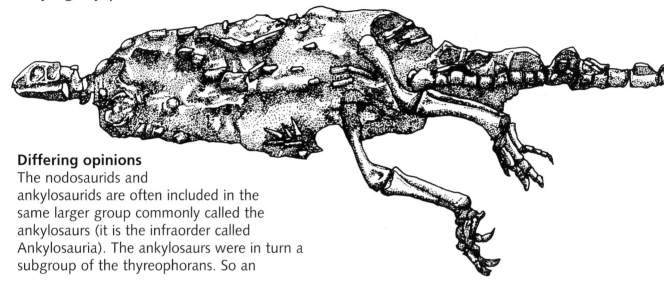

Differing opinions

The nodosaurids and ankylosaurids are often included in the same larger group commonly called the ankylosaurs (it is the infraorder called Ankylosauria). The ankylosaurs were in turn a subgroup of the thyreophorans. So an

Groups of thyreophorans

The general name of armored and plated dinosaurs is usually applied to four main subgroups, or families, of dinosaurs. They make up the main group (suborder) known as the thyreophorans.

- **Scelidosaurids** They were smaller, lightly built plant-eaters, part-armored and from relatively early in the Age of Dinosaurs. They included *Scutellosaurus* and *Scelidosaurus*.
- **Stegosaurids** Commonly known as the plated dinosaurs, the stegosaurids (some known as stegosaurs) were medium-to-large, four-legged plant-eaters with big, flat plates or spikes of bone probably set upright along their backs. They included *Stegosaurus, Tuojiangosaurus, Kentrosaurus, Panoplosaurus,* and possibly *Huayangosaurus* (although this type is sometimes placed in its own family as a huayangosaurid).
- **Nodosaurids** One of the two main families of armored dinosaurs, the nodosaurids were tanklike, four-legged plant-eaters with lumps or nodules of bone as armor and usually spines too, especially on the shoulders, but no tail clubs. They included *Hylaeosaurus, Sauropelta, Nodosaurus, Polacanthus, Edmontonia,* and possibly *Minmi.*
- **Ankylosaurids** The other main family of armored dinosaurs, the ankylosaurids were also tanklike, four-legged plant-eaters that lived later than most nodosaurs. They had heavy protective plates and shields of bone. They lacked body spines but had a hammerlike tail club. They included *Ankylosaurus, Euoplocephalus, Pinacosaurus,* and possibly *Minmi.*

▲ Still in its tomb

The fossilized skeleton of *Scelidosaurus* originally described by Richard Owen was for many years partly encased in limestone rock.

"ankylosaur" can be a nodosaurid or an ankylosaurid.

As mentioned at left, the stegosaur *Huayangosaurus* is sometimes included in its own family, the Huayangosauridae. Most other stegosaurs are grouped in the family Stegosauridae. These two families are then commonly called the stegosaurs (infraorder Stegosauria).

If these ideas are followed, the ankylosaurs (Ankylosauria) and stegosaurs (Stegosauria) are both still subgroups of the thyreophorans.

The first armored dinosaurs

The most ancient or primitive family of thyreophorans was the Scelidosauridae. They were small, lightly armored types that included *Scelidosaurus* and *Scutellosaurus* from the Early Jurassic Period and other types such as *Tatisaurus* and *Echinodon* that are only vaguely known from scarce remains.

Origins of the scelidosaurids

Where did these first armored dinosaurs, the scelidosaurids, come from? They may have evolved from small ornithischian dinosaurs similar to heterodontosaurs (described in chapter 7 of this book). The heterodontosaurs were probably able to walk and run on their two rear legs alone. But as the thyreophorans began to develop bony armor, these new dinosaurs became too heavy for two-legged movement (bipedal locomotion) and instead had to get about on four legs (quadrupedal locomotion).

Early on several counts

Scelidosaurus was one of the earliest thyreophorans. It was also one of the earliest of the entire group of ornithischian (bird-hipped) dinosaurs living around 200 million years ago. And it was one of the first dinosaurs whose fossils were named for science. The man who studied them, in 1859, was none other than Richard Owen, who had coined the term Dinosauria in 1841.

About *Scelidosaurus*

Scelidosaurus had a small head, longish neck and tail, and a long and heavy body supported by four strong limbs, the rear pair being much longer and sturdier

Scelidosaurus head and teeth

The head of *Scelidosaurus* was protected by clusters of thornlike lumps. These bony or horny structures in the skin are known by the general name of scutes. Crocodiles and turtles have them. So do some fish, such as sturgeons. They are usually larger than the standard reptile or fish scales.

The skull of *Scelidosaurus* was short and deep, with extra bony plates fused to the main skull and lower jaw for further protection. The teeth were small and pointed, and the front of the mouth was shaped like a bird's or turtle's beak.

When it wanted to reach food, *Scelidosaurus* could probably lift its head and front body up on its hind legs. It snipped off low-growing tender leaves, shoots, and buds with its narrow, horny beak, and chewed by simple up-and-down jaw movements. The teeth were not especially good at grinding up plant food. Digestion probably took place mostly in the muscular foregut (gizzard or stomach), perhaps aided by small stones (gastroliths) for the purpose.

than the front pair. Most of the upper body, from the neck to the end of the tail, had lengthways rows of cone-shaped, bony lumps in the skin. *Scelidosaurus* may have been able to rear up and run on its hind legs for short distances to avoid predators.

▼ Cone-shaped protectors

The conical lumps in the skin of *Scelidosaurus* would make it awkward for a large predator to grab a mouthful of flesh. Just behind the ear are three lumps clustered in a "tricorn" pattern.

→ The ankylosaur group

The ankylosaurs – the earlier nodosaurids and the later ankylosaurids – were the "walking tanks" of the Age of Dinosaurs.

The major dinosaur group (infraorder) Ankylosauria, or ankylosaurs, includes two main families – the earlier, more primitive nodosaurids and the later and more advanced ankylosaurids. They were truly "walking armored vehicles" and evolved the toughest, most thorough body protection of any animal before or since.

Fused lizards

Ankylosaur means "fused lizard," or "jointed lizard." The ankylosaurs, like other dinosaurs, were not true lizards, although they were of course members of the reptile group. The name ankylosaur refers to the bony plates or shields, fused or welded to each other, that were embedded in the skin and over the skull.

A typical ankylosaur stood low near the ground and walked on four sturdy, upright legs. It had a broad head, short neck, and heavy, barrel-shaped body, tipped by a long, muscular tail.

Armor details

The shieldlike armor extended from the skull, along the neck, back, and tail, often along the flanks too, and in some ankylosaurs, even under the belly. It was usually formed from a mosaic of thick bony plates, lumps, or studs. They are known as dermal plates since they were set within the skin rather than growing on top of or under the skin.

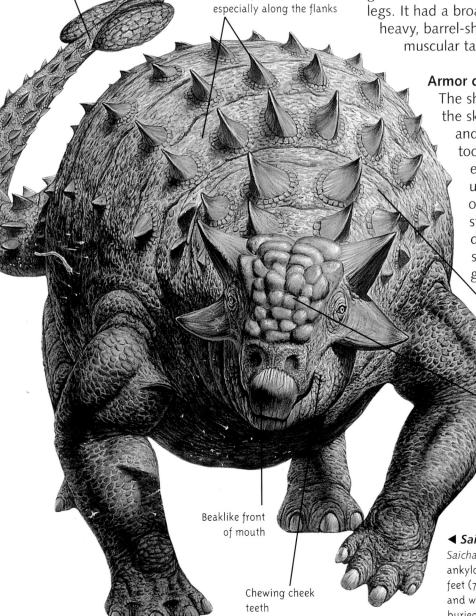

Extensive bony armorplating reaching to the end of the tail

Some bony plates extended into long, sharp spines, especially along the flanks

Some bony plates were wide and shieldlike

Unusual bony palate, shaped like a pear or an hourglass, between the mouth below and the nasal passageways above.

Beaklike front of mouth

Chewing cheek teeth

◄ *Saichania*

Saichania (see page 195) was an Asian ankylosaur from Mongolia. It was about 23 feet (7 meters) long. Some specimens died and were fossilized after being trapped and buried in desert sandstorms.

◀▼ Armor today
Crocodiles and alligators (left) have bony plates, called scutes, similar to those of the armored dinosaurs. They occur mainly along the neck, back, and upper flanks and along the sides of the tail. Turtles and tortoises (below) have gone one step further with an almost all-around, rigid protective casing in two main parts. Over the back is the domed carapace. On the underside is the flatter plastron.

Ankylosaur cousins

The ankylosaurs had features in common with their relatives the ornithopods (the dinosaur group that included the well-known *Iguanodon*). These features included:

- a birdlike pelvis (a key characteristic of the whole ornithischian dinosaur group)
- a toothless, horny beak like a turtle's at the front of the mouth
- fleshy cheeks or an elongated beak to retain food while chewing with the teeth at the back of the mouth
- in some types a trellislike pattern of bony, rod-shaped tendons along the vertebrae, or backbones, to reinforce the back and hip region.

Smaller, normal reptile scales filled any gaps between these large plates or scutes. In life some scutes were covered by leathery skin. Others were probably covered by horn in the way that the bony plates forming the shell of a turtle or tortoise are covered with another layer of horny plates.

In addition to this amazing defensive armor many ankylosaurs had sharp spines on the shoulders and other body areas, which they could use to threaten or jab into their enemies.

▲ *Polacanthus* armor
A dorsal plate (left) and part of the dorsal shield (right) of *Polacanthus*.

The ankylosaurids also had massive, bone-splintering clubs on the ends of their tails.

Nodosaurid evolution

As described on page 186, there were two families of Ankylosauria, the nodosaurids are described on the following pages; the ankylosaurids, some of which are described are in this chapter.

The nodosaurids, or "nodular lizards," were the earlier and more primitive group. They evolved in Europe in the Middle Jurassic Period and spread to Asia and North America and then on to Australia and Antarctica through the Cretaceous Period. None had the defensive tail clubs typical of the ankylosaurids. There were about 20 genera (groups of species) in the nodosaurid family, ranging in length from less than 5 feet (1.5 meters) to more than 25 feet (7.6 meters).

Early nodosaurids

Nodosaurids seem to have evolved during the Middle Jurassic Period in Europe, probably from scelidosaurid-type ancestors.

One of the earliest nodosaurids was possibly *Sarcolestes*, from Early-Middle Jurassic rocks in England. But its fossils are scarce, being mainly part of a lower jaw, a few teeth, and a bony plate from the side of the mouth. There are also fragmentary remains of nodosaurids of the Middle and Late Jurassic period in Europe – but none from the rich fossil sites of this age in North America, Asia, or East Africa.

A founder member

An early nodosaurid that has left reasonable fossils was *Hylaeosaurus*. Its remains were found in Sussex, southern England, in the 1820s, and named by the finder of *Iguanodon*, Gideon Mantell, in the 1830s. This was even before the dinosaurs were recognized as a distinct group of reptiles by Richard Owen (see page 185), who also described the fossils of *Scelidosaurus*. Along with *Iguanodon* and *Megalosaurus*, *Hylaeosaurus* was one of the "founder members" of the Dinosauria.

The original skeletal remains of *Hylaeosaurus* were left encased in their slab of rock, preventing proper study. Some experts suggest that *Hylaeosaurus* is really a specimen of the similar nodosaurid *Polacanthus*. Others say that *Hylaeosaurus* is a distinct type of nodosaurid similar to *Sauropelta*.

▶ **An interesting comparison**
A model of *Hylaeosaurus* constructed in the nineteenth century for the Crystal Palace Exhibitions in London, England, is incorrect in many respects, for example in the lack of spines.

Hylaeosaurus reconstructed

From the evidence available, *Hylaeosaurus* had a massive, barrel-shaped body. Its four short, pillarlike legs ended in widely spread out, hoofed toes, which were probably all wrapped up in strong tissues like the feet of an elephant. The neck was short and stubby, the tail long and muscular.

The skull of *Hylaeosaurus* was narrow and covered in fused slabs of bone, like a helmet from the suit of armor of a medieval knight. The true skull bones inside the "helmet" were much reduced to lighten the head's weight. This resulted in air cavities (spaces) inside the skull. They may have been used as resonating chambers to amplify the sounds and calls of *Hylaeosaurus*, for example, when it wanted

▶ **A prickly customer**
Hylaeosaurus may have been covered in knobs and spines along its neck, back, and flanks, as shown here. However, the exact pattern of protection is not fully known because of the lack of "prepared" fossils, that is, fossils extracted from the surrounding rock.

Forest lizard

Another nodosaurid was *Silvisaurus*, "forest lizard." Its fossils come from 95-million-year-old rocks of the Middle Cretaceous Period in Kansas. It was quite small, about 10 feet (3 meters) long, and its skull, neck, back, flanks, and tail were covered in typical bony armor-plating, decorated with short, sharp spikes. *Silvisaurus* was a primitive member of the family, as shown by several teeth in its front upper mouth, which more advanced nodosaurids lost.

to attract a mate during the breeding season.

Hylaeosaurus had tiny, piggy eyes, small nostrils, and a rounded, beaklike front to its mouth. The teeth were similar to those of other nodosaurids, small and leaf-shaped, and found only toward the rear of the mouth.

The armor of *Hylaeosaurus*

The neck, back, and tail of *Hylaeosaurus* were probably covered in curved bands of bone, each bearing horny knobs or spines. There may have been a row of long spines along each flank extending to the sides of the tail.

There may also have been spines along the upper surface of the tail.

Too heavy to flip over

Nodosaurids were slow creatures, with few or no offensive weapons. They relied on their armor for protection. If threatened, *Hylaeosaurus* would crouch or sit on the ground. Its armor, great body weight, and wide base would make it exceptionally difficult for a predator to dislodge or tip over to get at the less-well protected belly.

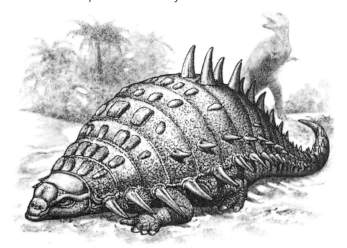

▲ Immovable object

Like a giant seashore limpet, *Hylaeosaurus* sits tight on the ground, relying for protection on its armor, weight, and immovability. A predator would have to get a claw or tooth between the armor plates or under the edge of the dinosaur's body to get enough leverage to tip it over.

DATA BASE

 **Name** *Hylaeosaurus*
Pronounced HIGH-lee-oh-SORE-us
Meaning "woodland lizard"

 Length (nose - tail-tip) 15 feet (4.6 meters)
Standing height 5 feet (1.5 meters)
Weight 2 tons (2 tonnes)

What it ate
Plant-eater, probably consuming tender low vegetation

When it lived Early Cretaceous Period 130-120 million years ago
Where it lived Europe (England)

Order Ornithischia (bird-hipped dinosaurs)
Suborder Thyreophora
Infraorder Ankylosauria
Family Nodosauridae

⇒ A defense of spines

Polacanthus ("many spines") was a well-named nodosaurid. Its massive body spines presented a formidable hazard to predators.

Like other armored dinosaurs, *Polacanthus* was a heavily built, quadrupedal animal that cropped low-growing plants with its turtlelike beak. In addition to its body armor of bony nodules, it had a row of vicious-looking spines along each side of the neck and flank and triangular spikes along the top of the tail. Among the nodosaurids the closest relative of *Polacanthus* was probably *Sauropelta* from North America.

▼ **Fossilized bones of *Polacanthus***

Front and back?

Fossils of *Polacanthus* were found in 1865 on the Isle of Wight in southern England – and in the same rocks as *Hylaeosaurus* (see page 16). This led to the suggestion that *Polacanthus* and *Hylaeosaurus* were the same animal because only the back part of the former and the front part of the latter have been firmly identified. At the same time, there was no good evidence that these two dinosaurs were indeed the same animal.

Further fossils of *Polacanthus* uncovered more recently include some armor-plated skin or hide, backbones, or vertebrae (left), leg bones, and long spines. But again, these are from the rear body parts only.

Legs and feet

No front legs of *Polacanthus* have been found. But fossils of the back leg bones show they were short and sturdy, like other nodosaurids. The feet would be rounded and fleshy for weight-bearing, like those of an elephant, and supported by hoofed toes that curved outward.

The size and build of *Polacanthus* made it a slow, lumbering creature. But it may have been agile enough to turn or rush sideways at an attacker, leading with its sharp shoulder spines. It may also have swished its spiky, well-armored tail.

▼ **Where were the spikes?**

Most of the front half of *Polacanthus* is guesswork. The large side spikes may have been arranged over the shoulders and back rather than along the sides.

The lifestyle of *Polacanthus*

Because of the lack of fossils from the head and front end of *Polacanthus*, proposals about its lifestyle and diet are based on

The smallest nodosaurid

Struthiosaurus, the "ostrich lizard," was only 6.5 feet (2 meters) long, making it probably the smallest known nodosaurid. It was a miniature version of its larger relatives such as *Sauropelta*.

Struthiosaurus lived during the Late Cretaceous Period and its fossils have been dug up across Europe — in France, Hungary, Austria, and Romania. At the Romanian site the fossils of other types of dinosaurs, including sauropods and ornithopods, suggest that they were also very small compared with their cousins elsewhere. This has led to the suggestion that these creatures evolved on islands in the shallow seas that covered much of Europe at the time. During evolution many island species seem to become either "dwarfs" or "giants." Examples that exist today are the small Shetland ponies and the giant Galapagos tortoises.

(*Struthiosaurus* should not be confused with *Struthiomimus*, one of the "ostrich dinosaurs," which is mentioned in chapter 8 of this book.)

specimens we have available we can only guess at their pattern and arrangement. The restoration shows the heavy spines arranged in pairs protruding from the sides of its neck, shoulders, and back. There were also two rows of smaller spines running along the tail.

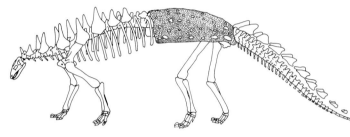

▲ *Polacanthus* hip shields

▲ *Polacanthus* skeleton
This diagram shows the shield of fused bones over the hips (ilium).

knowledge about its close relatives, such as *Sauropelta*. Perhaps *Polacanthus* chopped off mouthfuls of low-growing vegetation, chewed them with its weak teeth, and then finished digesting the food in its stomach or in a gizzard, a muscular second stomach that some animals have for grinding food. It may also have swallowed stones to aid the process (gastroliths).

How many spines?

Polacanthus fossils show that the animal probably had long body spines, but from the

Another composite skeleton

Like the skeleton of *Nodosaurus* on the previous pages, this skeletal reconstruction of *Polacanthus* contains parts "borrowed" from other, similar dinosaurs. The skull, front legs, and shoulder region are mostly missing from the original fossil specimens. As in *Nodosaurus*, the ilium bones were enlarged and in this case covered with a mosaic of small, rounded nodules of bone.

DATA BASE

Name	*Polacanthus*
Pronounced	POLE-ah-KAN-thus
Meaning	"many spines"

What it ate
Plants, mainly low ferns and cycads

Length	(nose - tail-tip) 13 feet (4 meters)
Standing height	5 feet (1.5 meters)
Weight	2 tons (2 tonnes)

When it lived	Early Cretaceous Period 120-110 million years ago
Where it lived	Europe (England), North America (South Dakota)

Order	Ornithischia (bird-hipped dinosaurs)
Suborder	Thyreophora
Infraorder	Ankylosauria
Family	Nodosauridae

What were the ankylosaurids? ➤

⇨ What were the ankylosaurids?

Ankylosaurids became successful mainly during the Cretaceous Period, replacing their armored and plated nodosaur relatives as the main browsers of low-growing vegetation in North America, Asia, and Australia.

The ankylosaurids (Ankylosauridae) were the second family of ankylosaurs. More than a dozen types are known. They were generally slightly larger than their cousins the nodosaurs, ranging from about 18 feet (5.5 meters) up to more than 30 feet (9.1 meters) in length. They began to take over from the nodosaurids and their other relatives, the remaining stegosaurids, toward the end of the Cretaceous Period in Asia and North America.

Types of armor

Ankylosaurids were generally short, wide, stocky animals. Like nodosaurids, they resembled living armored vehicles. Their armor included bands of bony plates and knobs running across the body, but hardly any longer spines, as in nodosaurids. The bands were hinged by leathery skin, like those of an armadillo, so the neck, body, and tail could bend and flex.

A key feature of ankylosaurids was the large, heavy, bony lump at the end of the muscular tail. The animal probably used it as a club or hammer to swing at enemies. The armor near the end of the tail was thinner to give the tail flexibility.

Ankylosaurus described

Ankylosaurus gave its name to the entire group of armored dinosaurs. It was extremely heavy and well-built, with a body as much as 16 feet (nearly 5 meters) wide at the hips. It was probably one of the largest and heaviest

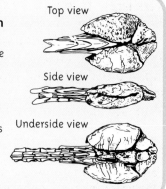

A formidable weapon
These three views of an *Ankylosaurus* tail show the double-club design at its end. This was almost certainly a weapon that could be swung at the legs of adversaries such as predators and possibly at rivals of its own kind during breeding contests.

Top view

Side view

Underside view

ankylosaurids and also one of the last, dwelling in North America during the Late Cretaceous Period.

Fossil bones of the legs, hips, and shoulders, together with evidence from footprints, indicate that ankylosaurids walked with their legs held straight underneath the body, not bowed out to the sides like a modern lizard.

Ankylosaurus armor

Thick bands of bony armor ran crossways over the upper head, neck, back, and tail

▼ **Offensive weapon**
We can imagine *Euoplocephalus*, an ankylosaurid from North America (see pages 28–31), in an encounter with a tyrannosaur. *Euoplocephalus* might keep its back toward the circling attacker, ready to kick out with a hind leg or to strike with the clubbed tail.

of *Ankylosaurus*. The armor was flexible, like chain mail, made up of hundreds of close-set, oval, bony plates in the leathery skin. These plates varied in size: some were as small as coins, others were larger than your hand. Some bore ridged, pointed knobs.

The skull of *Ankylosaurus* was about 30 inches (75 centimeters) long, with a blunt snout, broad face, and toothless beak. Two spines stuck out sideways at the back of the head and another at each cheek.

◄ ► Heavy weapons
The skull of *Ankylosaurus* (left) and part of the body of *Euoplocephalus* (right).

Jurassic star

In the early 1990s fossils of what could be one of the world's oldest and smallest armored dinosaurs were discovered in northwest China. It lived around 170 million years ago during the Jurassic Period. This armored creature, which may have been an ankylosaurid, was nicknamed *Jurassosaurus* after a certain dinosaur movie that was famous at the time.

Shoulder and hip muscles and bones

The hip region of an ankylosaurid had at least eight sacral vertebrae (backbones) fused to each other and to the ilium (front part of the pelvis or hipbone). This formed an immensely strong, boxlike arrangement to bear the great weight of the armor, to anchor the powerful muscles of the hind legs, and to anchor the tail muscles that swung the clubbed tip. The hips had become so highly specialized for these purposes that they were no longer like those of a typical ornithischian or bird-hipped dinosaur.

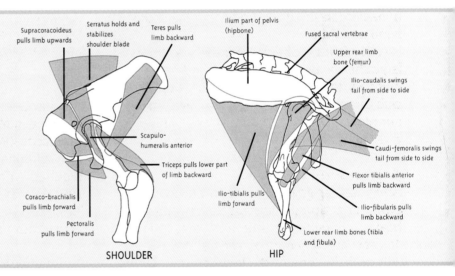

Supracoracoideus pulls limb upwards

Serratus holds and stabilizes shoulder blade

Teres pulls limb backward

Ilium part of pelvis (hipbone)

Fused sacral vertebrae

Upper rear limb bone (femur)

Ilio-caudalis swings tail from side to side

Scapulo-humeralis anterior

Triceps pulls lower part of limb backward

Coraco-brachialis pulls limb forward

Pectoralis pulls limb forward

Ilio-tibialis pulls limb forward

Caudi-femoralis swings tail from side to side

Flexor tibialis anterior pulls limb backward

Ilio-fibularis pulls limb backward

Lower rear limb bones (tibia and fibula)

SHOULDER

HIP

DATA BASE

Name	*Ankylosaurus*
Pronounced	ANN-kee-low-SORE-us
Meaning	"stiff lizard"

What it ate
Plants – low, bushy vegetation

Length	(nose - tail-tip) 33 feet (10.1 meters)
Standing height	8 feet (2.4 meters)
Weight	4-5 tons (4.1-5.1 tonnes)

When it lived	Late Cretaceous Period 65 million years ago
Where it lived	North America (Alberta, Montana)

Order	Ornithischia (bird-hipped dinosaurs)
Suborder	Thyreophora
Infraorder	Ankylosauria
Family	Ankylosauridae

⇒ Dinosaur wars

Thousands of wonderful dinosaur fossils found in North America toward the end of the nineteenth century were the result of a long, bitter feud between two eminent paleontologists.

In the "dinosaur wars" two men, called Edward Drinker Cope and Othniel Charles Marsh, struggled to find ever-more impressive fossils to outdo each other.

During the middle of the nineteenth century the scientific world woke up to the existence of a prehistoric landscape inhabited by enormous reptiles, all now extinct. British animal anatomist Richard Owen (see page 187) coined their group name, Dinosauria, in 1841. More and more fossils were discovered. These vast beasts, with their nightmarish size, power, and ferocity, soon caught the public imagination. The first wave of "Dinomania" swept across Europe and North America from the 1850s. Fame and fortune waited for those who found the best fossils and produced descriptions of ever bigger, stranger "monsters."

▲ **Paleontologists at war**
Edward Drinker Cope (left) and Othniel Charles Marsh (right) started out as colleagues and ended as rivals.

▼ **Late Cretaceous scene**
An *Elasmosaurus* in the water is surrounded by *Ichthyornis* (birds) and *Criorhynchus* (pterosaurs).

Head on the tail

In 1868 (or perhaps 1870) a young American paleontologist (fossil expert) proudly described a marine reptile that he had reconstructed called *Elasmosaurus* (see illustration below). The paleontologist, Edward Drinker Cope (1840-97), noted that the beast had a very unusual spine. The vertebrae, or backbones, seemed to be the wrong way around!

Cope asked another paleontologist, Othniel Charles Marsh (1831-99), for his opinion on the new find. When Marsh saw the reconstruction he suggested that Cope had put the head at the wrong end – on the tail! Worse for Cope, Marsh was right! Cope was devastated, and their rivalry began.

Finds in Colorado

Cope went to work in Philadelphia, studying carnivorous dinosaurs. He had already described several ceratopsian, or horned, dinosaurs from Montana and others from New Jersey. Meanwhile, Marsh, supported by his wealthy uncle George Peabody, became professor of paleontology at Yale College (later University) and studied fossil finds from New Jersey and Kansas.

In 1877 rich deposits of dinosaur bones were found independently in Colorado by two schoolteachers. Arthur Lakes discovered fossils near Morrison, and O. W. Lucas discovered his near Canyon City.

Double trouble

Hoping to get the best analysis of his fossils, Lakes sent some of the remains to Marsh at Yale and others to Cope in New Jersey. Marsh immediately realized the importance of the finds and paid Lakes to keep his discovery secret. So Lakes wrote to Cope, asking him to send his bones to Marsh. But Cope had already examined them and was busy writing his descriptions for publication. He was furious to hear that his rival Marsh was also studying them.

In the meantime, the reverse happened. Lucas sent some of his finds to Cope, and Marsh heard about them. So a tangled web began to form of arguments about who had found which fossils, how important they were, and who deserved the most recognition and fame.

A head start

Cope and Marsh each began a frantic rush to describe and publish his new discoveries before the other. The finds of Lucas were bigger and more complete than the fossils of Lakes, so at first Cope had the lead.

Then Marsh came to hear of more rich fossil deposits at Como Bluff, Wyoming. He quickly located the sites, hired teams of diggers, and took the lead from Cope. There were tales of workers hired by the rival teams to sabotage each other's finds, destroy fossils, wreck tents and campsites, stop food and other supplies from reaching them, plant fake fossils, and send each other off on false trails. There were problems also of a scientific nature, as the paleontologists rushed to name new kinds of dinosaurs on the flimsiest of evidence.

On to Montana

Cope decided to explore elsewhere. In 1876 he turned from the Jurassic rocks of Wyoming to the Cretaceous rocks of Montana. But he had little success. Marsh, meantime, continued to find Jurassic fossils. So Cope returned to these Jurassic sites.

In hindsight, Cope should have stuck with his instincts. In the 1880s Marsh and his team went to investigate Montana's Cretaceous rocks – and began yet another run of success.

Overall, thanks to the efforts of Marsh and Cope, some 130 main types (genera) of dinosaurs came to light in North America. But the two paleontologists never overcame their rivalry. If their "dinosaur wars" had ended earlier, and they had worked together, who knows what they might have achieved?

> ### So many dinosaurs
> Over a period of more than 25 years the frantic race between the two men and their teams led to the discoveries of huge numbers of Jurassic dinosaurs, including *Allosaurus, Ceratosaurus, Camarasaurus, Apatosaurus, Diplodocus, Stegosaurus* (see page 200), and *Camptosaurus*. They also discovered Cretaceous dinosaurs such as *Ornithomimus, Nodosaurus*, and many ceratopsians.

▼ *Stegosaurus*
Stegosaurus finds were among those involved in the "dinosaur wars."

⇒ Rise of the stegosaurs

The stegosaurs were the "plated dinosaurs" with tiny heads, weak teeth, and tall, arched backs bearing huge, saillike plates of bone.

Small brain but big success

Stegosaurs are famous for their small brain size. The brain was only as big as a walnut, which is tiny for a creature almost 30 feet (9 meters) long and weighing 2 tons (2 tonnes). The great brain-to-body ratio (see page 39) implies that stegosaurs were "stupid" or "dim-witted."

But words like this, which we apply to people and animals today, have little meaning for the Age of Dinosaurs. They do not relate to "success" in evolution, because stegosaurs were a very successful group. They numbered at least 15 main kinds, lasted for almost 100 million years, and spread around the world.

Teeth in the beak

There were possibly two subgroups, or families of stegosaurs. They were the Stegosauridae and the Huayangosauridae (see page 186). They probably both arose in China during the Early Jurassic Period.

The Huayangosauridae were the most primitive. They may have been descended from early ornithopods (see page 186). The only well-known member is *Huayangosaurus*. It had a deep, short, beaked snout and the primitive feature of teeth in the upper jaw within the beak. In other, more advanced stegosaurs the beak was entirely toothless.

Huayangosaurus described

Huayangosaurus lived during the Middle-Late Jurassic Period in China. It was about 15 feet (4.6 meters) long, with a heavy body and sturdy legs. The front legs were almost as long as the rear pair. This is another feature that marks it out, since in other stegosaurs the front legs were much shorter, bringing the shoulders and head near the ground. *Huayangosaurus* also had certain bones in the skull and hips that were not found in other stegosaurs.

Stegosaur features

The stegosaurs were medium-sized members of the thyreophoran dinosaur group. A typical stegosaur (member of the infraorder Stegosauria) was:

- between about 15 and 25 feet (4.6 and 7.6 meters) in total length;
- quadrupedal, standing and moving on all four legs;
- small-headed, with a famously tiny brain, a beaklike front to the mouth, and tiny cheek teeth in the rear.
- massive-bodied — although the main body was much slimmer or narrower, side to side, than the body of an ankylosaur, especially in the hip region (see page 194);
- strong-legged, especially the back legs, which held the hips much higher than the shoulders;
- muscular-tailed, with long, sharp spikes at the tip;
- plate-backed — these large, flat slabs, plates, triangles, or spikes of bone along the back and tail are the key feature of stegosaurs;
- a plant-eater.

Huayangosaurus skeleton

This is the most primitive stegosaur as yet discovered. Several skeletons are known that demonstrate its comparatively large forelimbs, small pointed plates, and spikes. *Huayangosaurus* stood only 5 feet (1.5 meters) tall but weighed nearly 1 ton (1 tonne).

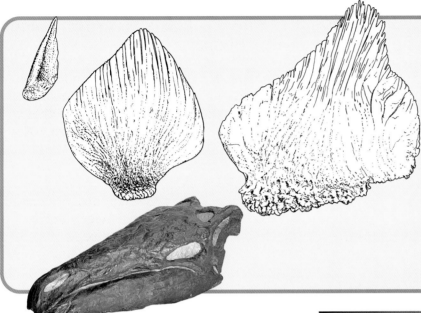

Types of stegosaur plates

Primitive stegosaurs had more spikelike plates than the advanced stegosaurs, which had narrow, broadened plates. The dorsal (back) plate of *Huayangosaurus* is shown on the left, the neck plate of *Stegosaurus* with a short, wide base is in the center, and a tail plate of *Stegosaurus* with its long, narrow base, is on the right. From the different kinds of bases we can tell how they were positioned on the body, either slanted or directly upright.

Stegosaurus skull
Skull cast of a *Stegosaurus stenops* from the U.S.

How were the plates arranged?

Fossils of *Huayangosaurus* show sets of small, flat, bony plates and spikes in the skin. Many almost complete specimens of this dinosaur have been found, but none is quite good enough to reveal the exact pattern or arrangement of the plates and spikes. Perhaps they were set upright in a line along the back, like those of *Stegosaurus*, as shown on the following page.

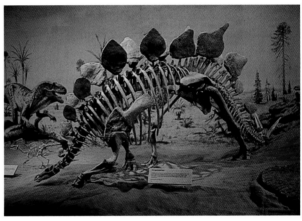

▲ **Bone sails**
Stegosaurus had the typical stegosaur saillike bones along its arched back.

DATA BASE

Name	*Huayangosaurus*
Pronounced	HOY-ang-oh-SORE-us
Meaning	"Huayang lizard"

What it ate
Low-growing plants

Length	(nose - tail-tip) 13-15 feet (4-4.6 meters)
Standing height	5 feet (1.5 meters)
Weight	1,700 pounds (800 kilograms)

When it lived	Middle-Late Jurassic Period 155 million years ago
Where it lived	Asia (China)

Order	Ornithischia (bird-hipped dinosaurs)
Suborder	Thyreophora
Infraorder	Stegosauria
Family	Huayangosauridae (or Stegosauridae)

The dumbest dinosaur? ▶

→ The dumbest dinosaur?

With its tiny brain, huge body, and the diamond-shaped back plates almost the size of tabletops, *Stegosaurus* was one of the most distinctive animals from the Age of Dinosaurs.

The stegosaurids, like the huayangosaurids on the previous page, probably arose in China during the Early Jurassic Period. They spread westward to India, Europe, and Africa, and then on to North America, where they reached the height of their success during the Late Jurassic Period. They went into decline in the Cretaceous Period, although a few isolated types held on until the time of the mass extinction at the end of the Cretaceous.

Stegosaurid features

The stegosaurids had no teeth in the beaklike front part of the mouth. They had the characteristic plates or spines along the back. There are some 15 well-known types (genera). They probably lived in herds, plodding slowly about the landscape as they nipped off choice bits of plants with their narrow beaks.

How high?

The front legs of *Stegosaurus* were so short that the tiny head was held only a few feet above the ground. So most

stegosaurid food must have been very low-growing! However, some experts suggest that these dinosaurs could rear up on their much longer, stronger rear legs, supported by the muscular tail. Supporters of this "rearing *Stegosaurus*" idea point out that the bones of the tail had strong yet flexible joints and protected undersides, which could press against the ground and form a stable tripod with the rear legs.

If *Stegosaurus* could really rear up on its back legs, it might have been able to reach vegetation as high as 14 feet (4.2 meters). In that case it would have been like an enormous, fat, plate-backed, scaly, reptilian version of a kangaroo!

Tiny brain

The skull of *Stegosaurus* housed a tiny brain weighing less than 3

◄ **High hips**
This rear view shows the long back legs of *Stegosaurus*.

ounces (about 85 grams). This brain had to control a body weighing around 2 tons (2 tonnes; see panel below right). Did this mean that *Stegosaurus* was a slow, lumbering creature?

Very probably. But *Stegosaurus* was also the most highly evolved of its group. Its features must have fitted the conditions of the time. Its kind must have competed with many other plant-eaters and survived attacks from huge predators such as *Allosaurus* for several million years.

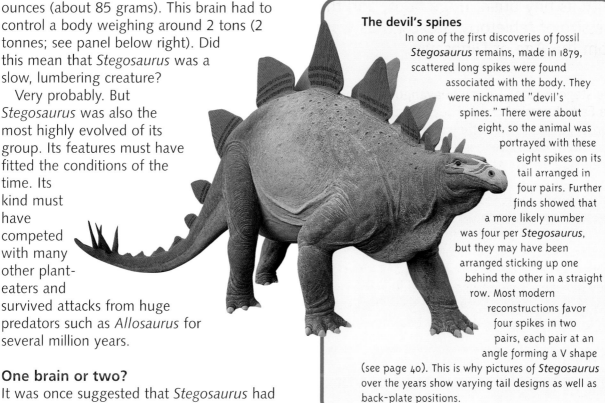

One brain or two?

It was once suggested that *Stegosaurus* had two brains. One was in the usual place in the skull. But it was so small that the animal needed a second, in the hip region. However, this "second brain" was probably just a widening of the body's main nerve, the spinal cord, within the vertebrae (backbones) of the hip. It was more of a relay station or coordinating center, where the nerves controlling the back legs and tail joined the spinal cord.

A similar nerve junction is found in other reptiles and in amphibians, birds, and mammals. It happens to be especially prominent in *Stegosaurus* because of this dinosaur's unusual body proportions.

Plates and armor

Fossils of large, finlike or diamond-shaped plates of bone have been found with *Stegosaurus* skeletons. They were probably arranged somehow along the back – see page 202. In addition, recent research has shown that *Stegosaurus* had patches of the more usual thyreophoran body armor. These included circular, bony plates in the skin over the hip area and a mosaic of small, rounded, bony studs covering the throat.

The devil's spines

In one of the first discoveries of fossil *Stegosaurus* remains, made in 1879, scattered long spikes were found associated with the body. They were nicknamed "devil's spines." There were about eight, so the animal was portrayed with these eight spikes on its tail arranged in four pairs. Further finds showed that a more likely number was four per *Stegosaurus*, but they may have been arranged sticking up one behind the other in a straight row. Most modern reconstructions favor four spikes in two pairs, each pair at an angle forming a V shape (see page 40). This is why pictures of *Stegosaurus* over the years show varying tail designs as well as back-plate positions.

Brains and bodies

In the modern animal kingdom does a big brain mean that a creature is what we call clever or intelligent? Does the animal show adaptable behavior and the ability to learn?

Not necessarily. The biggest animal brain of all belongs to the sperm whale, whose cleverness is difficult to study! But other examples suggest that it is not brain size itself that matters. It is more the comparison between the weight of the brain and the weight of the body it controls — what is known as the brain:body ratio. There is a very rough link between the brain-body ratio and what we call "intelligence" in animals.

Animal	Brain: body ratio
Stegosaurus	1:25,000
Sperm whale	1:5,000
Cow	1:1,200
Elephant	1:600
Troodon	1:200 (a theropod dinosaur, see chapter 8)
Chimpanzee	1:120
Dolphin	1:100
Human being	1:50

Bare bones of *Stegosaurus*

Stegosaurus was the largest of the stegosaurids and weighed as much as a large rhinoceros of today.

Tail spikes

The stegosaurid tail was tipped with a fearsome defensive weapon of bony spikes. *Stegosaurus* itself had two pairs of these caudal spikes, forming two V shapes. Each spike was more than 3 feet (about 1 meter) long. Other stegosaurids had three or more pairs, and in some kinds the spikes were shorter and stouter.

The bones inside the tail had large areas for muscle attachment, indicating that the tail could be swung to and fro with speed and power. The lashing spikes would have been lethal against large predators such as *Allosaurus* and *Ceratosaurus*, as well as against packs of smaller hunting dinosaurs.

The largest of its kind

Stegosaurus was the largest of the stegosaurids, as heavy as the biggest rhinos of today. Because the hind legs were twice as long as the forelegs, the hips arched high above the ground. The tail or spikes at the tail end could be swung at enemies. The back plates are shown in the upright position here, and staggered, with one plate half behind the other, rather than in pairs.

Skull of *Stegosaurus*

The thin, narrow skull was only 16 inches (40 centimeters) long, and the cavity that housed the brain was less than 2 inches (5 centimeters) long. The jaws and their muscles were

Skeleton of *Stegosaurus*

This side view shows the tiny skull of *Stegosaurus* compared with the bulky body. The sacral vertebrae (backbones in the hip region) had tall upward extensions, called neural spines. They may have anchored muscles that could lever and lift the front part of the body off the ground. Along the base of the tail the tall neural spines of the vertebrae anchored tail-lashing muscles. The rear legs were twice as long as the front legs, giving a "humped-hipped" appearance.

▼ A hip-based dinosaur

Most of the bulk of *Stegosaurus* - its rear leg and tail-base muscles and its massive belly slung between the back legs - was in the hip region. This left the animal's front end relatively light and supports the idea that *Stegosaurus* could rear up on its back legs.

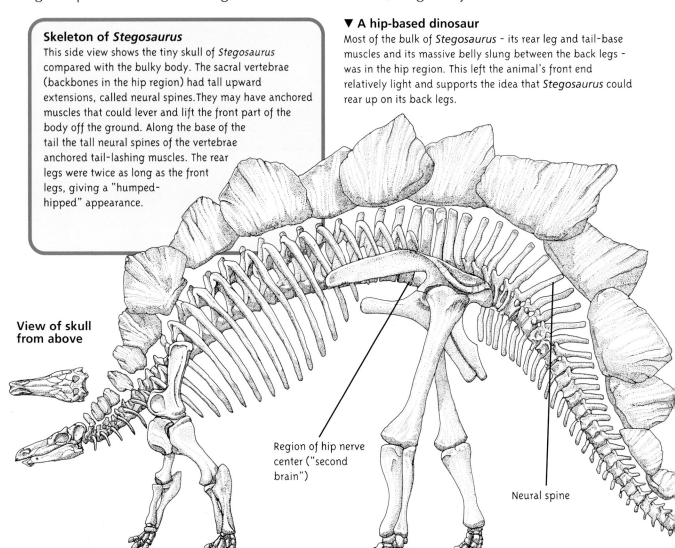

View of skull from above

Region of hip nerve center ("second brain")

Neural spine

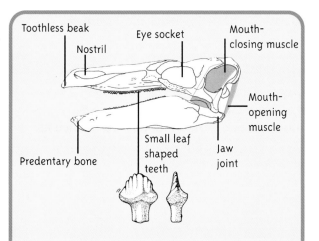

Stegosaurus skull and teeth
The skull of *Stegosaurus* was rather small and the jaws quite weak for such a large animal. The jaw muscles were fairly simple, and there was no obvious lower jaw projection to which they could attach. The cheeks may have been muscular. The teeth were numerous, leaf-shaped, and serrated, but not organized into a grinding battery. At the front of the skull there was a narrow, toothless beak. Probably *Stegosaurus* used stomach stones rather than teeth to grind up its food.

also thin and not especially strong. The toothless, horny beak at the front cut off selected tender buds, shoots, and other soft parts from plants such as seed-ferns, cycadeoids, and conifers. There were no herbs, grasses, or other flowering plants during the Jurassic Period.

Serrated teeth

The weak jaws of *Stegosaurus* carried many small, thin, leaf-shaped cheek teeth. Each was edged with tiny serrations or ridges. The teeth could chop soft food repeatedly, but not really crush or grind it. Stegosaurs may have swallowed stomach stones to help break down their food in the gut into powder.

Toes and hooves
The pillarlike legs of *Stegosaurus* ended in broad, rounded foot pads with short toes, five at the front and three at the rear. Some of the toes had hooflike claws. The main foot pad probably had a cushionlike wedge of flesh around it, similar to an elephant's foot.

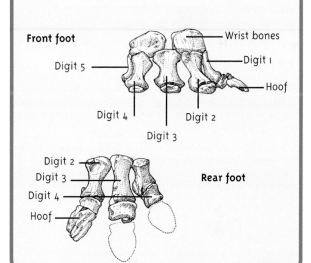

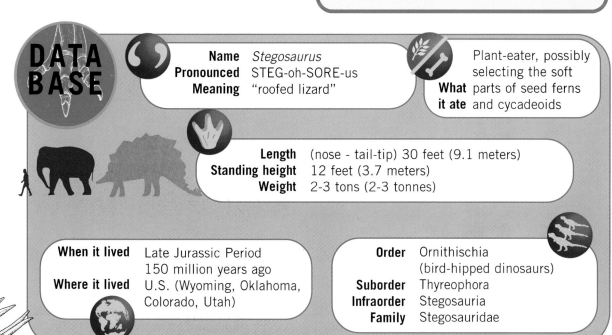

DATA BASE			
Name	*Stegosaurus*	**What it ate**	Plant-eater, possibly selecting the soft parts of seed ferns and cycadeoids
Pronounced	STEG-oh-SORE-us		
Meaning	"roofed lizard"		

Length	(nose - tail-tip) 30 feet (9.1 meters)	
Standing height	12 feet (3.7 meters)	
Weight	2-3 tons (2-3 tonnes)	

When it lived	Late Jurassic Period 150 million years ago	**Order**	Ornithischia (bird-hipped dinosaurs)
Where it lived	U.S. (Wyoming, Oklahoma, Colorado, Utah)	**Suborder**	Thyreophora
		Infraorder	Stegosauria
		Family	Stegosauridae

African stegosaurids ▶

⇒ African stegosaurids

By the Late Jurassic Period stegosaurids had spread from Asia to many other regions. *Kentrosaurus* (sometimes called *Kentrurosaurus*) was a group member from Africa.

Kentrosaurus was a smallish stegosaurid, only some 16 feet (nearly 5 meters) long. Its fossils were discovered in about 1908 in East Africa. Over the following few years thousands of bones were unearthed in the Tendaguru Hill locality of Mtwara, now in Tanzania. These stone-bones were scattered and jumbled, but many belonged to *Kentrosaurus*. Weighing some 250 tons (255 tonnes), they were carried by porters on foot to the Indian Ocean 40 miles (64 kilometers) away for shipment to Germany. The Tendaguru Hills have yielded the fossils of many other kinds of dinosaurs, including small meat-eating coelurosaurs and giant, long-necked, plant-eating sauropods such as *Brachiosaurus*.

Two whole skeletons were assembled from these numerous remains. However, many of the fossils were lost during the Second World War.

Plates to spines

Kentrosaurus seems more similar to *Tuojiangosaurus* than to *Stegosaurus*. There were six pairs of flat, bony back plates over its neck, shoulders, and ribs. But along the back and hips they changed into about seven pairs of sharp spines up to 2 feet (60 centimeters) long. There may also have been another pair of spines on either the hips (as shown in the main illustration) or further forward on the shoulders.

The two-brain theory

Internal casts of the inside of the skull show that like *Stegosaurus*, *Kentrosaurus* had a tiny brain for its body size. It also had an enlarged spinal cord, as shown by internal casts of the fossils of two sacral vertebrae (hip backbones). However, this was probably a relay station or nerve junction (see page 201), rather than a "second brain."

◀ Looking over its shoulder

Kentrosaurus probably fed on low-growing ferns and shrubs along river valleys. It may have reared up to reach the tender shoots of trees, propping itself up on its tail, which, together with the legs, would have made a kind of tripod. This reconstruction shows the back plates in pairs, becoming taller and more spiky from the neck rearward toward the tail.

▶ *Kentrosaurus* **in a sunny clearing**
If stegosaurids could eat only low-growing leaves, they would probably prefer forest clearings where small plants thrived in the sunlight.

The lifestyle of *Kentrosaurus*

Other fossils found with those of *Kentrosaurus* show that during the Late Jurassic Period the climate of East Africa was warm with wet and dry seasons. *Kentrosaurus* had to eat whatever vegetation it could find during the drought. It also had to defend itself from predatory dinosaurs such as *Ceratosaurus*. *Kentrosaurus* may have threatened these enemies by turning and reversing toward them. Its sharp spines would bristle like a huge porcupine's, and the spiked tail would lash out in defense.

Kentrosaurus skeleton
The down-curved neck and short front legs meant that the head of *Kentrosaurus* was very low near the ground. However, the undersides of the tail backbones (caudal vertebrae) had chevrons (extensions like the keel of a ship) on their undersides. They could have supported the tail as it pressed on the ground, when *Kentrosaurus* reared up on its back legs to feed. This drawing shows a long spine on the hip, but it may have been on the shoulder.

DATA BASE

Name	*Kentrosaurus*
Pronounced	KENT-row-SORE-us
Meaning	"spiky lizard"

What it ate
Low-growing river-valley vegetation

Length	(nose - tail-tip) 16 feet (4.9 meters)
Standing height	5 feet (1.5 meters)
Weight	1 ton (tonne)

When it lived	Middle-Late Jurassic Period 156-150 million years ago
Where it lived	Africa (Tanzania)

Order	Ornithischia (bird-hipped dinosaurs)
Suborder	Thyreophora
Infraorder	Stegosauria
Family	Stegosauridae (Tuojiangosauridae?)

Introduction to the ceratopsians ▶

⇒ Introduction to the ceratopsians

The "horn-faced" dinosaurs were big, bulky, four-legged plant-eaters. They were among the last of the major dinosaur groups, flourishing mainly during the last 30 million years of the Age of Dinosaurs.

"Ceratopsian" means "horned face." This is not a term of abuse but a description of the bony-cored, horn-covered projections on the faces and heads of these dinosaurs. (The name "ceratopian" has also been used, but the more accepted term now is "ceratopsian" with an "s.")

The ceratopsians were large, bulky, heavy, and powerful dinosaurs. They stood, walked, and ran on their four sturdy legs. They were herbivores, or plant-eaters. Perhaps the animals of today that are most similar in general body shape to the ceratopsians are the big herbivorous mammals such as rhinoceroses, hippopotamuses, musk oxen, buffalo, and yak.

Horns and frills

Most ceratopsians had horns on their faces; the number and shape of the horns varied. They also had huge frills or wavy-edged shields extending from the back of the skull over the rear of the neck. Some of these frills had horn knobs or spiky projections.

The face horns and neck frills may have had several uses. Perhaps they were for defense

> ### Ceratopsian families
> The dinosaurs known by the general name of ceratopsians, group Ceratopsia, included three main subgroups or families. They were:
> - psittacosaurids, or "parrot-faces,"
> - protoceratopsids, or "first horned-faces,"
> - ceratopsids, or "horned-faces."
>
> There is a difference between ceratopsian, meaning a member of the general group Ceratopsia, and protoceratopsid or ceratopsid, meaning a member of these respective families.

against the big hunting dinosaurs of the time such as *Tyrannosaurus*. They may also have been important for social life. The evidence is that many ceratopsians lived with others of their own kind in groups or herds.

Evolution of the ceratopsians

The first dinosaur of the ceratopsian type, *Psittacosaurus*, appeared in Asia during the Middle Cretaceous Period some 115-110 million years ago. It was a small creature with features of its ancestral group, but also features that could be seen later in the larger ceratopsians.

Early ceratopsians similar to the Asian *Protoceratops* spread from Asia across to North America via the land bridge that spanned the Bering Strait during this time. It was in North America in the last 30 million years of the Cretaceous Period that ceratopsians became successful and very numerous.

The end of the era

In fact, the last 30 million years of the Cretaceous Period marked the close of the Age

▲ New plant-eaters for new plants

During the Cretaceous Period a new group of plants appeared and spread across the land. They were the flowering plants (angiosperms) — the flowers, herbs, bushes, and nonconiferous trees that now dominate our landscape. Ceratopsian success may have been partly due to their ability to eat these new plants. Each ceratopsian had a sharp, hooked, parrotlike beak at the front of the mouth and cutting, bladelike teeth further back, worked by massive jaw muscles. This eating equipment could deal with the tough, stringy, fibrous stems and trunks of the new plants. The artist's impression shows a *Triceratops* family in a landscape dotted with plants.

of Dinosaurs. The ceratopsians were among the last of the main dinosaur groups. Their final members perished in the great mass extinction 65 million years ago that brought the Cretaceous Period and the entire Mesozoic Era to an end.

Fortunately for us, the ceratopsians left thousands of fossilized remains – horns, teeth, skulls, and other bones, even entire skeletons of both males and females, also nests, eggs, tiny hatchlings, youngsters, and droppings, footprints, and other fossilized signs. Such remains provide fascinating glimpses into the lives of these great animals.

◄ Plenty of fossils

The ceratopsians were very heavy, "bony" animals. They had tough, thickset, sturdy skeletons, and their horns and frills were based on bony structures. This is one reason why their remains are relatively plentiful and in good condition, compared with the thinner and more fragile bones of the slender, lightweight dinosaurs. This is a skull of *Protoceratops*.

▶ Earliest of the group

Psittacosaurus was the earliest known ceratopsian. It was about the size of a very large dog today. It lived in dry, almost desertlike conditions in Asia. Plants grew only along waterways or in the cool dampness of shady cliffs and outcrops. Parts of the region are similar desert or semidesert today.

What were the ceratopsians?

The ceratopsians were a subgroup of a larger group of dinosaurs that we call the Marginocephalia. It also included the bone-headed dinosaurs, or pachycephalosaurs, with thick crests or helmets of bone on their heads.

In turn, the marginocephalians were a subgroup of one of the two great groups of dinosaurs, the Ornithischia, or "bird-hips." Other members of the Ornithischia, which were all plant-eaters, included:

- the ornithopods, or "bird-footed," dinosaurs, itself a large group including the well-known *Iguanodon*, also (possibly) the fabrosaurs, heterodontosaurs, hypsilophodonts, dryosaurs, camptosaurs, and the hadrosaurs, or "duckbill," dinosaurs;
- the plated dinosaurs or stegosaurs, with upright plates of bone along their backs;
- the armored dinosaurs or ankylosaurs, with massive bony plates like shields.

Dinosaurs

Ornithischians   Saurischians

Ornithopods   Ankylosaurs
Stegosaurs

Marginocephalians

Ceratopsians   Pachycephalosaurs

Why horns and frills?

Evolution favors body features that help a creature survive in its environment. So the long, pointed horns and huge neck frills of many ceratopsians must have had some important use, otherwise they would not have reached such dramatic proportions. After all, these structures were a great "investment" by the animal. The dinosaur had to put in large quantities of food minerals and other resources to build up the bony centers and outer horn as they grew and to maintain them during adulthood.

Also, the horns and frills required modifications of other body parts, including a stronger skull, sturdier neck, and stouter front legs to bear the weight. In turn, more powerful muscles in the entire skull, neck, and forelimb area were needed to carry and move the extra weight.

Over the years there have been various proposals for their use, including temperature control (see page 220).

Nests and eggs

Dinosaurs were reptiles, and most of today's reptiles breed by laying eggs. The first fossilized dinosaurs eggs known to science were discovered in the 1920s in Mongolia. They belonged to *Protoceratops*.

The Mongolia fossil-finding expedition of the 1920s, described on the previous page, made many astounding discoveries. Among them were the first known dinosaur eggs, preserved for more than 80 million years in specially made, dug-out nests. Evidence shows that they belonged to *Protoceratops*.

The eggs

There were about 18 to 30 eggs in each nest. They had been carefully laid in layers, either in a spiral shape or in circles one within the other. Each egg was sausage-shaped and about 8 inches (20 centimeters) long. The fossilized remains showed that the shell was thin and wrinkled. In life it was probably slightly flexible and leathery, like most reptile eggshells today, rather than hard and brittle like a bird's eggshell.

Some of the eggs were whole. Recent studies with medical-type scanners have revealed the presence of tiny embryos (unhatched babies) preserved within.

▼ At the nest

Protoceratops probably lived in groups, roaming the range for food and then returning to the same nesting site to breed. The males may have showed off their large neck frills in visual displays to dominate rival males and impress females when mating (see panel on page 211). Meanwhile, the females dug nests, laid their eggs, and covered them with sand, as we shall see on the next page.

▶ Skull of a juvenile

This *Protoceratops* skull measures about 1 foot (30 cm) from nose to back of frill. By the time this juvenile was an adult, the skull would be about 1 foot 6 inches (46 cm) long.

The nest

The *Protoceratops* nest was a shallow, bowl-shaped depression scooped out of the sandy landscape. A parent – most likely the female – dug the nest. It seems that the same nest area was used time after time, the new nests being dug over the old ones, or old ones renovated. The eggs may have been covered with soil for protection and temperature control. They would incubate and hatch in the heat of the sun.

The breeding colony

There were many *Protoceratops* nests gathered at the same site. This suggests a breeding colony where many *Protoceratops* came together to reproduce. They were not the only dinosaurs to do this, as we shall see on the next page.

The nests of *Psittacosaurus*

Fossilized eggs and babies of the ceratopsian *Psittacosaurus* have also been discovered. As with *Protoceratops*, the eggs were laid in nests. The preserved skulls of two *Psittacosaurus* youngsters are hardly larger than human thumbs. This would put the length of the whole baby at around 10-16 inches (25-40 centimeters). The skulls have very large eye sockets. The vertebrae (backbones) are not well formed, so it is doubtful that the babies were strong enough to move. Yet, amazingly, their teeth already show signs of wear. Possibly, one or both parents brought food to the babies while they were still in the nest, as hadrosaurs did. The picture shows fossilized *Protoceratops* eggs and eggshell from the Gobi Desert.

More about breeding ▶

⇨ More about breeding

Life was never easy for the nest-builders when there were also nest-raiders about.

Fossils of the "duckbill" hadrosaurs and other dinosaurs show mass nesting sites similar to those of *Protoceratops*. However, modern reptiles do not set up breeding colonies. This behavior is more characteristic of modern birds such as gulls.

The nest-raider
Protoceratops was not the only type of dinosaur present in the area 80 or so million years ago. One of the nests contained the remains of another dinosaur – the smallish, lightly built hunter *Oviraptor*. In fact, this dinosaur was named "egg predator/thief" because people imagined that it could have been raiding the nest to steal and eat an egg or two. It is possible that the crushing damage to the bones of this *Oviraptor* specimen was done before preservation, rather than after. The cause was the *Protoceratops* parent attacking the intruder in defense of its nest.

◀ **Mother protector**
The female *Protoceratops* probably guarded her nest against predators, if necessary by fighting them off.

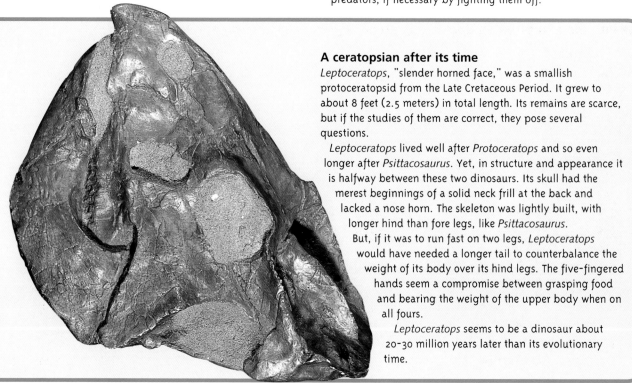

A ceratopsian after its time
Leptoceratops, "slender horned face," was a smallish protoceratopsid from the Late Cretaceous Period. It grew to about 8 feet (2.5 meters) in total length. Its remains are scarce, but if the studies of them are correct, they pose several questions.

Leptoceratops lived well after *Protoceratops* and so even longer after *Psittacosaurus*. Yet, in structure and appearance it is halfway between these two dinosaurs. Its skull had the merest beginnings of a solid neck frill at the back and lacked a nose horn. The skeleton was lightly built, with longer hind than fore legs, like *Psittacosaurus*.

But, if it was to run fast on two legs, *Leptoceratops* would have needed a longer tail to counterbalance the weight of its body over its hind legs. The five-fingered hands seem a compromise between grasping food and bearing the weight of the upper body when on all fours.

Leptoceratops seems to be a dinosaur about 20-30 million years later than its evolutionary time.

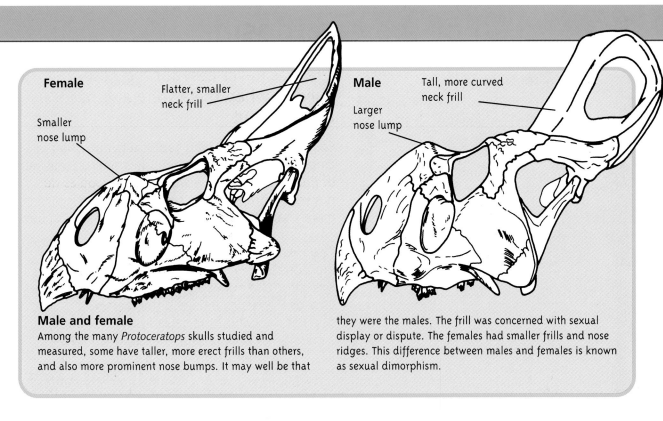

Female

Flatter, smaller neck frill

Smaller nose lump

Male

Tall, more curved neck frill

Larger nose lump

Male and female

Among the many *Protoceratops* skulls studied and measured, some have taller, more erect frills than others, and also more prominent nose bumps. It may well be that they were the males. The frill was concerned with sexual display or dispute. The females had smaller frills and nose ridges. This difference between males and females is known as sexual dimorphism.

Another nest-raider

A third type of dinosaur on the scene was another small-to-medium carnivore, also a member of the theropod group, *Velociraptor*, the "speedy predator/thief." In one unique find it seems that a *Protoceratops* and a *Velociraptor* died together in combat. The *Protoceratops* could have bitten and locked its beak into the arm of *Velociraptor*. The raptor struggled and kicked with its clawed hind legs, embedding one of its toe claws into the ceratopsian's neck.

If these ideas are correct, it seems that the mother *Protoceratops* guarded her nest against predators. Again, this behavior is rare among today's reptiles, but extremely common in birds. (Both *Velociraptor* and *Oviraptor* are mentioned in chapter 8 of this book.)

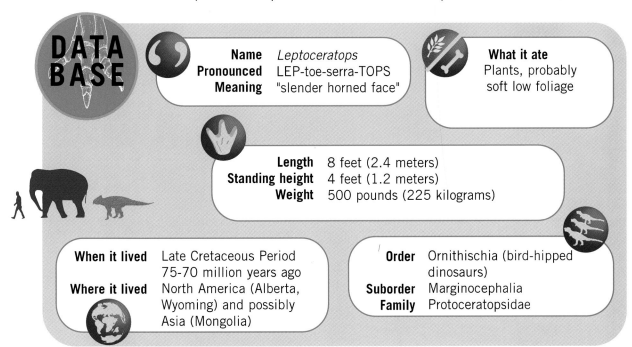

DATA BASE

Name	*Leptoceratops*
Pronounced	LEP-toe-serra-TOPS
Meaning	"slender horned face"

What it ate
Plants, probably soft low foliage

Length 8 feet (2.4 meters)
Standing height 4 feet (1.2 meters)
Weight 500 pounds (225 kilograms)

When it lived Late Cretaceous Period 75-70 million years ago
Where it lived North America (Alberta, Wyoming) and possibly Asia (Mongolia)

Order Ornithischia (bird-hipped dinosaurs)
Suborder Marginocephalia
Family Protoceratopsidae

The spread of the ceratopsids ➤

The spread of the ceratopsids

As the Cretaceous Period went on, the main ceratopsian family – the ceratopsids – began to evolve, thrive, and spread. *Triceratops*, with its long horn and large frill, was the most typical member of the family.

Until a few years ago it was believed that protoceratopsids arrived in North America from Asia toward the Middle-Late Cretaceous Period some time after 100 million years ago. Then some types evolved into the ceratopsids proper, with their fully quadruped (four-legged) stance, massive neck frills, long face horns, toothless beaks, and hoofed toes.

◀ **Streamlined skull**
The skull of *Eoceratops was* long and streamlined, with a smooth sweep down the neck frill to the horns. The central parts of the horns were bone and so preserved as fossils. In life an outer sheathlike layer of horn (like our fingernails) would make the whole horn longer and sharper.

A changing picture
However, recent fossil finds in Utah are changing this view. The remains are dated to a 25-million-year span in the Middle Cretaceous Period. They fill a considerable gap in which fossils of certain dinosaur groups in North America are generally scarce. The fossils include those of tyrannosaurs, small sauropods, duckbilled hadrosaurs – and ceratopsians. They show that ceratopsians had spread to North America, presumably from Asia via the Bering region, earlier than once believed.

◀ More about breeding

Two subgroups

Once the ceratopsid group had got into its stride in North America, it seemed to split into two subgroups, one with short neck frills and the other with longer neck frills.

This division is convenient, seems simple, and is described below. However, in the details of the structure of the skull, neck frill, and horns the distinction between the two subgroups has never been especially clearcut. In fact, it too has been changed by recent information. Such grouping of animals is important in all areas of the life sciences, since it helps us understand evolutionary relationships.

The short-frills

The short-frilled types included (traditionally) *Triceratops*, *Centrosaurus*, *Monoclonius*, and *Styracosaurus*. They lived from about 85 million years ago in North America and were very abundant, as fossil accumulations such as those in Alberta, Canada, show.

These dinosaurs had short, bony neck frills, with small "windows" in the bone or no windows at all – like *Triceratops*. They also had long nose horns and small eyebrow horns – apart from *Triceratops*. The edges or margins of the frills bore bones of various shapes, forming lumps, bumps, bulges, hooks, small spikes, and even extra full-blown frill horns.

◀ **A new subfamily**
Until recently grouped with the short-frilled ceratopsids, *Triceratops* is now classed in a new subfamily, the chasmosaurines. *Triceratops*, with its three facial horns, is the best-known ceratopsian. It was also one of the largest.

The long-frills

The long-frilled types included *Pentaceratops*, *Torosaurus*, *Chasmosaurus*, *Anchiceratops*, and *Arrhinoceratops*. They lived from about 80 million years ago, also in North America. They had very long bony, neck frills with large windows. The frills were usually decorated with elaborate bones. Like *Triceratops*, they all had long eyebrow horns and short nose horns.

But *Triceratops*, one of the last of all dinosaurs, falls between the two groups. It had a short, solid neck frill but the long eyebrow horns and short nose horn of the long-frilled

▲ **Frill-horned ceratopsid**
Styracosaurus had a nose horn and also six long horns in its neck frill, not on the face like the horns of *Triceratops*.

types. Another ceratopsid, *Pachyrhinosaurus*, with massive bony lumps or bosses on its face but no actual horns, is also hard to place.

Another changing picture

Recently, the individual bones that make up the neck frills have been studied in the better-preserved ceratopsid specimens. The results indicate that the length of the neck frill or the size of its windows are not, in themselves, a suitable basis for grouping these dinosaurs. What seems to be important is the length of a bone that forms all or part of the side of the frill, called the squamosal bone.

Revised subfamilies

Using this newer basis, the two subfamilies of ceratopsids are:
- chasmosaurines, with a long squamosal bone. They also had relatively long frills overall, longer eyebrow horns than nose horns, and shallow, long faces.
- centrosaurines, with a shorter squamosal bone. They also had relatively short frills overall, shorter eyebrow horns than nose horns, and deep, short faces.

These new features put *Triceratops* into the chasmosaurine group, where its long brow horns fit neatly. Until, perhaps, a further change takes place …

A very big ceratopsid ▶

A very big ceratopsid

Think of a well-known dinosaur. It may be a fierce meat-eater such as *Tyrannosaurus*. It may be a long-necked giant like *Diplodocus*. Or it may be *Triceratops*.

Triceratops was one of the largest, most abundant, and best-represented of all ceratopsians, and indeed, of all dinosaurs. It was also one of the very last dinosaurs, surviving right to the edge of the mass extinction at the end of the Cretaceous Period 65 million years ago.

The discovery of *Triceratops*
Early fossil finds of *Triceratops*, including the bony cores or centers of its great face horns, came from Green Mountain Creek, near Denver, Colorado. They were studied in 1887 and thought to be the horns of a giant type of North America bison (buffalo) that had only recently become extinct. They were even named as *Bison alticornis* ("high-horned bison") by the fossil expert Othniel Charles Marsh. He was in great competition with his archrival, Edward Drinker Cope, to discover and name as many new kinds of dinosaurs as possible.

More excellent finds
In 1888 another fossil prospector, John Bell Hatcher, investigated a find of more horn cores at Niobrara County, Wyoming. Working under the direction of Marsh, Hatcher dug into the site and over the following four years uncovered the fossils of about 30 *Triceratops* skulls and skeletons, some almost complete. Since then another 20 or so well-preserved specimens have been added to the tally of *Triceratops*, making it one of the best-known and most thoroughly studied of all dinosaurs.

How many types of *Triceratops*?
One of the largest ceratopsids, *Triceratops* probably weighed more than 5 tons (5.1 tonnes), as heavy as the largest African male elephants today. Minor variations among the fossils, especially the horns and neck frills, once led experts to propose that there could have been as many as 16 species within the genus

◄ **Peaceful feeding**
For most of its day *Triceratops* would feed peacefully on low-growing vegetation. Its sharp beak snipped off plant matter, and the shearing cheek teeth chopped it up before it was swallowed. Microorganisms in the vast gut would digest the food further. This side view shows the great length of the beast, which could reach 30 feet (9.1 meters), and the sturdy pillarlike legs.

Triceratops. But the variety almost certainly represents normal differences between individual skulls and also between adult males, adult females, and juveniles. Perhaps there were only two or three species in the genus, especially *Triceratops horridus* ("terrifying three-horned face").

Skull, horns, and frill

Triceratops had a short nose horn and two very long, pointed forehead or brow horns. The bony cores or centers of the brow horns measured 3 feet (90 centimeters) in length. In life they would have been covered in horn, which would have made them considerably longer and also sharper.

The neck frill of *Triceratops* was relatively short, not quite reaching the shoulders, but solid and heavy and flared to the sides. It had an edging of bony, studlike lumps.

The entire skull and frill of *Triceratops* were huge. In the largest specimens it measured some 6 feet 6 inches (2 meters) from the front tip of the beak bones to the rear edge of the frill. A fossil skull of this size, having been turned from bone to stone, weighs about 1 ton (1 tonne).

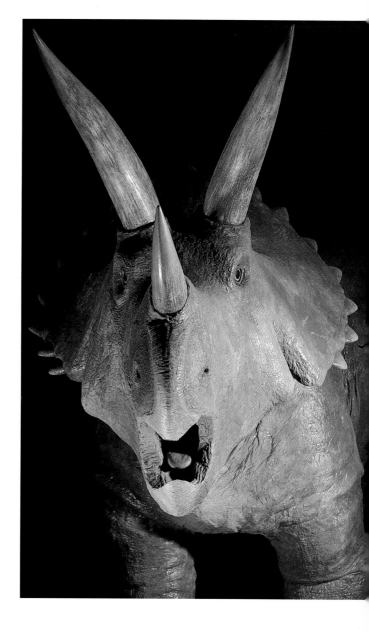

▶ **An alarming view**
A predator about to tackle *Triceratops* would come face to face with this fearsome sight. The sharp, beaklike mouth was ready to snip and shear, the nose horn was waiting to stab, the great eyebrow horns stood tall and sharp, and the neck frill flared out to the sides and made *Triceratops* look even more massive.

▶ ***Triceratops* charges**
If defensive posturing and threats did not work against an attacker, *Triceratops* could lower its head and charge. Perhaps, like today's rhino, *Triceratops* was capable of surprising speed over short distances. A charging rhino could outrun most humans in a short sprint.

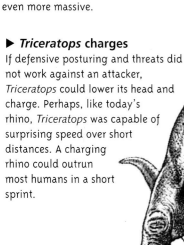

Large and familiar

There are few dinosaurs that are as thoroughly familiar and well studied as *Triceratops*.

Inside the head

Some skulls of *Triceratops* show the shape of the cavity in the upper rear that housed the brain. This, in turn, gives clues to the size and shape of the brain and the proportions of the brain parts devoted to functions such as dealing with senses or movements. Studies suggest that *Triceratops* was faster and more agile than the lumbering stegosaurs, but slower and with less keen senses than the ornithopod and theropod dinosaurs.

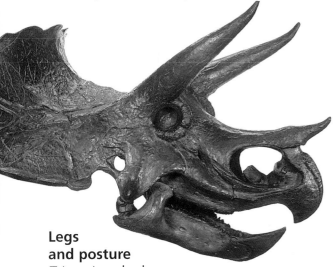

Legs and posture

Triceratops had three hoofed fingers on each front foot and four hoofed toes on each hind foot. Its legs were thick and strong, like an elephant's, supporting more than 1 ton (1 tonne) of body weight each.

It is unlikely that ceratopsids and other quadrupedal dinosaurs had their front legs directly underneath the shoulders, straightened, and with the elbow joints facing backward, as in mammals. The joints between the limb bones suggest that the front legs were bent or bowed slightly to the sides, and that the elbow joints faced to the sides as well.

This could allow three basic postures for the front limbs. For fast walking or running they were almost straight, with elbows pointing slightly outward and toes inward. For slow walking the elbows were bent more, and the legs bowed further out to the sides. For standing the limbs would bend even more, and the elbows would stick out almost at right

◀▶ Front-heavy skeleton

In relation to their overall size ceratopsians had large, heavy heads. Including the frill, the head of *Triceratops* was one-fifth of its total length. In some sauropod dinosaurs the proportion was only one-fortieth!

Triceratops skull

The head of *Triceratops* narrowed to a pointed beak at the front. The frill was low and flaring, but not especially long. It was also solid, lacking the windows or gaps found in other ceratopsids. The brow horns were enormous, the nose horn much smaller. The view from above shows the narrowness of the snout and beak, and the characteristic ceratopsid "pointed cheeks" formed by the long, tapering bones at the side of the face.

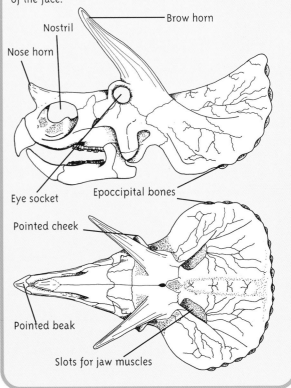

Nostril
Brow horn
Nose horn
Eye socket
Epoccipital bones
Pointed cheek
Pointed beak
Slots for jaw muscles

angles. That would give a very stable stance, like that of a bulldog.

Sizing up the enemy

Triceratops had eyes on the sides of its head, like modern large plant-eaters such as horses. This gave good all-round vision and helped it keep watch for enemies. But both eyes could not look at the same object. Animals whose two eyes face forward, such as cats and dogs and ourselves, have stereoscopic or binocular

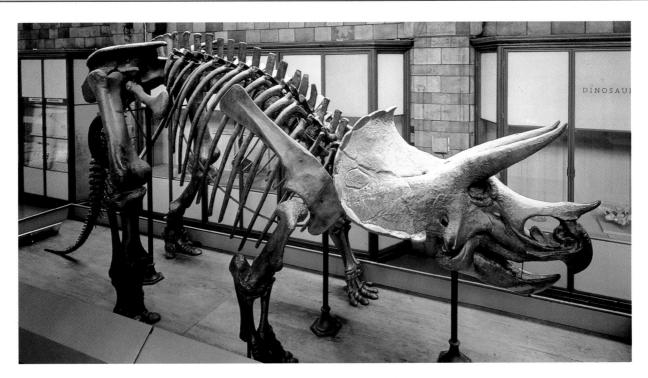

vision that helps us judge distances so accurately. *Triceratops* would not have had that ability. Perhaps it had to move its head from side to side in order to gauge the distance and direction of objects such as herd rivals or predators.

Herd behavior

Triceratops may have used its long brow horns in pushing contests with rivals at breeding time, or to settle disputes about leadership in the herd (see page 218). As the horns locked, the solid neck frill would act as a shield to protect the shoulders and flanks from injury. There was also a hollow in the skull above the brain, which could have acted as a shock absorber during such trials of strength.

Some fossil specimens of *Triceratops* show signs of old wounds on the cheek and frill regions of the head. They may be evidence of injuries caused by battles with enemies or herd rivals.

DATA BASE

Name	*Triceratops*
Pronounced	TRY-serra-TOPS
Meaning	"three-horned face"

What it ate Fibrous plants, herbaceous plants, and leaves of low trees

Length	30 feet (9.1 meters)
Standing height	7 feet 6 inches (2.3 meters)
Weight	5.3 tons (5.4 tonnes)

When it lived Late Cretaceous Period 67-65 million years ago
Where it lived North America (Alberta, Saskatchewan, Montana, North Dakota, South Dakota, Wyoming)

Order Ornithischia (bird-hipped dinosaurs)
Suborder Marginocephalia
Family Ceratopsidae

Life in the herd

How do we know that ceratopsids such as *Triceratops* gathered in large groups? What would their daily life be like?

"Bonebeds" are huge accumulations of fossils at one site, representing hundreds or even thousands of individuals. The layers of rock consist more of fossils than of matrix (the surrounding stone). Bonebeds are known for many kinds of prehistoric animals, including various dinosaurs, such as the sauropods and hadrosaurs.

Ceratopsid bonebeds

North America has yielded at least nine bonebeds of large numbers of ceratopsians. They include *Anchiceratops*, *Centrosaurus*, *Chasmosaurus*, *Monoclonius*, *Styracosaurus*, and *Pachyrhinosaurus*. At one site in Alberta

there are the remains of more than 1,000 *Pachyrhinosaurus*.

In most cases the bonebed contains mostly fossils of one type of ceratopsian and very little else. The jumbled bones, horns, hooves, and other remains are from apparently healthy individuals of both sexes and different ages, from perhaps less than a year old through juveniles to full adulthood.

However, there were no eggs or hatchlings. This suggests the dinosaurs traveled in a group, or migrated, to a certain area for breeding. Then they moved on when the youngsters were big and strong enough to keep up with the herd.

Perished together

The likely explanation for these fossil collections is a watery catastrophe in a limited area such as a flash flood that hit the single-species herd of animals. A general flood would wash together the remains of many types of animals.

We can imagine several ways in which these fossil beds were formed. In the face of danger, such as a sudden and violent flash flood, the natural response of individuals in the herd would be to crowd together for protection and security. They may have tried to swim to safety but drowned because of exhaustion. The rushing waters washed the bodies onto a bank or bar, then receded. Many fossils bear the tooth marks of scavengers that feasted on the rotting carcasses. The bones were perhaps washed away again by further floods that disarticulated them (pulled adjacent bones apart at their joints).

◄ **Over the edge**
In a fierce battle between two *Triceratops* the stronger male pushes the weaker one over a stream bank. They may be fighting to demonstrate to the rest of the herd which is the stronger and fitter.

Daily life

From the many clues provided by the fossils of ceratopsians and the remains of other animals and the plants of the time a picture emerges of daily life in the herd. The ceratopsids lived in a group with others of their kind, browsing in the cool forests of Late Cretaceous western North America. The inland sea of the time was shrinking as the climate became drier.

The dinosaurs munched low herbaceous plants and perhaps reached up to drag at low branches with their horns, to strip off twigs and leaves.

When enemies appeared

Ceratopsids were too heavy and bulky to flee from fast predators. Their nose horns could offer defense in individual cases. But again, they may have used the tactic of safety in numbers.

Living in a herd ensured that as some members fed or rested, others were on guard. At the sign of danger they would crowd together, the young and vulnerable in the middle. The adults stood around them, facing the attacker. With heads lowered, they could swing their heads in a defense display that drew attention to the long face horns and sharp neck-frill spikes. Today, musk oxen gather in a circle and protect their young when faced with predators such as wolves.

Rivals and mates

When it came to breeding time, the neck frills and face horns of ceratopsids could have several uses. As visual signals they would signify which individuals belonged to which species, and to which sex, and whether they were sexually mature. The skin of the frill may have been brightly colored to act as a "flag."

The head gear may also have been used in threat displays, especially among rival males trying to gain access to females. Two rivals could face each other, heads lowered to raise the outline of the frill above the body in an impressive show of size. The head would be swung to show off the face horns.

If it came to physical contact, the horns would lock together in a pushing and wrestling match, much as rutting deer today

▲ Head to head

Herds of animals may have fought off a common enemy, but there was still rivalry between individuals within a herd, as between these two chasmosaurs.

have their shoving contests. Each dinosaur would adopt its wide-footed stance for stability as it fought. These threats and fights may have also been useful for defending the nest site from rivals and the nest itself, the eggs, or babies from predators.

On the move

Groups of such huge herbivores would have needed massive amounts of food. They may have traveled slowly and regularly, feeding as they went. Or they could use the "locust strategy" and stay in an area until it was stripped almost bare, then move on.

At certain times the herd may have set off on a longer migration to exploit seasonal food sources elsewhere or to reach their breeding sites. Estimates put the daily distance covered by a steadily walking *Centrosaurus* at about 70 miles (110 kilometers). Such migrations would have been safer in large numbers. Perhaps separate smaller groups banded together into vast multiherds at migration time. Some modern large herbivores, such as wildebeest and caribou (reindeer), do this.

Hearts and windows

Styracosaurus had one of the most remarkable ceratopsid neck frills. It was short and heart-shaped, with two small windows and various spikes radiating from its edges.

Styracosaurus was very similar in size and body shape to a rhinoceros. It also had one long nose horn but only low ridges on the eyebrows, like *Centrosaurus*. And it lived during the Late Cretaceous Period and in the same general region of North America as *Centrosaurus*.

A spiky frill

The neck frill of *Styracosaurus* had two large windows, perhaps to reduce weight. But the frill was unique among ceratopsids in the size and number of "decorations" around its edges. At the top were two great hornlike spikes, longer than the nose horn. There were two more large spikes on each side along the edge below the main spike. They were followed by a selection of smaller, blunter spikes further down the frill edge to the level of the eyes.

These frill spikes had cores formed by greatly elongated epoccipital bones, as found along the frill margins of other ceratopsids. The topmost, largest frill spikes, with their covering in life of horn, probably reached 3 feet (about 1 meter) in length.

Styracosaurus's lifestyle

Styracosaurus was a typical ceratopsid. It may have used its nose horn to ward off enemies

Temperature control

Ceratopsian dinosaurs, being reptiles, were probably "cold-blooded." More accurately, their body temperature would be affected by the temperature of the surroundings rather than being constantly high as in warm-blooded mammals and birds.

Various dinosaurs had large areas of body surface that may have helped control body temperature by taking up or losing heat. They included the "sail-backs" of the ornithopod *Ouranosaurus* and the carnosaur *Spinosaurus*, the back plates of *Stegosaurus* and other stegosaurs, and the head crests of hadrosaurs such as *Parasaurolophus*.

Did the ceratopsian neck frills also work as heat exchangers? Some fossils such as those of *Triceratops* show the marks of blood vessels on the upper surface of the frill. If the ceratopsian was too hot, it could move to the shade and lose or radiate excess body heat from the large surface area of the frill. When cold, it could stand in the full rays of the sun and absorb heat to warm up quickly. That would allow it to become active before its predators and competitors.

◄ **Impressive beast**
This front view of *Styracosaurus* shows the large spikes around the edge of the frill and the menacing nose horn. With the nose tipped down, the frill stands up vertically, increasing the dramatic effect. In life the frill may have been brightly colored or patterned. The front legs are set apart in a solid-looking stance.

and rivals by charging at them, as a rhinoceros does. The spikes around the frill edges added greatly to the impression of size and fierceness. The display reduced the possibility of getting into a physical battle, a great advantage in the animal world. Once actual fighting starts and wounds are caused, the risks of disability and death rocket.

The spiked frill of *Styracosaurus* would protect its neck and flanks from attack by predators, probably better than an unspiked version. Also, rival *Styracosaurus* males might have tried to lock or jab each other with their frill spikes during mating contents.

A variety of frills

Some experts suggest that *Styracosaurus*, *Centrosaurus*, and *Monoclonius* were so similar that they should all be placed in the same genus. In terms of overall evolution the different frill shapes were relatively minor and due mainly to species, sex, and age.

In addition, recent fossil finds could show that there was a ceratopsid like *Styracosaurus* – but with only two large frill spikes and a

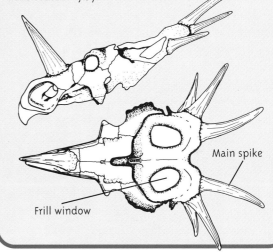

***Styracosaurus* skull**
The long frill spikes of *Styracosaurus* look like efficient weapons. But the bone of the frill, with its two gaps or windows, was not particularly solid. Great leverage on the spike could have snapped it off, broken the frill, or wrenched the dinosaur's neck terribly. More likely the spikes were for visual display or for head-wrestling contests. With them the animals would act out a set of rituals rather than going for all-out attack, which could have caused injury.

Main spike

Frill window

forward-curving nose horn that arched over the beak. Further discoveries like this may bring some answers but probably also pose further questions.

DATA BASE

Name	*Styracosaurus*
Pronounced	STY-rack-oh-SORE-us
Meaning	"spiked lizard "

What it ate
Fibrous plants

Length	18 feet (5.5 meters)
Standing height	7 feet (2.1 meters)
Weight	2.7 tons (2.7 tonnes)

When it lived	Late Cretaceous Period 75-72 million years ago
Where it lived	North America (Alberta, Montana)

Order	Ornithischia (bird-hipped dinosaurs)
Suborder	Marginocephalia
Family	Ceratopsidae

The dinosaur big-head ▶

The dinosaur big-head

Because of its massive neck frill, the ceratopsid *Torosaurus* had the longest skull of any land animal that ever lived on earth.

Like *Triceratops*, *Torosaurus* was one of the last dinosaurs to survive. Its remains, found in Wyoming, have been dated to the very end of the Cretaceous Period, 67-65 million years ago. This dinosaur was named "bull lizard" for its long, pointed eyebrow horns. However, perhaps more significant is the enormous neck frill, which was almost twice the length of the main skull.

The record-holder
Only a few good specimens of *Torosaurus* have been found, and these have consisted of skulls with frills. The earliest were discovered near the end of the nineteenth century by John Bell Hatcher in Niobrara County, Wyoming (see page 214). This site also yielded many specimens of *Triceratops*.

One skull-and-frill specimen of *Torosaurus*, known as the species *Torosaurus gladius*, measures 8 feet 6 inches (2.6 meters) in total length. This makes it the longest skull of any known land animal, even the great mammoths of recent prehistory. (However, it is smaller than the skulls of the great whales.) Another fossil

specimen, named *Torosaurus latus*, had a skull that was probably (after restoration) about 8 feet (2.4 meters) long. More than half of this length was the frill.

Details of the frill
The massive, sweeping frill of *Torosaurus* stretched halfway along the back of the animal. It had a window in each side, longer in *Torosaurus gladius*, more rounded in *Torosaurus latus*. The frill had a plain, smooth edge or margin, undecorated by spikes,

▶ **Torosaurus on the move**
This side view shows the immense size of the swept-back neck frill of *Torosaurus*. This dinosaur was the largest of the long-frilled ceratopsids. But it was not quite as bulky as *Triceratops*, weighing perhaps 1 ton (1 tonne) less. These two types of horned dinosaurs, *Torosaurus* and *Triceratops*, lived alongside each other in Late Cretaceous North America.

DATA BASE

Name *Torosaurus*
Pronounced TOR-oh-SORE-us
Meaning "bull lizard"

What it ate
Plants

Length (to tail-tip) 25 feet (7.6 meters)
Standing height 10 feet (3 meters)
Weight 4.5-5 tons (4.6-5.1 tonnes)

When it lived Late Cretaceous Period
67 million years ago
Where it lived North America
(Wyoming)

Order Ornithischia
(bird-hipped dinosaurs)
Suborder Marginocephalia
Family Ceratopsidae

lumps, or other adornments. In one specimen, the inner surfaces of the frill had irregular holes and dimples. They could be signs of a disease such as a type of bone cancer, multiple myeloma.

Horns and skull

Torosaurus had two very long eyebrow horns and a short nose horn, rather similar to the horns of *Triceratops*. The skull of *Torosaurus gladius* differs slightly from that of *Torosaurus latus* in the

shape of the eyes, the position of the brow horns, and the angle of the frill. But these differences could well be normal variations between members of one species perhaps due to age or sex rather than differences between two species.

Torosaurus skull

This specimen (which lacks its lower jaw) shows how the neck frill swept back from the rear of the skull, but at a low angle, staying close to the dinosaur's shoulders and back. The frill gaps or windows are small in proportion, especially when compared with those of *Chasmosaurus*. Its edges or margins are smooth and plain, unlike the decorated types such as *Styracosaurus*. The nose horn is little more than a large pyramid-shaped bump.

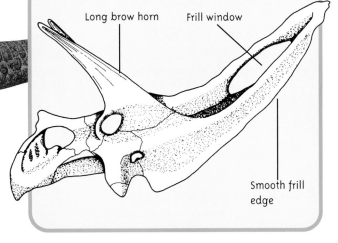

Long brow horn   Frill window

Smooth frill edge

⇨ The last ceratopsians

Anchiceratops was yet another ceratopsid known from fossils discovered in the Red Deer River region of Alberta, Canada.

Anchiceratops lived in the same region as, although perhaps slightly before, the well-known ceratopsid *Chasmosaurus*. It was also similar to *Chasmosaurus* in many ways, although it differed in various details. In size it was about 3-4 feet (1 meter) longer overall than *Chasmosaurus*, but similar in bodily proportions. It had longer eyebrow horns and a slightly shorter nose horn.

The frill of *Anchiceratops*
The neck frill of *Anchiceratops* was relatively tall and narrow from side to side. It had smallish gaps or windows to save weight. As in other ceratopsians, the frill may have had several uses – perhaps a degree of protection, also display against rivals or enemies, and a visual sign of the species, age, and sex of the owner. The visual effect would be heightened if the skin covering the frill was brightly colored or patterned.

▲ Forward horns
The nose and eyebrow horns of *Anchiceratops* all curved forward. This view shows especially well the pointed cheekbone below the eye, which early fossil hunters thought might be yet another horn. In fact, this projecting point was probably a flange to anchor the powerful jaw muscles that would spend many hours each day chewing. The beak at the front of the mouth was long and narrow.

Eight spikes
There were three pairs of prominent epoccipital bones on the upper rear margin or edge of the neck frill, forming tall cones (or short spikes). There was also another pair of such bones on the upper front of the frill, pointing nearly straight up to the sky. This pair

DATA BASE

Name	*Anchiceratops*
Pronounced	ANN-key-serra-TOPS
Meaning	"lizard with the close-set horn" (close as in near, not shut)

What it ate — Possibly swamp vegetation such as cypresses, ferns, giant redwoods, and cycads

Length	(to tail-tip) 20 feet (6.1 meters)
Standing height	7 feet (2.1 meters)
Weight	2.7 tons (2.7 tonnes)

When it lived	Late Cretaceous Period 80-75 million years ago
Where it lived	North America (Alberta)

Order	Ornithischia (bird-hipped dinosaurs)
Suborder	Marginocephalia
Family	Ceratopsidae

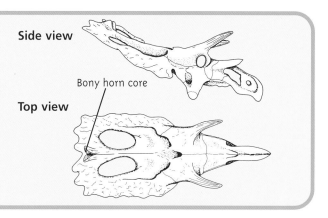
of decorations was in a position on the frill similar to the longer, curved, tonguelike projections on the frill of *Centrosaurus*.

Unlike *Chasmosaurus*, there were no nodules, lumps, or spikes around the side edges of the frill of *Anchiceratops*.

The habitat of *Anchiceratops*

Fossils of *Anchiceratops* were found in rocks where there were also deposits of coal. The coal was formed from the compressed, fossilized remains of layers of decomposing plants, usually the soft, luscious plant growth that occurred in swampy or marshy habitats. This could imply that *Anchiceratops* may have lived in or near swamps, feeding on marsh vegetation such as cypresses, ferns, cycads, and similar water-loving plants.

▲ Sniffing the air
Anchiceratops raises its head to sniff the breeze and peer about for food, herd members, enemies, and anything else that could be of interest. The upper rear edge of the frill had a neat row of six blunt spikes, and just below them in the center was another pair of lumpy, forward-facing spikes. The nose horn of *Anchiceratops* was relatively low and directed forward.

→ End of an era

About 65 million years ago a great change happened on earth. It affected the world's climate, seas, landscape, plants, and animals. It was the end of an era – what we now call the Mesozoic Era, or the time of "Middle Life." It also marked the end of the Age of Dinosaurs.

▲ Late Cretaceous scene
This artist's impression shows an upland Cretaceous landscape crossed by rivers and streams with exposed banks of sand and mud and shallow seas beyond bordered by a quietly smoking

The history of the earth itself is known mainly from the studies of rocks. In particular, it is known from the changing types and layers of rocks, which formed over hundreds of millions of years.

The history of life on earth is known mainly from fossils. They are the long-dead remains of plants, animals, and other living things, turned to stone and preserved in the rocks.

Rocks and fossils have enabled scientists to produce the geological timescale, which runs from the time when the earth was formed 4,500 million years ago to the present day.

volcano. These were ideal conditions for the preservation of dinosaurs and other animals. Their remains were washed into the river or sea, covered with sediments, and gradually became fossilized.

Evolution of life
Life on earth has never stood still. Fossils show that new kinds, or species, of living things have appeared gradually over time. This is called evolution by natural selection.

Some kinds of plants and animals lasted tens or even hundreds of millions of years. Others appeared and then died out much more quickly. This process of evolution has been so active that more than 98 percent of all the kinds of plants and animals that have ever existed on earth have come and gone. They are extinct.

Eras and periods
Changes in the rocks mark the beginning and end of the Mesozoic Era. The era began about 250-245 million years ago and ended 65 million years ago, when it gave way to the Cenozoic Era, the time of "Recent Life."

The Mesozoic Era consisted of three shorter timespans, or periods. They were the Triassic, Jurassic, and Cretaceous Periods. So, the end

of the Cretaceous Period was also the end of the Mesozoic Era.

After this came the Tertiary Period, which was the first period in the Cenozoic Era.

The Age of the Dinosaurs
The dinosaurs were part of the changing pattern of life on earth. Different kinds of dinosaurs survived through almost the whole Mesozoic Era from about 230 to 65 million years ago. Hence the Mesozoic Era is sometimes known as the Age of the Dinosaurs. Indeed, the dinosaurs were one of the most numerous, long-lived, and successful groups of animals that the world has ever seen.

A time of change
About 65 million years ago "something big" happened on our globe. Exactly what it was and how big and how sudden is not clear. But it was enough to mark a clear and worldwide transition in the rocks and fossils between the Cretaceous Period and the Tertiary Period.

After the end of the Cretaceous Period, there were no more dinosaur fossils. Not only dinosaurs – many other kinds of animals and plants disappeared from the fossil record. The disappearance of many kinds of living things at around the same time has happened several times on earth and is known as a mass extinction (see page 228).

Slow or fast? One cause or many?

Some experts say that the changes around the end of the Cretaceous Period happened gradually, lasting perhaps a few million years. Others say that they took only a few thousand years. That sounds like a long time, of course, but in relation to the history of the planet it is fairly abrupt. Some think that there was one main cause. Others point to a mixture of different causes.

The various ideas and reasons about the death of the dinosaurs are discussed in this book.

Recent extinctions

Animals and plants have always become extinct. It is part of natural evolution. However, in the past few centuries the rate of extinction has become much faster. This is due to the activities of humans. We hunt, collect, persecute, and kill for "sport." We destroy the countryside and wild places. We pollute the air, soil, and water. All of these activities harm plants, animals, and their habitats. Examples of extinctions caused by humans include

▲ Startled into action
A group of *Triceratops* is driven into the water when a *Tyrannosaurus* suddenly appears from behind a fallen tree.

the flightless bird called the dodo in the 1680s, the passenger pigeon in 1914, the thylacine, or Tasmanian wolf, in about 1933, and the Balinese tiger in 1952.

Many changes

During most of the Mesozoic Era many kinds of dinosaurs came and went. The earliest kinds, such as *Herrerasaurus* and *Coelophysis*, were around in the Triassic Period. They were mostly quite small. The biggest sauropod dinosaurs, such as *Brachiosaurus* and *Apatosaurus*, plated dinosaurs like *Stegosaurus*, and great carnosaur meat-eaters like *Allosaurus*, all lived during the Jurassic Period. The Cretaceous Period saw the rise of ornithopods such as *Iguanodon*, horned dinosaurs like *Triceratops*, and the massive and fearsome predator *Tyrannosaurus*.

▼ Cretaceous diversity
As the continents drifted further apart, the dinosaurs of certain areas became more distinctive. Pictured here are (heads from left to right) *Triceratops* from North America, *Carnotaurus* (South America), *Titanosaurus* (Africa and India), and *Saichania* (Asia).

Mass extinctions

The death of the dinosaurs, along with many other kinds of living things, was not the only mass extinction to happen on earth.

Extinction is the complete and worldwide disappearance of a species or other group of living things. It is a natural part of evolution, as new species appear and others die out.

A mass extinction is the disappearance of hundreds or thousands of species all within a relatively short time. The evidence for mass extinctions comes from fossils.

Negative evidence

The evidence for mass extinctions is that many kinds of fossils vanished from the rocks, never to reappear. This evidence is negative, in the sense that the lack of fossils is not absolute proof that the animals and plants really became extinct. For example, they could have become so rare that the chances of their becoming fossils were even lower than normal – just about zero. However, if there were other changes at the same time, for example if one type of rock was replaced by a very different type, then we can be fairly sure that mass extinctions really did occur.

The fossil record shows several mass extinctions through earth's history, especially:

- at the end of the Cambrian Period, about 505 million years ago;
- at the end of the Devonian Period, about 360 million years ago;
- in the middle and toward the end of the Permian Period (marking the end of the Paleozoic Era, or "Old Life" era) about 250 million years ago (see panel on page 230);
- at the end of the Cretaceous Period, as discussed in this book.

Cuvier's studies

One of the foremost scientists of the early nineteenth century was a French baron, Georges Cuvier (1769-1832). He was a comparative anatomist. Comparative anatomy is the study of the structures (anatomy) of living things, especially comparing their similarities and differences. It can be carried out with existing plants and animals and also with fossils.

In the early 1800s Cuvier studied many rocks and fossils, especially Tertiary Period rocks around Paris. He saw that one set of slowly changing yet similar fossils existed through several layers of rock. Then there was an abrupt alteration in both the rocks and the fossils, as new kinds replaced the earlier ones.

The fossils provided extremely strong evidence that other, quite different species had lived long

◀ **A great authority**
Baron Georges Cuvier was respected across Europe as a biologist and an authority on fossils. In particular, he described *Mosasaurus*, a huge, fierce, long-fanged, lizardlike sea reptile from the Age of Dinosaurs (mentioned in chapter 6 of this book). Using the fossils, Cuvier built up a picture of what the animal looked like in life. It encouraged more scientists in using fossils to reconstruct long-extinct creatures. Cuvier was also involved in the study of one of the first dinosaurs to be given a scientific name, *Iguanodon* (see chapter 7).

ago on earth and had become extinct. The pattern of sudden changes suggested mass extinctions.

No dinosaurs or evolution

Cuvier did not know about dinosaurs or believe in evolution. The name dinosaur, meaning "terrible lizard," was not suggested until 1841, nine years after his death. It was proposed by British anatomist Richard Owen for extinct creatures that were certainly reptiles, as shown by their fossils, but that did not fit into any of the usual reptile groups such as lizards or crocodiles. The idea of evolution by natural selection was not put forward in scientific form until 1859, when the English naturalist Charles Darwin wrote his book *On the Origin of Species*.

Early ideas on extinctions

Cuvier, like many scientists of his time, followed the ideas of the Bible. To explain changing fossils in the rocks, he suggested "catastrophism." According to this theory, many kinds of living things were created on earth, but then they were all destroyed by a catastrophe, such as a massive flood, or fire, or volcanic eruption. A new, improved set of

▲ Digging up proof
The discovery of the remains of *Mosasaurus* in a chalk quarry in Maastricht, Netherlands, supported Cuvier's belief that there had been repeated extinctions of animals in earlier times.

▼ A catastrophe from God?
Could volcanic activity on an enormous scale have wiped out the dinosaurs? Catastrophic destruction seems to be suggested by the Bible.

living things was created to follow them, but they all died out too, in another catastrophe. And so on. This notion explained the changes in fossils through time. It also fitted in with religious teachings, the most recent catastrophe being the Great Flood described in the Bible.

→ All part of evolution

Scientists now think that a mass extinction is a not a catastrophe for life on the planet but simply an ongoing event in evolution.

◀ A lakeside scene
Two sharp-toothed *Dimetrodon* in the foreground may be about to attack one of the plant-eating *Edaphosaurus* in the background. The scene is present-day Oklahoma during the Permian Period.

Part of nature
Today most scientists view mass extinctions, such as the one involving the dinosaurs at the end of the Cretaceous Period, as part of evolution by natural selection. Extinctions are the result of changes in, on, or even around our planet. Animals and plants must adapt or die in an ever-changing world where continents drift around the globe, mountains are thrust up and worn down, volcanoes erupt, sea levels rise and fall, ocean currents alter their patterns, and global climates are sometimes warm or cool, sometimes wet or dry. Most of these processes happen incredibly slowly. But we can detect them today, so we assume they happened in the past.

The Permian mass extinctions
The greatest mass extinctions occurred during and near the end of the Permian Period around 250 million years ago. Many larger animals disappeared, including the pelycosaurs ("sail reptiles"), such as *Dimetrodon*, whose skeleton is shown here. So did many kinds of land plants. In the oceans more than two-thirds of all animals and plants died out, including the last of the trilobites.

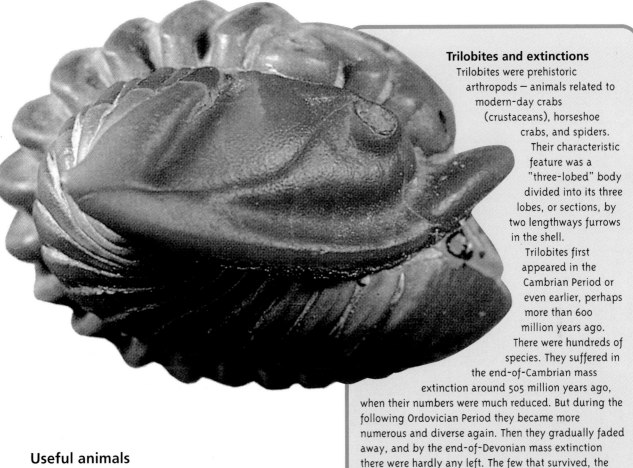

Trilobites and extinctions

Trilobites were prehistoric arthropods – animals related to modern-day crabs (crustaceans), horseshoe crabs, and spiders. Their characteristic feature was a "three-lobed" body divided into its three lobes, or sections, by two lengthways furrows in the shell.

Trilobites first appeared in the Cambrian Period or even earlier, perhaps more than 600 million years ago. There were hundreds of species. They suffered in the end-of-Cambrian mass extinction around 505 million years ago, when their numbers were much reduced. But during the following Ordovician Period they became more numerous and diverse again. Then they gradually faded away, and by the end-of-Devonian mass extinction there were hardly any left. The few that survived, the last of the trilobites, perished in the mass extinction at the end of the Permian Period.

Useful animals

Some of the most numerous fossils are formed by shelled animals of the oceans, such as sea snails and bivalve molluscs like mussels and oysters. This is partly because their shells are hard and resist decay and partly because shallow seas often provide good conditions for preservation and fossilization. These types of animals are called marine invertebrates – sea-dwelling creatures without backbones.

A huge scientific study of marine invertebrate fossils looked at more than 200,000 species in some 3,000 families, stretching over 500 million years of time from the beginning of the Cambrian Period to the present day. As this study dealt with so many animals of so many different types, scientists could make detailed and accurate statements about what they had learnt and be confident that they had got things right. By contrast, when they have just a few dinosaur fossils to study, their conclusions involve a lot of guesswork.

A repeating pattern?

The study found a pattern in the development and numbers of marine invertebrate species, which was repeated over time. The pattern was that the species increased in number and in diversity, then decreased rapidly as a result of extinctions. This happened on average every 26 million years. In some cases the extinctions were minor. In other cases they formed the well-known mass extinctions such as those at the end of the Permian Period and the end of the Cretaceous.

Whatever affected marine invertebrates in this way could also have affected animals on land. Why has there been this oddly regular pattern of extinctions? One idea is that they have been caused by a cycle of events, not on earth but deep in space, such as one or more meteoroids hitting the earth and causing great destruction.

The "bone-headed" dinosaurs ▶

The "bone-headed" dinosaurs

The pachycephalosaurs were one of the last main groups of dinosaurs on earth, surviving right up to the great extinction.

Pachycephalosaur means "thick-headed lizard." The outstanding feature of the pachycephalosaur dinosaurs was the very thick roof of the skull, made of extra-deep bone. It formed a dome of bone that looked a little like a motorcyclist's crash-helmet or a building worker's hard hat. That is why these dinosaurs have sometimes been called "dome-heads," "bone-heads," "thick-heads," or "helmet-heads." Some types of pachycephalosaurs also had decorative frills or knobs of bone around the head and on the snout.

Cousins

The pachycephalosaurs were members of the main dinosaur group called the Ornithischia, or "bird-hipped" dinosaurs. This large group included ornithopods such as *Iguanodon*, plated dinosaurs such as *Stegosaurus*, armored dinosaurs like *Ankylosaurus*, and horned dinosaurs such as *Triceratops*. They were all plant-eaters. The pachycephalosaurs may have been plant-eaters too, but fossils of their teeth suggest a more varied died of small, easily chewed food.

Why a thick head?

Why did bone-headed dinosaurs have such thick skull bone? Almost certainly, it was to absorb knocks and jars as they butted and rammed with their heads. Probably they did this to battle with rivals of their own kind, perhaps for mates at breeding time or for higher status in the social group or for a patch of territory to ensure survival.

Or they may have charged in defense at enemies, head down, to ram and injure them or to frighten them away. These different ideas are described over the following pages.

Origins

Pachycephalosaurs may have appeared in East Asia as early as the Late Jurassic Period some 150 million years ago. One possibility is that they evolved from some type of ceratopsian, or horned, dinosaur. This is why the bone-heads and horn-heads are put together as the larger dinosaur group known as the Marginocephalia (see chapter 11 above).

From East Asia the bone-heads spread to Europe, possibly Africa (one specimen coming from Madagascar), and definitely North America. Most of the better-known types lived in North America and East Asia at the end of the Cretaceous Period. However, even these "better-known" bone-headed dinosaurs are not at all well known compared with some other dinosaurs. Their fossils are few and fragmentary.

▼ **Heads you lose**
Two pachycephalosaurs bang skulls in a ritualized headbutting contest.

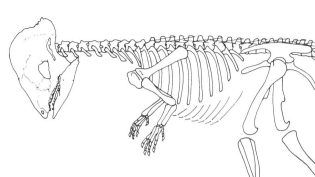

Early bone-heads

Chaoyangosaurus may be an early bone-head from China. It had jutting cheekbones and lived during the Late Jurassic Period.

Yaverlandia (named after Yaverland Point) may be a bone-head from England. Its fossils date from the Early Cretaceous Period. It had only a slight thickening of the upper skull and two low, rounded bulges on the outer surface of the skull. It may indicate a different origin for the bone-head group, namely, that they evolved from the small dinosaurs known as hypsilophodonts (described in chapter 7 of this book). Alternatively, *Yaverlandia* may have not been a pachycephalosaur at all, but an armored dinosaur or ankylosaur (see chapter 10).

Ready to ram

A bone-head such as *Stegoceras* (left) would lower its body as it got ready to butt like a battering-ram. The thickened, reinforced top of the skull would take the full impact of the blow. The jolt would pass along the bones of the neck and back, which were held in a straight line. These bones (vertebrae) and the joints between them were strongly reinforced to absorb the shock.

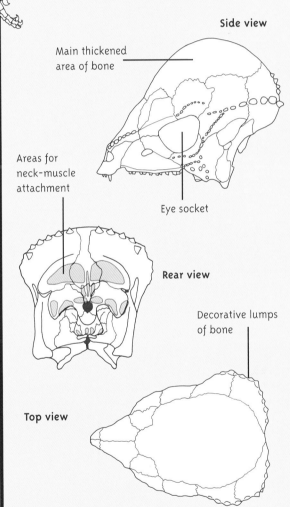

Side view

Main thickened area of bone

Areas for neck-muscle attachment

Eye socket

Rear view

Decorative lumps of bone

Top view

Bone-head skull

These three views of the fossil skull of *Prenocephale* show how the roof was enlarged into a dome. The extra bone was part of the original skull, which had become thicker. It was not another layer of bone added onto the surface, as in the armored dinosaurs or ankylosaurs. *Prenocephale* was slightly smaller than *Homalocephale* (see pages 234-235), and lived at the same time and place — the Late Cretaceous Period in Mongolia.

⇨ The even-headed bone-head

The name *Homalocephale* means "even head." This pachycephalosaur did indeed have a flatter crown to its skull. But the skull cap was still made of considerably thickened bone.

The bone-headed dinosaur *Homalocephale* did not have a bulging dome on top of its head like many of its cousins. But it did have a very thick area of bone in this region, shaped more like a flat wedge. The grain of the bone (that is, the way the fibers of bone tissue lined up) in the skull cap was at right angles to the surface for greater shock-absorbing strength.

The skull was also decorated with small bony lumps, pits, and knobs around the sides and rear. They may have developed as the animal grew and again there may have been differences that indicated the sex and age of the individual.

Unique neck

The joint between the skull and the neck of *Homalocephale* was unique among dinosaurs. It had a wide range of movement, which allowed the head to be held facing forward, with eyes and nose pointing to the front, or facing downward, with the top of the head to the front. There were strong, thick, straplike ligaments, called nuchal ligaments, running between the back of the head and the neck to support the head.

Strong, stiff back

Further to the rear, the joints between the backbones had grooved surfaces to stop them twisting, which meant the back was very stiff. The vertebral tendons running alongside the backbones were ossified, or hardened with bone, to increase this stiffness. The hips of *Homalocephale* were also unusually broad and strong. Any sudden physical shock would have passed down from the head, neck, and back through the hips and down through the legs to the ground.

◄ Flathead

This reconstruction of *Homalocephale* shows that the head was flatter than the dome heads of *Stegoceras* and *Pachycephalosaurus*. Even so, the bone across the top of the skull was thicker than in other dinosaurs. The small teeth, like those of *Stegoceras*, indicate a diet of soft plants or perhaps a mixture of leaves, shoots, fruit, and small animals such as insects.

Homalocephale skull roof

Dinosaur battering ram

All of these features point to head-to-head butting or pushing in *Homalocephale*. The whole body seems designed as a living battering-ram for delivering a powerful head blow. *Homalocephale* would run toward its opponent with its head held nose down, facing the ground, and with neck, back, and tail standing stiffly out behind.

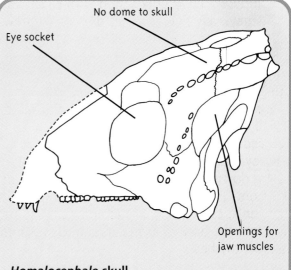

No dome to skull

Eye socket

Openings for jaw muscles

Homalocephale skull

The skull of *Homalocephale* (above and left) lacks the high dome of certain other bone-headed dinosaurs. It has large eye sockets, tiny teeth, and small knobs of bone forming two lines on each side, one down the cheek area and one behind the eye sloping up and back across the temple region.

Other bone-headed dinosaurs

- *Stygimoloch* (from Montana) had horns around the back of its skull.
- *Majungatholus* (from Madagascar) also lived during the Late Cretaceous Period.
- *Ornatotholus* (from Alberta) may have been a female version of *Stegoceras*, with a rough, pitted skull.
- *Goyocephale* (from Mongolia) was a flat-headed type with a rough, pitted skull and a pair of large, stabbing teeth in both the upper and lower jaw.

DATA BASE

Name *Homalocephale*
Pronounced Home-ah-LOW-sef-ah-LEE
Meaning "even head"

What it ate
Plant-eater or possibly omnivorous, feeding on fruit, leaves, seeds, insects, and other items

Length (nose - tail-tip) 10 feet (3 meters)
Standing height 5 feet (1.5 meters)
Weight 140 pounds (64 kilograms)

When it lived Late Cretaceous Period 70 million years ago
Where it lived Asia (Mongolia)

Order Ornithischia (bird-hipped dinosaurs)
Suborder Marginocephalia
Family Homalocephalidae

Largest and last bone-head ▶

Largest and last bone-head

Pachycephalosaurus was a very large bone-headed dinosaur and has given its name to the whole group. It was also one of the last of its kind.

Several fossil skulls of *Pachycephalosaurus* have been uncovered in Alberta, Canada. But very few remains of the rest of its skeleton have been discovered. Guesswork from comparisons with other bone-headed dinosaurs suggests that *Pachycephalosaurus* was a stocky animal with a short, thick neck, short arms, a bulky body, long legs, and a heavy, rigid tail. It was probably about as tall and as long as a large drafthorse of today.

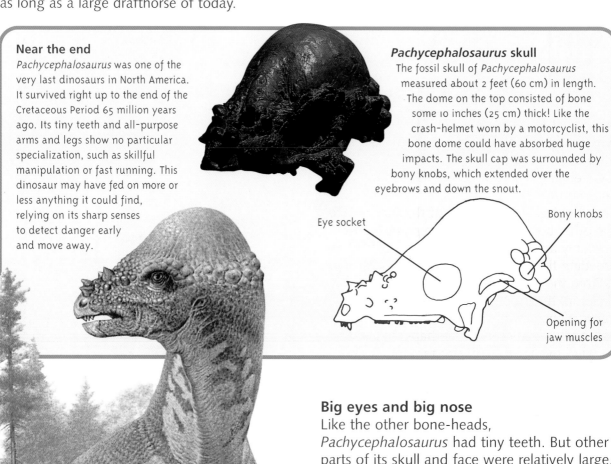

Near the end
Pachycephalosaurus was one of the very last dinosaurs in North America. It survived right up to the end of the Cretaceous Period 65 million years ago. Its tiny teeth and all-purpose arms and legs show no particular specialization, such as skillful manipulation or fast running. This dinosaur may have fed on more or less anything it could find, relying on its sharp senses to detect danger early and move away.

Pachycephalosaurus skull
The fossil skull of *Pachycephalosaurus* measured about 2 feet (60 cm) in length. The dome on the top consisted of bone some 10 inches (25 cm) thick! Like the crash-helmet worn by a motorcyclist, this bone dome could have absorbed huge impacts. The skull cap was surrounded by bony knobs, which extended over the eyebrows and down the snout.

Eye socket

Bony knobs

Opening for jaw muscles

Big eyes and big nose
Like the other bone-heads, *Pachycephalosaurus* had tiny teeth. But other parts of its skull and face were relatively large, especially the eye sockets. The eyes faced partly forward, rather than sideways, for a degree of stereoscopic, or binocular, vision. This is where the fields of vision seen by each eye overlap, allowing accurate judgement of distance. The shape of the braincase shows that the olfactory lobes were also big. They are the sections of the brain that deal with smell. So *Pachycephalosaurus* probably had good senses of sight and smell.

In difficult country
Pachycephalosaurus may have lived in small groups, where one animal was always likely to be looking, listening, and sniffing for danger while the others fed. Its main

◄ A crash-helmet with knobs on
This reconstruction clearly shows the bony knobs that extended most of the way around the head at eyebrow level.

▼ French connection
This reconstruction of *Pachycephalosaurus* is on display at the Palais de la Découverte, Paris.

▼ Walk in the woods
Pachycephalosaurus, the largest and one of the last of the pachycephalosaurs, takes a walk in the Alberta woods.

defense at close quarters would be to charge at attackers with head lowered and deliver an enormously forceful knock-out blow with its great thick skull. Like the other bone-heads, *Pachycephalosaurus* probably also battled with rivals of its kind at breeding time or for dominance in the group.

From the scarce fossil remains of its skeleton, the proportions of the legbones of *Pachycephalosaurus* suggest that it was not an especially speedy runner. Perhaps it avoided enemies by living in difficult terrain, among rocks or thick, thorny undergrowth, as goats and bighorn sheep do today.

DATA BASE

Name	*Pachycephalosaurus*
Pronounced	PAK-ee-seff-ah-LOW-sore-us
Meaning	"thick-headed lizard"

What it ate Plant-eater, possibly omnivorous, feeding on fruit, leaves, seeds, insects, and similar items

Length	(nose - tail-tip) 15-20 feet (4.6-6.1 meters)
Standing height	9 feet (2.7 meters)
Weight	800-900 pounds (360-410 kilograms) (very approximate as there are so few fossils of the body and limbs)

When it lived	Late Cretaceous Period 65 million years ago
Where it lived	North America (Alberta)

Order	Ornithischia (bird-hipped dinosaurs)
Suborder	Marginocephalia
Family	Pachycephalosauridae

The end-of-Cretaceous world

The 80 million years of the Cretaceous Period involved enormous changes on earth, with continents shifting and the landscape brightly colored with flowering plants and many new kinds of insects.

The Age of Dinosaurs consisted of three huge periods of prehistoric time. They were the Triassic, Jurassic, and Cretaceous Periods (see page 226). For much of this time, the great landmasses or continents of the world were joined together, forming the supercontinent of Pangaea. Through the Jurassic Period a vast body of water began to form in the southern region of Pangaea. It was the Tethys Sea. It made Pangaea into a type of sideways U shape. The northern arm of the U is known as Laurasia and the southern arm as Gondwanaland.

The great break-up

During the Late Jurassic and Early Cretaceous Periods, Pangaea at last began to split into the two subgroups of continents, Laurasia and Gondwanaland. As the Cretaceous Period went on, these two subgroups split further into the continents we know today. Also, these continents began to drift to the places where they are today.

Changes during the Cretaceous

Toward the end of the Cretaceous Period the North Atlantic Ocean was forming as North America drifted away from Europe. Similarly, the South Atlantic opened up as South America slid further away from Africa. The "island" of India moved northward toward Eurasia. The Tethys Sea disappeared as Africa collided with Eurasia.

◄ **Continental drift**
(Top) Two hundred million years ago almost all the land on earth was contained in Pangaea. (Center) By 110 million years ago Pangaea had split into Laurasia and Gondwanaland, which themselves were beginning to split up. (Bottom) The continents are shown in their present positions – but they are continuing to move.

Another factor in the changing world was sea level. This was affected both by climate and by mountainbuilding and similar activity. The sea began to rise in the second half of the Cretaceous Period. By the end of the period, much of the earth's land surface – probably more than at any other time – was covered by shallow seas. So, on a global map of land and sea, the continents looked smaller than they are today. They also had different shapes, since many low-lying areas of land were flooded.

Land and sea

Land animals became isolated on these small "islands." Evolving in separated groups, they became more diverse. Sea life was especially successful because of the increased areas of shallow water. Marine reptiles such as mosasaurs, in particular, grew to huge sizes. Many winged reptiles or pterosaurs fed mainly from the sea, and they too were very widespread and successful.

Because there were large tracts of shallow ocean, tiny sea organisms thrived. When they died, their microscopic chalky shells piled up on the sea floor. These shelly remains eventually became squeezed and hardened into great layers, or strata, of chalk rock. Indeed, the Cretaceous Period is named after the term *kreta* or *creta*, meaning "chalk."

Drier and cooler

However, as the Cretaceous Period closed, the level of the sea plummeted. During the following Tertiary Period it continued to fall until it reached its present level. Also, plant fossils show that the climate was cooling a lot by the end of the Cretaceous Period. These climate changes were probably due to the movements of the earth's continents, which in

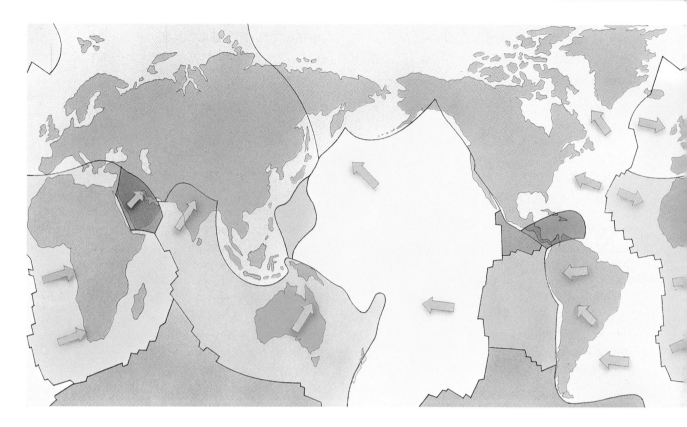

▲ Plate tectonics

The process of continental drift happens because the hard outer layer of the earth, called the crust, is not one vast ball-shaped piece. It is made up of 12-20 huge curved parts, known as lithospheric plates, with jagged edges. These fit together like an immense spherical jigsaw.

Massive temperatures and pressures from deep in the earth have kept the plates moving. Also, some plates have grown as new rock has been added to their edges. Others shrank as their edges were rubbed away or forced down to melt back into the planet's interior. These massive earth movements cause earthquakes, volcanoes, tsunamis (tidal waves), and similar events.

The entire process is called plate tectonics. It explains continental drift and the ever-changing map of our world, and continues today.

turn changed the patterns of ocean currents. The oceans absorb the sun's warmth, and their currents have a tremendous effect on the way this heat is spread around the globe. For example, as Australia moved away from Antarctica, cold water currents could flow up nearer to the equator, cooling the southern tropics.

Plant life

On land the great plant success story of the Cretaceous Period was the appearance of flowering plants, or angiosperms. Before plants with proper flowers, the landscape had been dominated by conifers, ferns, and similar, mainly green plants. By the end of the Cretaceous Period, nine-tenths of plants were flowering plants. Many had bright petals and broad leaves, contrasting with the brown cones and needle leaves of pines, firs, and other conifers. Among the early types of flowering plants were probably magnolias and water-lilies.

Flowers and insects

Flowering plants continue to dominate in our world today. They include all our common flowers, herbs, and grasses. They also include bushes and trees with blossom and fruit, rather than cones, such as oaks, beeches, maples, ashes, and sycamores.

Closely connected with the spread of flowering plants during the Cretaceous Period was the rapid evolution of many new insect groups. Bees buzzed and butterflies flitted among the flowers, feeding on their nectar and carrying their pollen. Flowers and insects developed together – this is called coevolution (see pages 244-245). The world at the end of the Cretaceous period was more colorful and busier than it had been at the start.

What perished in the great extinction? ➤

→ What perished in the great extinction?

The dinosaurs are the best-known group of animals to disappear in the end-of-Cretaceous mass extinction. But many other kinds of animals died out and numerous plants too.

Dinosaurs are undoubted stars of the prehistoric world. Their death at the end of the Cretaceous Period is one of the great puzzles of earth's history. Many of the explanations about the mass extinction focus on dinosaurs alone. Yet dinosaurs were just one of the many groups affected. Any theory about the causes of the extinction must take into account the many other life forms that perished, such as the dinosaurs' reptile cousins – the flying pterosaurs and swimming ichthyosaurs. It should also explain why certain groups survived.

Fewer kinds of living things

The fossil record shows that overall about two-thirds to three-quarters of all kinds of living things perished at or near the end of the Cretaceous Period. True, a large proportion of them were reptiles. The Age of Dinosaurs, which could also be called the Age of Reptiles, was really at an end.

▲▶ Former times
Some groups of dinosaurs which had been very successful were already waning by the end of the Cretaceous, like sauropods (above). Various sharks had also come and gone, like *Pleuracanthus* (right), but some members survived the extinction.

Reptiles on land

In general, nearly every land animal more than about 3 feet (1 meter) in length or more than 55 pounds (25 kilograms) in weight perished. This included the vast majority of dinosaurs, as well as other large land reptiles. Small lizards, small land tortoises, and snakes (which had appeared only toward the end of the Cretaceous) escaped that fate. So did aquatic (water-dwelling) turtles in freshwater lakes and the salty water of the sea.

Reptiles in the air

The flying, flapping, soaring pterosaurs – which had been so widespread and numerous

– also perished. However, the birds as a whole, which had probably evolved from small dinosaurs during the Jurassic Period, managed to survive, although several large bird groups, or families, disappeared.

Reptiles in the sea

Most of the large marine reptiles, such as ichthyosaurs, plesiosaurs, mosasaurs, and big marine crocodiles, all died out by or at the end of the Cretaceous. In fact, some types were already declining or gone before this time. But, as mentioned above, smaller turtles and crocodiles survived.

There is little similarity between the stages of evolution in these groups. Some had only just appeared. Others were established and very diverse. Still others were already on the wane.

Other sea creatures
Many kinds of fish, including various sharks, were lost in the mass extinction. Since that time the bony fish (those with a skeleton

◄▼ Already in decline
Ichthyosaurs such as the Triassic *Cymbospondylus* (left) and the Jurassic *Stenopterygius* (below) had been changing and evolving through most of the Age of the Dinosaurs. However the ichthyosaur group went into decline well before the end of the Cretaceous.

of bone, not cartilage) have recovered spectacularly. They are now in the vast majority and include cod, barracudas, tunas, wrasses, gobies, and more than 20,000 other species. Sharks (which have cartilage skeletons) remain but are in the minority.

What of the marine invertebrates, or animals without backbones? The shelled sea-dwellers called ammonites and belemnites did not make it past the end of the Cretaceous Period. These large animals were molluscs, relatives of squid and octopus.

Many other types of mollusc "shellfish" also perished. So did nearly all of the lampshells, or brachiopods. These animals looked like bivalve molluscs such as oysters and clams. Brachiopods were once enormously common and widespread. They are now classed as a minority group of curious "living fossils."

However, many other marine invertebrates survived. They included molluscs such as whelks and other sea-snails, also crabs and prawns and other crustaceans, and starfish, sea urchins, and other echinoderms.

Other land creatures
Apart from birds and some reptiles, on land the mammals survived. The first mammals had appeared on earth at about the same time as the first dinosaurs. But they stayed small and scarce. Most were the size of mice or rats. None was bigger than a cat.

Amphibians such as frogs and newts have a reputation today for being especially sensitive to environmental changes and other disturbances, such as pollution and global warming. Yet they also survived the mass extinction.

Most land-dwelling invertebrates, such as insects, spiders, slugs, snails, and worms, were largely unaffected by the mass extinction.

◄ Flying through the water
Kronosaurus was a giant pliosaur with flipper-shaped limbs that probably flapped up and down to help the animal "fly" through the water. Its fossils have been found in rocks in Australia dating from the Early Cretaceous Period.

► Small survivor
Megazostrodon was one of the first mammals. It appeared more than 200 million years ago. Although mammals evolved at the same time as dinosaurs, they remained small and insignificant throughout the Age of Dinosaurs.

→ A sudden end?

How quick were the drastic events at the end of the Cretaceous Period? Did they take a few years, several centuries, or tens of millennia?

The evidence of rocks and fossils shows that about 65 million years ago, something happened to the earth and its living things. But what? Trying to make an accurate, detailed account of events so long ago is very difficult. Even extremely basic information can be hard to get, such as dating the layers, or strata, of rocks and identifying the bits of fossils in them.

Scientific studies are supposed to uncover the truth, but often they provide conflicting evidence. Sometimes the experts study the same evidence and then disagree about what it means. It is a complex patchwork of clues and information to knit together into one story that everyone can agree on.

Potential problems

Layers of rocks may be bent, twisted, or even turned upside-down. This means older fossils are on top of younger ones – the opposite of what we normally find.

Occasionally the fossils of a dinosaur are discovered in rocks dating from the Tertiary Period – the time after the Cretaceous, when all dinosaurs were supposed to be extinct. This is usually because the fossils, which had become very hard, have been worn, or eroded, out of one layer and then buried again later in a younger rock layer. This gives the false impression that the fossils date from a later time than they actually did.

▼ Even the biggest died out
The largest mosasaur grew to over 36 feet (11 meters) long and had a tremendous gaping mouth and rows of sharp teeth. This one is eying some curly-shelled ammonites, which might make a meal for it.

A long debate
Arguments about the speed of evolution have been around for as long as the idea of evolution itself.
- The English naturalist Charles Darwin (1809-82; below) proposed the theory of evolution by natural selection in his book *On the Origin of Species* (1859). He saw it as a very slow and gradual process. Species changed in many tiny stages and became new species as they evolved to cope with their changing surroundings.
- The great French anatomist and fossil expert Baron Georges Cuvier (see page 228) believed that life progressed in a series of catastrophes. A disaster such as a flood wiped out most living things, and God replaced them with a new set.

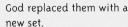

▲▶ Living diversity
(Above) Ichthyosaurs, such as *Ichthyosaurus* itself, lived about 150 million years ago, and most were already extinct some time before the Cretaceous Period. (Right) A floodborne log passes the reptile *Trilophosaurus*. Catastrophists believe that a disaster such as widespread flooding could have wiped out the dinosaurs.

Conflict and disagreement
A survey in one area on one group of fossilized animals may give different results from surveys in other areas on other groups. For example, some animals called ammonites, which were like sea snails, died out around the same time as the dinosaurs. A survey of ammonite fossils along the west coast of Europe showed that a sudden event abruptly killed one-half to three-quarters of them. However, similar surveys in other parts of the world show that ammonites declined gradually over the last 10 million years of the Cretaceous Period.

Views about the death of the dinosaurs and events at the end of the Cretaceous Period fall into two main groups. They are the gradualists and the catastrophists (see panel).

A sudden end?
The catastrophists believe that some sudden, worldwide disaster struck the earth. Exactly which disaster is discussed on the following pages. Animals and plants may have been poisoned, suffocated, starved, diseased, frozen, boiled, or zapped with radiation! But it was quick, lasting less than one million years – perhaps just a few years.

One survey of worldwide dinosaur diversity showed that at any one time, there were at least 50-100 species of dinosaurs in 20-30

groups or families. And this global dinosaur diversity continued right up to the end of the Cretaceous Period. However, these results do not agree with surveys based in North America (below).

Or a slow decline?
The gradualists believe that whatever killed the dinosaurs (and many other animals and plants) happened over a long period of time. The climate may have changed slowly.

Supporters of the gradualist idea point to their own surveys, which show that various dinosaur groups were on the wane as the Cretaceous Period drew to a close. And not only dinosaurs. One report suggests that certain types of sea animals were beginning to fade out for 30 million years beforehand. Belemnites and ichthyosaurs were probably extinct well before the end of the period.

A study of fossils in the Late Cretaceous rocks of North America suggests that dinosaurs decreased and mammals increased over the last eight million years of the period. Another study found that dinosaurs declined from 16 families to nine in the last 10 million years of the period.

At the very end, just a few dozen specimens of some 12 types of dinosaurs were left. They included *Saltasaurus*, *Tyrannosaurus*, *Pachycephalosaurus*, *Parasaurolophus*, *Gallimimus*, *Dravidosaurus*, *Ankylosaurus*, and *Triceratops*.

⇒ Plants, parasites, particles, predators

There seem to be endless theories about the mass extinction. Most of them are believable to an extent, but we cannot yet prove any of them.

◄ At home in the environment
A *Revueltosaurus* strides through a forest of palms, ferns, and low-growing trees. The dinosaurs were well adapted to living in this kind of environment. They may have come to rely on substances in these ancient plants, which disappeared as the new flowering plants spread.

Danger from deep space

There are many ideas about extraterrestrial causes for mass extinctions. They include:

- Periodic solar flares – vast tongues of flaming gas from the sun that emit extra heat and harmful rays.
- A tenth planet, in addition to the nine we know today. It would orbit through the Oort Cloud – the mass of rocky debris that lies beyond the orbit of the outermost known planet, Pluto. It could cause a massive shower of meteorites to head toward the other planets. Evidence for a

tenth planet has accumulated during the late 1990s.

- A supernova – the gigantic "death explosion" of a star. The Crab Nebula in the modern night sky is the debris of a supernova that was recorded by Chinese astronomers in 1054. If a supernova happened near earth, the resulting intense rays and magnetic shock wave could harm living things.
- A nearby collapsing star could also release huge bursts of atomic particles called neutrinos. They would bathe the earth like invisible rain and cause epidemics of cancer among animals and plants. (It is known from modern experiments that neutrinos can damage living cells and lead to cancer.)

Two suns?

Another group of ideas involves a twin for our nearest star, the sun. There are many examples of twin, or binary, stars in space. The sun and its supposed twin, nicknamed Nemesis – which nobody has detected yet – would orbit each other once every 26 million years. When the twin comes close, its immense gravity upsets the asteroids orbiting between Mars and Jupiter. They shower across the solar system, hitting planets as giant meteorites.

Another twin-star theory suggests that Nemesis disturbs the Oort Cloud (see above) and pulls meteorites toward the inner planets. The timing of such an event fits in with evidence that there is an increase in meteorite showers on earth every 26 million years.

Nemesis would not be a great shining ball like the sun. It could have evolved faster than its twin and aged more to become an almost-invisible "brown dwarf."

The end of the evolutionary road

Some ideas about dinosaur extinction were based on the notion of "evolutionary old age." Just as an individual animal becomes old and weak and finally dies – so does an animal

▲ **Varanid lizards raiding a hadrosaur nest**
If lizards, mammals, or other predators ate dinosaur eggs, it could bring the reign of the dinosaurs to a sudden end.

group. The group no longer has enough vigor or variety to alter and cope with a changing world. It uses up all of its possible genes. It is simply "worn out." So, after 155 million years as the main land animals, the dinosaur group reached the end of its natural life. It had begun to evolve dead-end designs that were too specialized to adapt.

◀ **A small mammal among the leaves**
The dinosaurs thrived as long as the ferns and leafy plants of the Cretaceous Period were available to eat. Flowering plants may not have suited them, however.

⇨ Dinosaurs in the future

Even if we cannot recreate dinosaurs from DNA, we can do the next best things. The crude static models of dinosaurs made in the nineteenth century have been improved beyond their makers' wildest dreams. Whether computer-generated, on-screen animations or handmade models, the dinosaur recreations of the twenty-first century are incredibly lifelike.

▲ Animated display
Visitors to the Canberra Science Museum, Australia, watch a lifesized animated model of *Ceratosaurus*. The model was based on studies of fossil remains and similar dinosaurs. It is jointed to allow some degree of movement.

Seeing fossils without digging
A developing technique called seismic profiling can help reveal fossils while they are still buried in the ground. Small shock waves or seismic waves are generated by a tiny explosion or a strong physical knock such as a hammer blow. The waves pass into and through the ground. Different types and shapes of rocks allow the waves from this "miniearthquake" to pass through them, or they may deflect or even reflect the waves.

Vibration sensors nearby, similar to earthquake detectors or seismographs, pick up the complex patterns of shock waves that result. The patterns are analyzed and assembled on a computer to give a picture of what is in the ground below, including any fossils. The technique is generally similar to the medical scan that reveals an unborn human baby in the womb. However, a baby scan is produced using ultrasound, not seismic shocks!

Modern electrical miniengineering and computer programming are two areas of science that have helped make dinosaurs more real than ever before. We see them walking, running, hunting, eating, drinking, and breeding. But only on a TV or movie screen or as animated electronic "animatronic" models. Animatronic models are based on a reconstructed dinosaur, built up from its skeleton out to its skin. (Some of the techniques for doing this are explained in chapter 1.

Realistic movements
An animatronics model has a flexible, or plasticized, covering that bulges and wrinkles just like real reptile skin and in the right places, such as around joints. The framework inside the model has joints and levers worked by handles or small electric motors. They move various body parts, not only the neck, legs, and tail but also detailed motions such as the eyes, tongue, and nostrils. Each joint is designed to copy the range of movement suggested by the fossil bones it is based on. So some dinosaurs have flexible, whippy tails while others have stiff tails like rods.

The skilled animators who control the models study similar animals today and also computer versions of moving dinosaurs. For example, small dinosaurs are made to walk or run like small lizards with quick, jerky, darting movements. Larger dinosaurs move more slowly and smoothly, since it takes time to get their great bulk in motion.

What does the future hold?
Can we know much more about dinosaurs than we do now? Can we make even better and more lifelike models or screen versions of them? Can we find out were they came from way back in history and which animals were their immediate ancestors in the Triassic Period? Will we know the reason why they all died out

Will we know the color of dinosaurs?

Perhaps. Recent research on very well-preserved dinosaur fossils has revealed microscopic ridges in the scales and skin. Similar pits and ridges are present in today's reptiles. They are so small that they are able to split light into its different colors of the rainbow, just as a prism splits white light into a spectrum. Such splitting is based on a property of light rays called interference. It helps give modern reptiles — and other creatures such as butterflies — their iridescent hues and sheens. Careful study of the sizes and patterns of the ridges in dinosaur fossils may suggest which colors they would have produced in life.

◀▼ Practical paleontology

(Above) A researcher adds finishing touches to a replica of a skeleton of *Titanosaurus*. (Below, upper) Using simple tools, a paleontologist gradually uncovers fossils of *Tarbosaurus* in the Gobi Desert of Mongolia. (Below, lower) Divers on the Isle of Wight, southern England, prepare to go underwater to search for *Iguanodon* remains.

during the mass extinction at the end of the Cretaceous Period?

The answers to these questions are: yes, yes, and probably, probably. Several major dinosaur fossils are uncovered each year. These new finds have continued to change and extend our ideas about dinosaurs. They may show how they spread around the world, or which groups evolved into another, or if some dinosaurs were warm-blooded. There is no reason why such finds should not continue into the future, showing us more about the ways they moved and fed and reared their young. Then we can more accurately represent dinosaurs in reconstructions.

There is also every reason to suppose that our scientific methods of rebuilding dinosaurs will improve. We will find new and more revealing clues to tell us how they lived and died. Many other branches of science will help, such as medicine, computer scanning, radio-dating, and comparative anatomy. The past and the present will teach us more in the future about the dinosaurs – the most fascinating animals ever to live on earth.

Glossary

Note These are explanations of terms as they relate to dinosaurs and other prehistoric animals. Some of the terms have more general biological, geological, or scientific meanings.

Advanced Appearing later in a sequence or more recently in time; one of the later of its kind.

Age of the Dinosaurs The time when dinosaurs were the dominant large animals on land. Usually taken to mean most of the Mesozoic Era, from the Middle-Late Triassic Period 230-220 million years ago to the end of the Cretaceous Period 65 million years ago.

Ankylosaur An armored dinosaur with lumps, plates, or slabs of protective bone in its skin, and a large bony lump on the end of the tail for use as a club.

Archosaurs ("ruling reptiles") A reptile group that included dinosaurs, pterosaurs, and also the crocodiles of today.

Articulated In a skeleton, having bones still in position next to each other, as they were when the animal was alive, rather than jumbled up or scattered.

Bipedal Walking or moving about on two legs, usually the back pair (like ourselves).

Carnivore An animal that eats mainly the meat or flesh of other creatures.

Carnosaur A general name for any medium-sized or large predatory or meat-eating dinosaur that ran on its two larger back legs, like *Allosaurus* or *Tyrannosaurus*. Not a true classification group.

Carpal Bone in the wrist.

Caudal To do with the tail. A caudal vertebra is a backbone in the tail.

Ceratopsian A horned and/or frilled dinosaur, with horns on the face or head and a large rufflike neck frill, such as *Triceratops*.

Cervical To do with the neck.

Clavicle The collarbone or similar bone in the upper chest and shoulder region.

Coelurosaur ("hollow-tailed lizard") A general name for a small, slim, and lightweight dinosaur such as *Coelophysis* from early in the Age of the Dinosaurs. Not a true classification group.

Cold-blooded (more accurately, "ectothermic") Referring to an animal that does not generate heat inside its body and whose body temperature therefore varies with the temperature of its surroundings.

Continental drift The slow movement over millions of years of the major landmasses about the surface of the earth. The earthís crust is made up of sections called lithospheric plates, which float about on the layer of molten rock underneath, carrying the continents with them. The process is called plate tectonics.

Convergent evolution The evolution of two or more different types of animals in such a way that they come to look or be similar because they occupy the same habitat or face the same problems. Two examples are the wings of bats and pterosaurs, which look similar on the outside but have different bone patterns, and the overall streamlined body shape of marlin (living fish), ichthyosaur (extinct reptile), and dolphin (mammal) for moving fast through the sea.

Cranium The topmost curved dome of the skull, mainly above the face and around the brain ñ the ìbrain case.î

Cretaceous One of the periods or timespans of the earthís history, lasting from about 144 to 65 million years ago; the last period of the Mesozoic Era and the Age of the Dinosaurs.

Digit Finger or toe.

Digitigrade Walking and running on the toes or even the toe-tips (digits).

Disarticulated In a skeleton, having bones jumbled up or scattered about, not in position next to each other, as they were when the animal was alive.

Dromaeosaur A small to medium-sized active, predatory dinosaur that walked on its back legs, with sharp teeth and claws, such as *Deinonychus*. Some dromaeosaurs are called raptors.

Ectothermic Of an animal, unable to generate heat inside its body. Its body temperature therefore varies with the temperature of its surroundings.

Endothermic Of an animal, able to generate heat inside its body. Its body temperature stays constant and usually high, despite the varying temperature of its surroundings. Today only mammals and birds are endothermic.

Evolution The slow process of change in living things, usually gradual and taking thousands or millions of years.

Extinction The dying out of every member of a group of living things, with the result that the species or group has gone forever.

Femur Thigh or upper legbone.

Fenestra A gap, hole, or ìwindow,î usually in a bone.

Fibula Bone in the lower leg, sometimes called the calfbone.

Gastric To do with the stomach or general belly region. Gastroliths are "stomach stones" swallowed by dinosaurs on purpose to help grind up food in the gizzard, stomach, and other digestive parts.

Geology The scientific study of the earth, its formation and history, its rocks and other materials, and the processes and events that shape them.

Hadrosaur A duckbilled dinosaur, an ornithopod-type dinosaur with a mouth shaped like a duckís beak.

Herbivore An animal that eats mainly plants, including leaves, fruit, stems, shoots, buds, roots, and so on.

Heterodontosaur A small, plant-eating dinosaur with teeth of different shapes, some long and sharp like tusks or fangs and others flatter for crushing food. A member of the larger ornithopod group.

Humerus Bone in the upper arm.

Hypsilophodont A small, slim, agile plant-eating dinosaur with front upper teeth in a beaklike mouth, plus rear upper and lower chewing teeth. A member of the larger ornithopod group.

Jurassic One of the periods or timespans of the earthís history, lasting from about 208 to 144 million years ago; the middle period of the Mesozoic Era and the Age of the Dinosaurs.

Keratin A body substance (protein) that forms our fingernails and toenails, also our hair and mammal fur, hooves, and horns, and also the feathers of birds and scales of reptiles.

Lumbar To do with the lower back.

Mandible Lower jawbone.

Matrix The rock around a fossil, encasing or containing it.

Maxilla Bone forming part or all of the upper jaw.

Metabolism A general name for the many chemical processes that go on inside a living thing.

Metacarpal Bone in the palm part of the hand.

Metatarsal Bone in the sole part of the foot.

Natural selection The way that the natural struggle for survival allows some individuals to live and breed and in so doing to pass their genes (coded information contained in the cells) to the next generation. Stronger and fitter individuals are inaturally selectedî to survive, weaker ones are not.

Nodosaur An armored dinosaur with lumps (nodules), plates, slabs, and spines of protective bone in its skin, but lacking a large bony lump on the end of the tail.

Occipital At the rear of the skull, usually low down near the neck.

Omnivore An animal that eats meat, plants, and any other food.

Orbit The hole or socket in the skull for the eye.

Ornithischian ("bird-hipped") A dinosaur with hipbones similar in general structure to those of a bird. There were several major groups of ornithischian dinosaurs, which were all plant-eaters, including the ornithopods, ceratopsians, stegosaurs, ankylosaurs, and pachycephalosaurs.

Ornithomimosaur An ostrich dinosaur, a small to medium-sized slim, lightweight dinosaur with long, powerful back legs, long neck and beaklike mouth, like *Struthiomimus*. It had the general shape and proportions of an ostrich.

Ornithopod ("bird foot") A large group of dinosaurs with birdlike feet, including *Iguanodon* and the hadrosaurs.

Pachycephalosaur A thick-headed, bone-headed, or helmet-headed dinosaur such as *Pachycephalosaurus* with a thickened layer of bone on the top of the skull, presumably for butting and battering.

Paleontology The scientific study of extinct life forms, especially as revealed by their fossils.

Pectoral To do with the shoulder region.

Pelvic To do with the hip region.

Pelvis Hipbone, made of individual bones joined or fused together.

Permian One of the periods or timespans of the earth's history, lasting from about 290 to 248 million years ago; the last period of the Paleozoic Era and the period before the Age of the Dinosaurs.

Phalanges Bones in the digits (fingers and toes).

Plantigrade Walking and running flat on the soles of the feet.

Predator An animal that hunts and kills other creatures – known as its prey – for food.

Prey An animal that is hunted and killed by another, the predator.

Primitive Appearing early in a sequence or long ago; one of the first of its kind.

Prosauropod A medium-sized to large dinosaur such as *Plateosaurus* showing development of the sauropod features of small head, long neck, barrellike body, stout, pillar-shaped legs, and a long, tapering tail.

Pterosaurs A extinct group of flying reptiles that lived throughout the Age of the Dinosaurs.

Quadrupedal Walking or moving about on four legs.

Radius Bone in the lower arm or forearm.

Raptor Variously interpreted as "thief," "predator," or "plunderer." Usually refers to the small to medium-sized active, predatory dinosaurs that walked on their back legs, with sharp teeth and claws, especially dromaeosaurs such as *Velociraptor*.

Saurischian ("lizard-hipped") A dinosaur with hipbones similar in general structure to those of a lizard. There were two major groups of saurischian dinosaurs – all of the meat-eating theropods and all of the large to giant-sized plant-eating prosauropods and sauropods.

Sauropod A large to giant-sized dinosaur with a small head, long neck, barrellike body, stout, pillar-shaped legs and a long, tapering tail, such as *Diplodocus*.

Scapula Shoulder blade bone.

Scute A bony or horny structure in the skin, such as a flat, shieldlike plate.

Sedimentary rock Rock formed from compacted, cemented particles or sediments, usually laid down in horizontal layers on the bottoms of seas, lakes, and rivers.

Sediments Pieces or particles of rock such as gravel, sand, or silt, worn off or washed away by weathering and erosion and eventually deposited on the ground.

Stegosaur A plated dinosaur, a large, four-legged plant-eater with plates or spikes of bone probably standing upright along its neck, back, and tail, as in *Stegosaurus*.

Sternum The breastbone or similar bone at the front of the chest.

Taphonomy The scientific study of collections, gatherings, and accumulations of objects, and how, when, where, and why they occur.

Tarsal Bone in the ankle.

Tertiary One of the periods or timespans of the earthís history, lasting from about 65 to 2 million years ago; the first period of the Cenozoic Era and the period after the Age of the Dinosaurs.

Theropod ("beast-foot") A general group of dinosaurs that mostly walked on their two back legs and included all the meat-eaters, from tiny *Compsognathus* through the small and medium-sized dromaeosaurs to the large carnosaurs.

Thoracic To do with the chest.

Tibia Bone in the lower leg, sometimes called the shinbone.

Torpor Deep sleep or long period of inactivity, for example during very cold weather.

Trace fossils A fossil that did not come from a body part but that reveals the activity or presence of a living thing, such as a footprint or nest.

Triassic One of the periods or timespans of the earth's history, lasting from about 248 to 208 million years ago; the first period of the Mesozoic Era and the Age of the Dinosaurs.

Ulna Bone in the lower arm or forearm.

Vertebra A backbone or spinal bone, one of the chain of bones making up the spinal column.

Warm-blooded (more accurately, "endothermic") Referring to an animal that generates heat inside its body and whose body therefore stays at the same, usually high temperature, despite the varying temperature of its surroundings. Today only mammals and birds are endothermic.

Index

Picture credits

Picture credits
The publishers gratefully acknowledge the following for the use of illustrations.
T top
B bottom
C centre
R right
L left

Ardea London 20, 50B, 57B, 67TR, 69CL, 70, 71CR, 83CL, 95BR, 128, 162B, 169TL, 181, 182, 190TR, 197, 201, 210BL, 212C, 213, 224. **Julian Baker** 238, 239. **W. T. Blows** 27TR, 57T, 79BR and TC, 189BL (2 images), 192C (3 images), 195TR, 199CR, 207T, 212TL, 221TC, 235TL, 247BR. **Britstock-IFA** 95CL. **Christiana Calvalho, Frank Lane Picture Agency** 101TL. **Sylvia and Stephen Czerkas**, *Dinosaurs: A Global View* (London, Dragon's World, 1991) 16CL, 16-17, 17T, 18TR, 19BL, 56, 73, 78-79, 87TR, 98, 108L (2 images), 184BC, 198, 199TL (3 images). *The Daily Telegraph* 99. **Denver Museum of Natural History** 165. **Digital Vision** 22CL, 23TR, 31BL and BR, 32BL, 33TL, 50CL, 63 (top 3 images), 67 (3 images), 68, 69TR and BR, 72CR, 74BL, 82BL, 92BL, 103BL, 111T and B, 112, 114B, 115, 117B, 120BL, 135TL, 142CR, 143BR, 145TL, 147, 162CL, 189TL and CR, 219BR. **Brian Franczak** 237CR. **Gay Galsworthy** 32TL **John Gurche** 96-97. **Mark Hallett** 50TL, 64, 72L, 90-91, 102, 146, 188, 218. **Douglas Henderson** 12R, 13TL and BR, 15C, 29CR, 30TL, 31TL and TC, 34CL and BR, 37B, 43, 46CR (2 images), 49, 85CR, 86, 98TR, 93T, 103TR, 106, 107, 116, 117T, 137CL, 141TR, 148, 149, 151, 172 (2 images), 174-175T, 178, 179TR, 184TC, 205TR, 207CR, 219TR, 226, 227TR, 229BR, 241T (2 images), 242B, 243TR, 244 (2 images), 245. **Imitor** 54CL, 196CL (2 images), 228. **Institut Royal des Sciences National de Belgique** 130-131 (3 images), 132T, 143TR **Steve Kirk** 54-55, 62L. **Mansell Collection** 242CR. **Natural History Museum Photograph Library** 15BL, 19BR, 40, 45B, 46B, 47T, 55TL, 65BL, 76BL, 82BR, 91CR, 97TR, 118, 120T, 135BR, 138BL, 139CR, 144, 152T, 154, 164, 173, 177, 193TR, 199CL, 209 T and B, 215TR, 216CL, 217, 240CR, 241BR, 243TL. **Natural History Photographic Agency** 25CL, 4CR, 63B. **Nauk, Warsaw, Poland** 11TR, 159BL, 185, 210TL, 247CR. *Newnes' Pictorial Knowledge* (London, George Newnes, c. 1945) 12L, 14CL, 29CL and BL. **Oxford University Museum of Natural History** 55CR, 229T. **Chris Pellant** 231. **David Peters** 240BR. **Planet Earth Pictures** 14BL, 15 (5 images), 25CR, 44TL and BL, 45TR, 103CR, 122CL, 155TR, 159TR, 160BL, 161, 174BL, 175TR, 183T, 237TL. **Royal Tyrrell Museum, Drumheller, Canada** 53, 61TR, 170, 180BL, 183BR, 195TL, 236TC. **Salamander Picture Library** 19TR, 22-23B, 24, 25TL, 27BL, 28BL and CR, 29T, 35T, 36-37, 38-39 (4 images), 47BL, 52, 58, 59, 60, 61C, 62 (4 images), 65BR, 66 (2 images), 72BL (2 images), 74-75, 76-77, 80-81 (3 images), 83CR and B, 84, 85BL, 89BR, 92-93, 94, 100C and B, 104TR, 105, 113 (4 images), 120CR (2 images), 121, 122B (2 images), 124-125, 125CR, 126-127 (7 images), 132B (2 images), 133, 134-135, 136 (2 images), 137TL, 138CR, 139T, 140, 141BR (2 images), 150, 152-153 (3 images), 155B (2 images), 156-157 (3 images), 158, 1600T and BR, 163, 168, 169CR, 171 (3 images), 174TL, 176, 180BR, 186, 187, 190BL, 191, 192B, 193CR, 194TR (3 images), 195C (2 images), 200, 202-203 (5 images), 204, 205C, 206, 208-209, 211 (2 images), 214, 215BR, 216CR (2 images), 220, 221CR (2 images), 222-223, 223BR, 225TR (2 images), 225BR, 230B, 232-233 (5 images), 234, 235CR, 236BL and CR **Sandown Museum, Isle of Wight** 26 (3 images), 79, 142BR, 143BL. **Science Photo Library** 25BR, 41B, 42, 71TR and BL, 109 (3 images), 110, 237C, 246, 247TL. **John Sibbick** 10-11, 11C, 13TR, 20BL, 21, 34CR, 35B, 75TR, 87BL, 88-89, 104BL, 114T, 166-167, 194BL, 196B, 227B, 230TL, 240CL. **South African Museum** 31C and CR, 48. **Superstock** 33R (4 images), 41T, 101TR, 119 (2 images), 122-123T, 123BR, 129, 142TR, 145CR, 179B (2 images), 247TR. **Peter Trusler** © *Australia Post* 1993 108BR

PRECAMBRIAN ERA

PALEOZOIC ERA

Cambrian Period:
590—505 millions of years ago

Ordovician Period:
505—438 millions of years ago

Silurian Period:
438—408 millions of years ago

Devonian Period:
408—360 millions of years ago

Carboniferous Period:
360—286 millions of years ago

Devonian Period:
286—245 millions of years ago

Triassic Period:
245—205 millions of years ago

Jurassic Period:
205—144 millions of years ago